EXPERIMENTS IN

BOOK 1

GROB

BASIC ELECTRONICS

Includes Experiments 1-34

FOURTH EDITION

Frank Pugh
Santa Rosa Junior College
Santa Rosa, California

Wes Ponick
Hewlett-Packard Company
Network Measuring Division
Santa Rosa, California

New York, New York   Columbus, Ohio   Mission Hills, California   Peoria, Illinois

Cover photos: Foreground Larry Keenan Associates/The Image Bank; Background Simon Fraser/Welwyn Electronics/Science Photo Library/Photo Researchers

Glencoe/McGraw-Hill

A Division of The ***McGraw-Hill*** *Companies*

Experiments in Grob Basic Electronics, Fourth Edition
Book 1, Experiments 1 to 34

Send all inquiries to:
Glencoe/McGraw-Hill
936 Eastwind Drive
Westerville, OH 43081

ISBN 0-02-802268-8

2 3 4 5 6 7 8 9 045 02 01 00 99 98 97

CONTENTS

PREFACE

Experiments in Basic Electronics is a lab manual for the beginning electronics student who does not have any previous experience in electricity or electronics. It has been developed especially for use with Bernard Grob's *Basic Electronics,* Eighth Edition, and the experiments are coordinated with the text in sequence and technical usage. There are 67 experiments in this edition, ranging from an introduction to electronic equipment and components to a primer on operational amplifiers. The emphasis throughout is on basic concepts. Although the experiments build on one another, with simple concepts being developed before more complex subjects are introduced, minor modifications in the sequence can be made as necessary to suit the requirements of an individual electronics program. All experiments have been student-tested at Santa Rosa Junior College.

Fifteen new or expanded experiments appear in this edition. These changes resulted from instructors' responses to a questionnaire distributed before work on the revision was begun. Most of the additions or changes have been made in the area of direct current, as requested by many of the respondents. We thank all the instructors, many of whom are associated with ITT Technical Institutes across the country, who provided us with opinions and suggestions for this edition.

Each experiment, which takes approximately three hours to perform, is organized as follows. First, the basic principles are explained in detail; then, the student is encouraged to apply electronics theory to troubleshooting; and finally, the student writes a comprehensive report. Techniques for good technical report preparation are discussed in the first group of experiments. Additional information about preparing reports is provided in Appendix D.

The authors would like to thank Dr. Rosemary Dardan, Assistant Dean of Science and Applied Technologies at Santa Rosa Junior College, for her unflagging encouragement. We also wish to thank David Newton of ITT Technical Institute, Nashville, Melvin Duvall of Sacramento City College, and Sharon Wujcik of Santa Rosa Junior College for their assistance with the preparation of this laboratory manual. In addition, we thank Jeanne Ponick, Ann Pugh, our children, and all the students at SRJC for their patience and support.

Frank Pugh
Wes Ponick

TO THE STUDENT

Experiments in Basic Electronics by Pugh and Ponick has been divided into two convenient books. Book 1 contains Experiments 1 through 34, which cover all the material on direct current. Book 2 contains the remainder of the experiments, 35 through 67.

The original manual has been separated logically, so that the material in each book corresponds to the two-volume version of *Basic Electronics,* Eighth Edition. The experiments manual retains the page numbers of the single-volume version. This has been done for ease of reference.

The text of Book 1 begins with Experiment 1 and continues through page 178 (Experiment 34). The text of Book 2 begins with page 179 and continues through the end of the text (Experiment 67). As in the two-volume student texts, the appendixes for the experiments manual appear in both books.

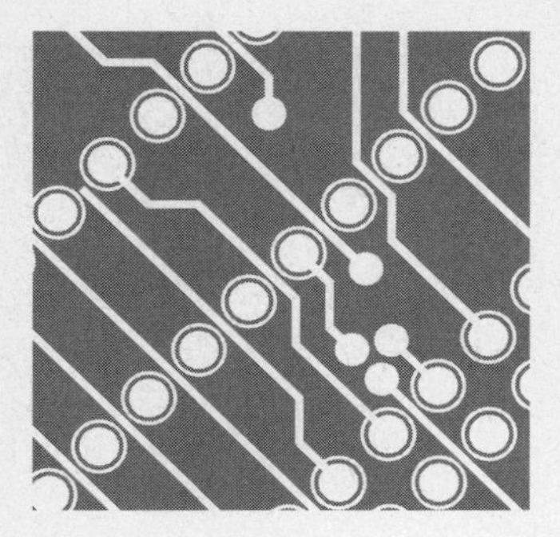

LAB SAFETY, EQUIPMENT, AND COMPONENTS

OBJECTIVES

At the completion of this experiment, you will:

- Know the basic safety concepts used in a lab.
- Be familiar with lab equipment and components.
- Know the resistor color code.

SUGGESTED READING

Chapters 1 and 2, *Basic Electronics,* B. Grob, Eighth Edition

INTRODUCTION

An electronics lab combines a classroom with a technician's workbench. Most classroom labs have similar equipment. You should become familiar with the equipment in your classroom lab, including safety equipment, safety policies, and practices.

SAFETY

Safety always comes first—in a lab class and at work. In fact, most large companies train their technicians in safety measures, including good ergonomic practices. You should not only know how to use the equipment safely but also how to sit at a lab station without stressing your arms, wrists, or eyes when working. Most of the time, this is a matter of common sense—avoid any stressful position for a prolonged time.

But most safety issues in an electronics lab come from the possibility of getting an electric shock. It is your responsibility to avoid this hazard by following these basic rules:

1. Do not plug in or turn on the power to any equipment without knowing how to use the equipment. This means asking for help when you do not know how to use something safely. Do not be afraid to ask for help.
2. Always check power cords. They should not be frayed, loose, or damaged in any way. In general, always inspect your equipment before using it.
3. Never wear loose jewelry or rings when working on equipment. Most jewelry is made of metal and may conduct hazardous current accidentally.
4. Do not keep drinks or open liquids near electronic equipment.
5. Do not touch any circuit or components unless you know that it is safe to do so. For example, touching some components (especially some chips) can damage them. Other components (large capacitors) can discharge a dangerous current through your body if you touch them—even if they are not connected to a circuit.
6. Never use a soldering iron without proper training.
7. Never disturb another person who is using equipment.
8. Always wear safety glasses or any other required safety equipment.

Your lab class may have a safety test, signs, or some other information that you should read or respond to as required. Although most electronics courses are not known to cause injury, it is still a good idea to be cautious and prepared. Be sure you know where first aid is available and what to do in an emergency.

EQUIPMENT

Every electronics lab, and every school, has different types of equipment. However, there are some basic meters that are common to all electronics labs. In one form or another, your school will have these meters. They may appear to be different only because they are made by different manufacturers. Typical equipment is shown in Grob's *Basic Electronics*.

Simple Meters (Single Purpose)

Ohmmeter: Used to measure resistance (in ohms). Remember that resistance is the opposition to current flow in a circuit. Resistors usually have color stripes on them to identify their values. One way to be sure your resistor is the correct value is to measure it with an ohmmeter.

Ammeter: Used to measure current (in amperes). Remember that current is an electric charge in motion.

Ammeters usually measure the current in milliamperes (0.001 A), because most electronics lab courses do not require large amounts of current.

Voltmeter: Used to measure voltage (in volts). Remember that voltage (force) refers to units of potential difference. Most voltmeters use more than one range, or scale, because voltage, unlike current, is often measured in larger values.

Multimeters (Multipurpose)

VOM (VOLT-OHM-MILLIAMMETER): A multipurpose meter used to measure dc and ac voltage, dc current, and resistance (see Fig. 1-1*a*).

VTVM (VACUUM TUBE VOLTMETER): Another, older type of multipurpose meter used to measure voltage and resistance only.

DMM (DIGITAL MULTIMETER): A digital multipurpose meter, also known as a DVM (digital voltmeter) (see Fig. 1-1*b*).

Other Equipment

DC Power Supply: A source of potential difference, like a battery. It supplies voltage and current, and it can be adjusted to provide the required voltage for any experiment.

Soldering Iron: A pointed electric appliance that heats electric connections so that solder (tin and lead) will melt on those connections. Used to join components and circuits.

Breadboard/Springboard/Protoboard: Used to assemble basic circuits, by either soldering, inserting into springs, or joining together in sockets. These boards are the tools of designers, students, and hobbyists.

Component Familiarization (Symbols)

The symbol for resistance or a resistor.

The symbol for a battery (cells) or a power supply.

\+ Positive symbol (associated with the color red).

− Negative symbol (associated with the color black).

Capacitor (or capacitance) symbol. Used in later study.

Inductor (or inductance) symbol. Used in later study.

Leads are simply insulated wires used to join the meters to the circuits, the power supply to the circuit, etc. They are conductors and have no polarity of their own. Leads have different types of connectors on the ends, such as alligator clips, banana plugs, and BNC connectors.

Ω = ohms (unit of resistance), Greek letter omega

∞ = infinity (used to indicate infinite resistance)

(*a*)

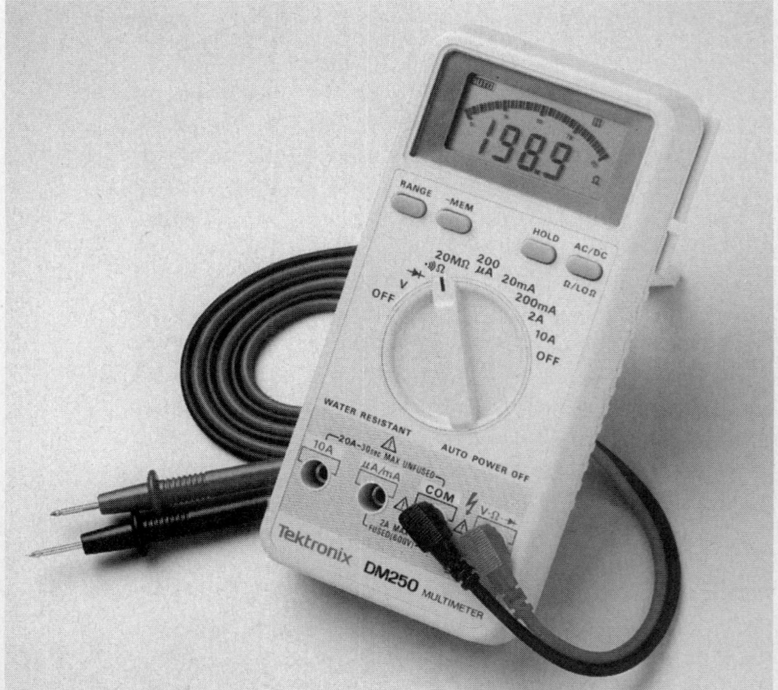

(*b*)

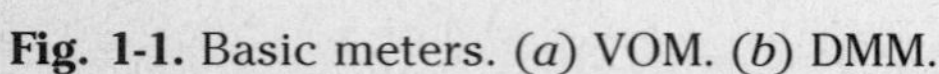

Fig. 1-1. Basic meters. (*a*) VOM. (*b*) DMM.

Common Symbols for Multipliers

Lowercase k = kilo = 1000 or 1×10^3
Uppercase M = mega = 1,000,000 or 1×10^6
Lowercase m = milli = 0.001 or 1×10^{-3}
Greek letter mu (μ) = micro = 0.000 001 or 1×10^{-6}

COMPONENTS

Certain basic components are used in electronics all the time. They are the resistor, the capacitor, the inductor, the diode, and the transistor (see Fig. 1-2). Along with these are also hundreds of variations and customized devices and chips.

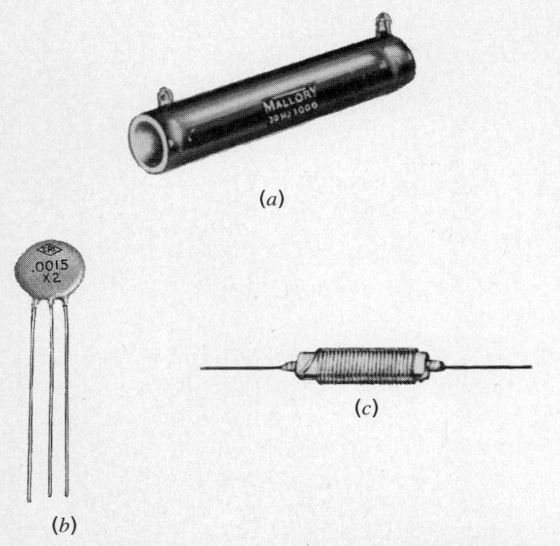

Fig. 1-2. Typical resistor (*a*), capacitor (*b*), and inductor (*c*).

Capacitors have the ability (capacity) to store electrical energy, and inductors have the ability to induce a voltage; these will be studied later. But the practical use of resistors is studied early in most lab classes. Learning about resistors and learning (memorizing) the resistor color code are critical for any technician.

In general, resistors limit or resist the flow of current in a circuit. That is why they are called *resistors*. Made of a carbon compound, resistors come in various sizes and power ratings. The most common resistors on circuit boards have the value of resistance color-coded (painted) on them. The value of resistance is the *ohm*, named for Georg Simon Ohm, the scientist who determined a law for resistance in 1828. The resistance value in ohms refers to the resistor's ability to resist the flow of electricity. The lower the value, the less resistance. In practical applications, one ohm (1 Ω) of resistance is very small and has little effect on most circuits. However, 1 million Ω has so much resistance that it resists all but the smallest amount of current flow.

PROCEDURE

Resistor Color Code

1. Answer questions 1 to 15.
2. After studying the resistor color code in Fig. 1-3, fill in Tables 1-1 and 1-2.
3. List the types of meters that you already know how to use and compare them to any meters in your lab.

After you finish, turn in your answers to procedure steps 1, 2, and 3.

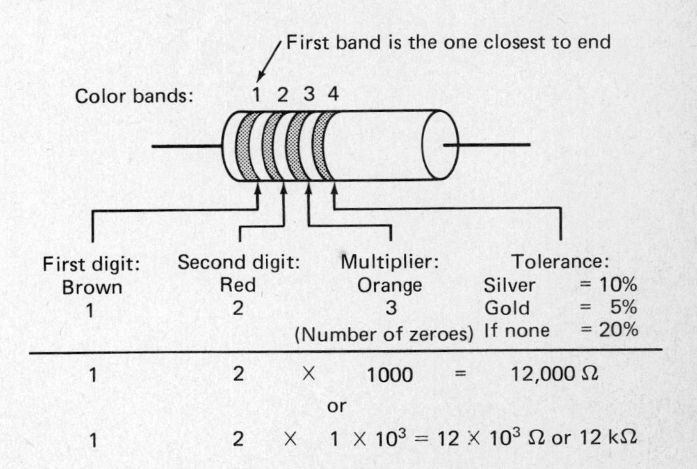

Remember: Multiplier means adding zeros.
Here, add three zeros.

Note: If the multiplier (third band) is gold, multiply by 0.1. Here, a gold band multiplier would mean 1.2 Ω. If the multiplier is black, multiply by 1.

COLOR CODE

Color	Value	Color	Value
Black	0	Green	5
Brown	1	Blue	6
Red	2	Violet	7
Orange	3	Grey	8
Yellow	4	White	9

Fig. 1-3. How to read color bands (stripes) on carbon resistors. Resistors come in various shapes and sizes. This is only one common form. The larger the physical size, the greater the wattage rating. Refer to Appendix C for other component codes, including the five-band carbon film resistors.

NAME ______________________________ DATE ______________

RESULTS FOR EXPERIMENT 1

QUESTIONS

Fill in the blanks (1–15) with the letter of the correct answer.

____ **1.** An instrument used to measure potential difference.

____ **2.** An instrument used to measure current.

____ **3.** An instrument used to measure resistance.

____ **4.** A passive component that opposes the flow of current.

____ **5.** An instrument used to heat solder and join components.

____ **6.** A source of dc voltage other than a battery.

____ **7.** A symbol for dc voltage source.

____ **8.** A symbol for resistance.

____ **9.** A color used to represent negative polarity.

____ **10.** An item used to temporarily build circuits on.

____ **11.** A Greek letter used to represent a unit of resistance.

____ **12.** An English letter used to represent 1000.

____ **13.** An English letter used to represent 0.001.

____ **14.** An instrument capable of measuring both voltage and current.

____ **15.** A symbol for infinity.

a. ammeter
b. —/\/\/—
c. power supply
d. voltmeter
e. −|‖|+
f. black
g. ohmmeter
h. breadboard
i. soldering iron
j. resistor
k. VOM/VTVM
l. m
m. k
n. Ω
o. ∞

REPORT

TABLE 1–1. Resistor Color Codes

First Digit Band 1	Second Digit Band 2	Multiplier Band 3	Tolerance Band 4	Resistor Value
Red	Brown	Brown	Gold	210 ±5%
Brown	Brown	Black	Gold	110Ω ±5%
Green	Blue	Red	Silver	5600 ±10%
Blue	Green	Yellow	Silver	650000 ±10%
Red	Red	Orange	Silver	22K ±10%
Orange	White	Brown	Gold	390K ±5%
Blue	Green	Black	Silver	650K ±10%
Brown	Black	Red	Gold	10K ±10%
Yellow	Violet	Green	Gold	475K ±10%
Brown	Black	Orange	Silver	10K ±10%
Orange	Orange	Orange	Silver	44000 ±10%
Brown	Black	Gold	Gold	10
White	Blue	Red	Silver	962K ±10%
Brown	Black	Yellow	Silver	104 ±10%
Brown	Green	Green	Gold	150 ±5%

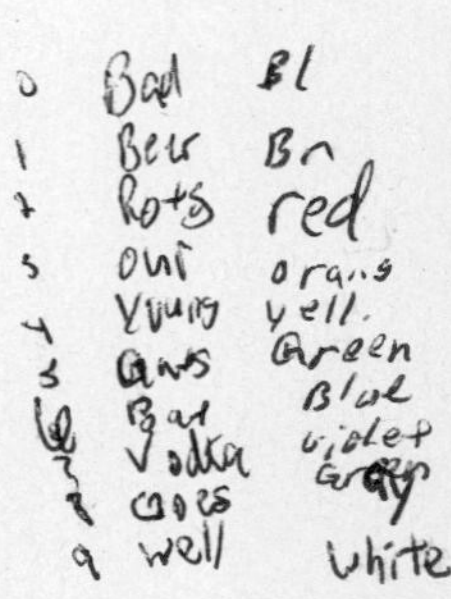

TABLE 1–2. Resistor Color Codes

Band 1 Color	Band 2 Color	Band 3 Color	Band 4 Color	Resistor Value
Blue	Green	Black	Gold	680 kΩ, 5%
Brown	Black	Black	Silver	10 kΩ, 10%
Brown	Black	Black	Gold	100 kΩ, 5%
Orange	Orange	Orange	Gold	3.3 MΩ, 5%
Brown	Red	Black	Silver	1.2 kΩ, 10%
Green	Red	Brown	Silver	820 Ω, 10%
Yellow	Violet	Black	Gold	47 kΩ, 5%
Orange	Orange	Brown	Silver	330 Ω, 10%
Yellow	Violet	Brown	Gold	470 kΩ, 5%
Green	Blue	Brown	Silver	560 Ω, 10%
Brown	Green	Blue	Silver	1.5 MΩ, 10%
Red	Red	Brown	Gold	220 Ω, 5%
Green	Blue	Silver	Silver	56 Ω, 10%
Brown	Red	Black	Gold	12 kΩ, 5%
Green	Blue	Brown	Gold	560 kΩ, 5%

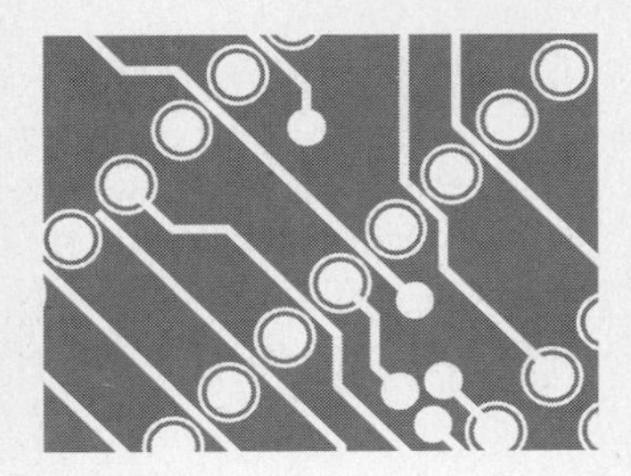

EXPERIMENT 2

RESISTANCE MEASUREMENTS

OBJECTIVES

At the completion of this experiment, you will be able to:

- Read nonlinear meter scales.
- Calibrate and/or operate an ohmmeter.
- Measure resistance in ohms.

SUGGESTED READING

Chapters 1 and 2, *Basic Electronics,* B. Grob, Eighth Edition

INTRODUCTION

This experiment will familiarize you with resistance measurements and the ohmmeter. Ohmmeters measure resistance in *ohms*, which is the opposition to current flow in a circuit. An ohmmeter works by sending a known value of current through a component and measuring the amount of current that returns. The difference is then used to determine the resistance. For example, if all the current sent is returned, the ohmmeter reading will be zero ohms (0 Ω) or no resistance. Or, if no current returns, the reading will be very large (millions of ohms) or infinity. Anything in between is determined by the internal circuitry and the applied voltage.

An ohmmeter can measure amounts of resistance from zero ohms, such as a short piece of copper wire (a *short circuit*) to infinite ohms, such as air (an *open circuit*). But, most of the time, you will use the ohmmeter to measure the value of resistors in ohms.

Types of Ohmmeters

For practical purposes, no single piece of equipment is dedicated to measuring ohms. Some older labs (schools) may use dedicated ohmmeters, but they are inadequate for use in the field and not found in modern test and production facilities. In general, ohmmeters are a functional part of multipurpose meters, which often also measure voltage and current. In fact, the only single-function ohmmeter that is practical is a continuity checker, which is used simply to verify that a circuit is closed (continuous) or open (no continuity).

Both digital and analog meters are used, with the digital meter currently the meter of choice. Analog meters use a meter movement and have nonlinear scales which are used only for resistance measurements—this is because the concept of infinite ohms cannot be fit onto a readable scale. In addition, all multifunction meters require that you adjust the function switch for volts, amperes, or ohms, and you may also be required to adjust the range. With the range properly set, you simply multiply the scale reading by the range setting. Ohmmeters can be part of the following types of multipurpose meters.

VOM (volt-ohm-milliammeter): This multifunction meter measures voltage, current, or resistance. As an ohmmeter, it can be digital or analog. Most versions use a magnetic meter movement with a needle or pointer and a nonlinear scale for resistance measurements. Other scales appear on the meter for voltage and current. Many VOMs combine function and range switches. The VOM is usually battery operated and portable. It also can usually measure low values of current, and both dc and ac voltages. See Fig. 2-1.

VTVM (vacuum tube voltmeter): This multifunction meter is based on vacuum tube technology and requires ac power to operate the vacuum tube inside. VTVMs usually have separate switches for function and range. For years the VTVM was considered the best bench tool for technicians because it measured both ac and dc voltages. However, it cannot measure current and is rarely used in modern workplaces since it has been replaced by digital meters that perform the same tasks. Like the VOM, the VTVM must be calibrated before measuring resistance. It also can measure power (in watts). See Fig. 2-2.

EQUIPMENT

Ohmmeter: DMM, VOM, or VTVM

COMPONENTS

30 resistors, all 0.25 W unless indicated otherwise:

(1) 10 Ω	(1) 4.7 kΩ
(1) 56 Ω	(1) 5.6 kΩ (0.5 W or less)
(1) 100 Ω	(3) 10 kΩ (0.5 W or less)

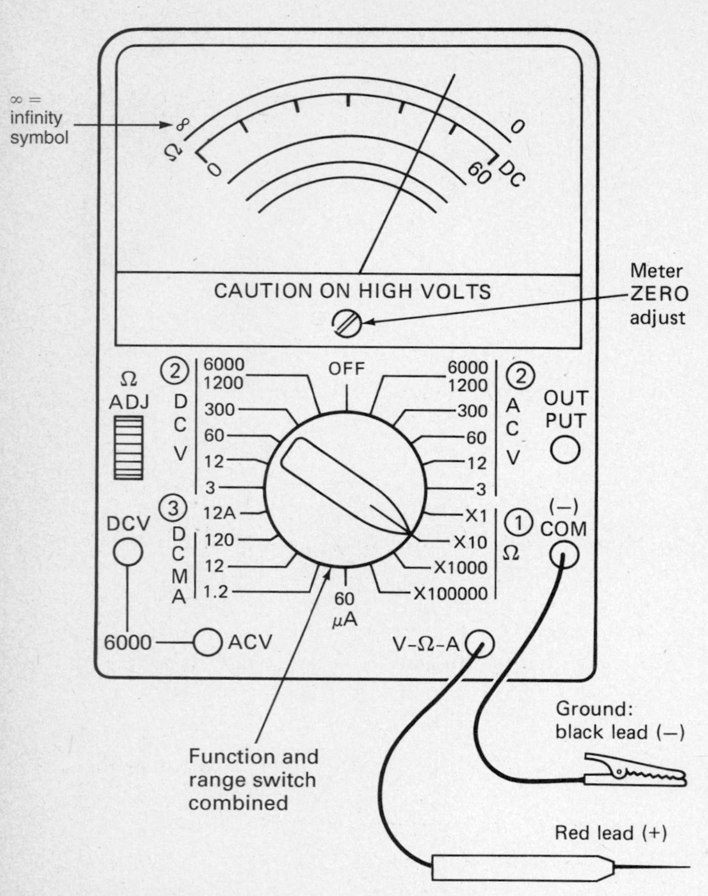

Fig. 2-1. VOM. Linear and nonlinear scale (ohms). A generic VOM measures resistance in ohms (Ω), ac and dc voltage, and current in amperes (A). The VOM shown is set for resistance: $R \times 10$.

(1) 220 Ω	(1) 22 kΩ (0.5 W or less)
(1) 390 Ω	(1) 33 kΩ (0.5 W or less)
(1) 470 Ω	(2) 47 kΩ (0.5 W or less)
(1) 680 Ω	(1) 68 kΩ (0.5 W or less)
(1) 820 Ω	(1) 86 kΩ (0.5 W or less)
(1) 1 kΩ	(2) 100 kΩ (0.5 W or less)
(1) 1.2 kΩ	(1) 220 kΩ (0.5 W or less)
(1) 1.5 kΩ	(1) 470 kΩ (0.5 W or less)
(1) 2.2 kΩ	(1) 1.2 MΩ (0.5 W or less)
(1) 3.3 kΩ	(1) 3.3 MΩ (0.5 W or less)

USING A VOM

Function/Range Switch: This rotary switch should be in the OFF position when not in use; otherwise, the VOM's battery may become depleted. Not only does this switch allow you to choose the desired functions (ohmmeter, voltmeter, ammeter), but it also indicates the range. VOMs often seem more difficult to use than VTVMs because they have so many switches and inputs located in a small area.

Ohms Adjust: This is the zero adjustment for measuring resistance (ohms). Use it to line up the needle directly on the zero line when using the VOM as an ohmmeter when the leads are shorted.

COM: This is the common or negative input. That is, it is the place where the black ground lead is plugged into the meter. Remember that VOMs, like most electronic instruments, have two inputs: a negative and a positive.

VΩA: This is the positive input. Plug the other lead (red, if available) into this jack. Note that the words *jack, input, terminal,* and *plug-in* are often used interchangeably. You will become used to this terminology as you continue. This plug-in is used whenever measuring volts, ohms, or amperes (dc milliamperes).

Other Inputs: Do not be concerned with the other inputs at this time. You will not be using them. However, notice that the zero adjust is not marked on the VOM itself. This is because it is not adjusted (balanced) like the VTVM. If your VOM needle is not on the zero line in the dc volts function, adjust it here with a screwdriver.

Scales: The VOM has several scales. The nonlinear scale at the top is used for resistance measurements in ohms. The linear scale below is usually used for dc voltage. And the milliamperes scale (current measurements) may be another scale altogether, depending upon the manufacturer.

Function Switch: This switch turns the VTVM on. Actually, it is a rotary switch and should be in the OFF position when not in use. However, VTVMs require some warm-up time and are often left on during lab hours. The function switch allows you to choose the function you want from the VTVM. Thus, setting the function switch turns the VTVM into either an ohmmeter or a voltmeter (AC or +DC or −DC). You will probably use it as either an ohmmeter or a +dc voltmeter during your beginning studies.

Range Switch: This switch determines the scale that will be used. Notice that Fig. 2-2 shows eight different range settings. Each range setting corresponds to the function switch setting. For example, "15 V, R × 100" can be used for either a voltage or a resistance (ohms) measurement. In this case, if the function switch is on OHMS, the range would automatically be R × 100, not 15 V.

Scales (Ohms and DC/RMS): The OHMS scale, marked Ω for resistance, is on top. It is a nonlinear scale (not equally divided). It goes from zero to infinity (∞). The scales below it are used for voltage and power measurements. DC and RMS are voltage measurements.

Zero Adjustment: This knob is a potentiometer that allows you to position the needle directly on the zero line before making a measurement.

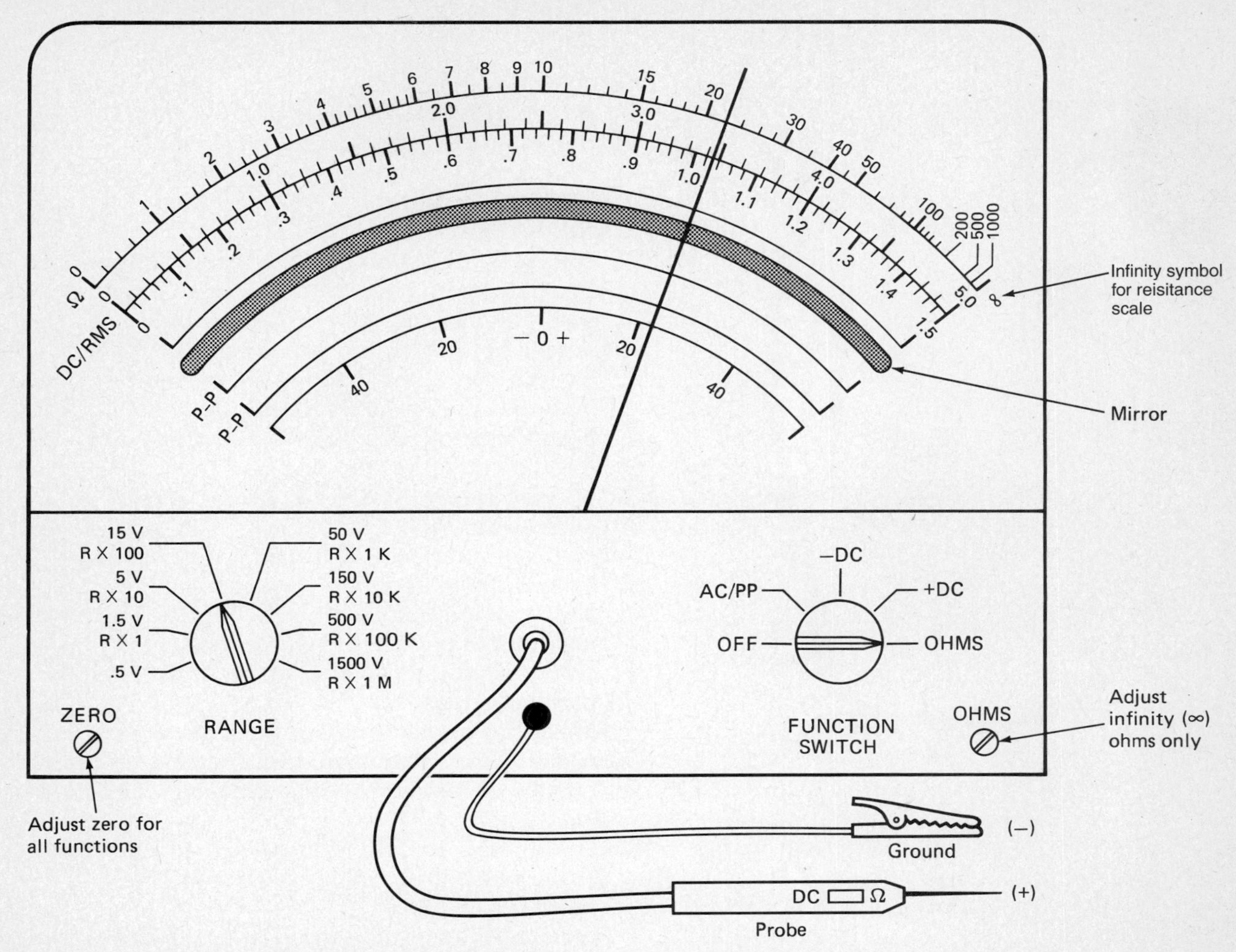

Fig. 2-2. VTVM (typical generic type). The top scale is nonlinear (0 to infinity), used for resistance (Ω). The remaining scales are linear (0 to 5, 0 to 1.5, etc.), used for voltage. Note that most VTVMs have a mirror strip between scales to prevent parallax errors. These visual errors are similar to those made by passengers in a car trying to read the speedometer from an angle. To avoid parallax errors, line up the needle with the mirror reflection and with the division line on the scale.

Ohms Adjustment: This knob, also a potentiometer, allows you to line up the needle on the other end of the scale, on the infinity line. It is only used for resistance measurements (ohmmeter function).

Ground Lead: This lead is usually connected first. It is the negative (−), or ground, side. First, connect this ground strap or lead to one end of the component you are measuring. Then, make connection with the probe (+).

Probe: Often called the *positive lead,* this pointed probe has a switch on it for measuring either ohms or dc voltage. After the ground lead is connected, it is easy to use this probe to make contact with the component you are measuring.

DVM or DMM (digital voltmeter or digital multimeter): This is the most common type of multimeter for field use. It can measure resistance, voltage, and current. It is usually small, portable (battery powered), and accurate. Of course, digital meters have an LED (light-emitting diode) display with the values displayed in digits. As with all meters, you must adjust the function and, sometimes, the range. The digital meter is the meter of choice for today's technician. See Fig. 2-3.

PROCEDURE

1. Reading Nonlinear Resistance Scales: Refer to Fig. 2-4. It shows the type of scales found on a VTVM. The top scale is nonlinear (uneven) and has an R label to indicate that it is used for resistance measurements only. The other scales below are used for voltage and power measurements. The scale goes from 0 (zero) to 1000, with infinity as the last increment or point on the scale. Notice also that the increment spacing is greater between

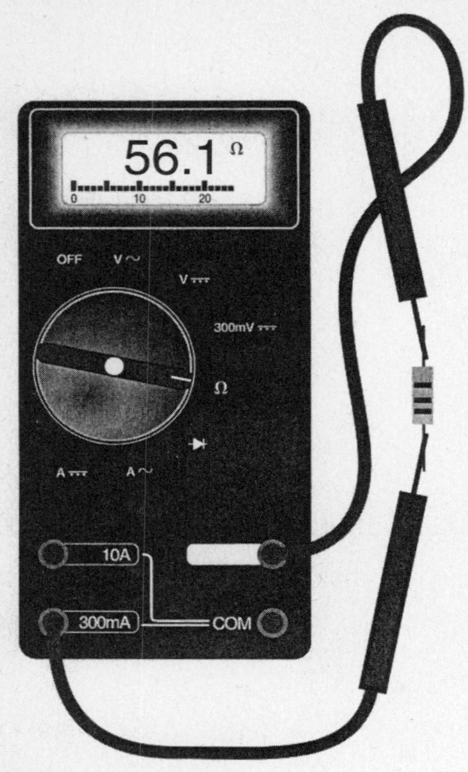

Fig. 2-3. DMM.

some numbers. This is due to the way the vacuum tube operates. For that reason, VTVM measurements are most accurate when the range is set so that the needle reading is near the center of the scale. There are 12 measurement readings in this figure. The first four readings have the values (answers in ohms) given where the range is shown multiplied by the needle position. Determine the best answers for readings 5 through 12, and be sure to record the values in Table 2-1 also.

2. Calibrate the Ohmmeter:

DMM: Digital Meter. Most handheld digital meters are easy to operate. First, become familiar with the meter and check with the instructor or the manual if you have any general questions. Digital meters normally require no calibration procedure. However, you should check to see whether the meter measures zero and infinite ohms correctly. Set the function to OHMS. With the leads shorted (connected), verify the reading of zero ohms. Next, disconnect the leads and verify infinite or many megohms. Try this in other ranges if applicable.

VTVM or VOM: Be sure that you are familiar with the meter operation as described in the sections above. Refer to the manual for more information. When you are ready, follow this procedure to calibrate the meter so that it will give the correct resistance measurements:

Turn on the VTVM by setting the function switch to the OHMS position. Notice that the needle will go toward the infinity (∞) line. This is because infinite resistance is the starting point; between the ground lead and the positive lead (probe), there is only air, or infinite resistance.

Switch the probe to the OHMS position.

After allowing the VTVM to warm up for 1 or 2 min, connect both leads together, resulting in a short circuit, or zero resistance. The needle should now go in the other direction, toward zero.

Keeping both leads connected (short-circuited), use the ZERO adjust to align the needle (pointer) with the zero line. Be sure to use the mirror for proper alignment and reduction of parallax error. If the pointer, the zero line, and the mirror reflection are one, you have zeroed the ohmmeter correctly.

Disconnect the two leads. The needle will move toward the infinity line. Now, use the OHMS adjust and align the pointer with the infinity line. Alignment of the pointer, the infinity line, and the mirror reflection of the needle (pointer) will eliminate parallax errors.

Repeat the zero adjustment once more (short-circuit the leads together), and the meter should now be calibrated.

3. Resistor Measurements:

Set the range for R × 10 if using a VOM/VTVM; DMM not required.

Connect the two leads across the 100-Ω resistor as shown in Fig. 2-5. It does not matter which side of the resistor you use; you may use either side. Also, never measure resistance when voltage is applied. You may damage the meter if you do.

Note: When measuring resistance, either end of the resistor can be connected. The resistor's polarity (+ or −) is due to the current passing through the resistor.

You should see the needle resting on or near the number 10 for DVM/VOM; DMM should read 100.

For VTVM/VOM: Multiply the number that the needle is indicating by the range setting. For example, if the needle is resting exactly between 9 and 10, at 9.5, multiply 9.5 × 10. The 10 is for R × 10. The result is 95 Ω. Do not be concerned if your measurement is not exactly 100 Ω. Remember that there may be differences due to manufacturing tolerances. Even a 100-Ω resistor, with 10 percent tolerance (silver, fourth band) may be 90 Ω and still be good.

For all: Measure all the resistors listed in the component section. Write the measured value next to the nominal (color band) value in Table 2-2.

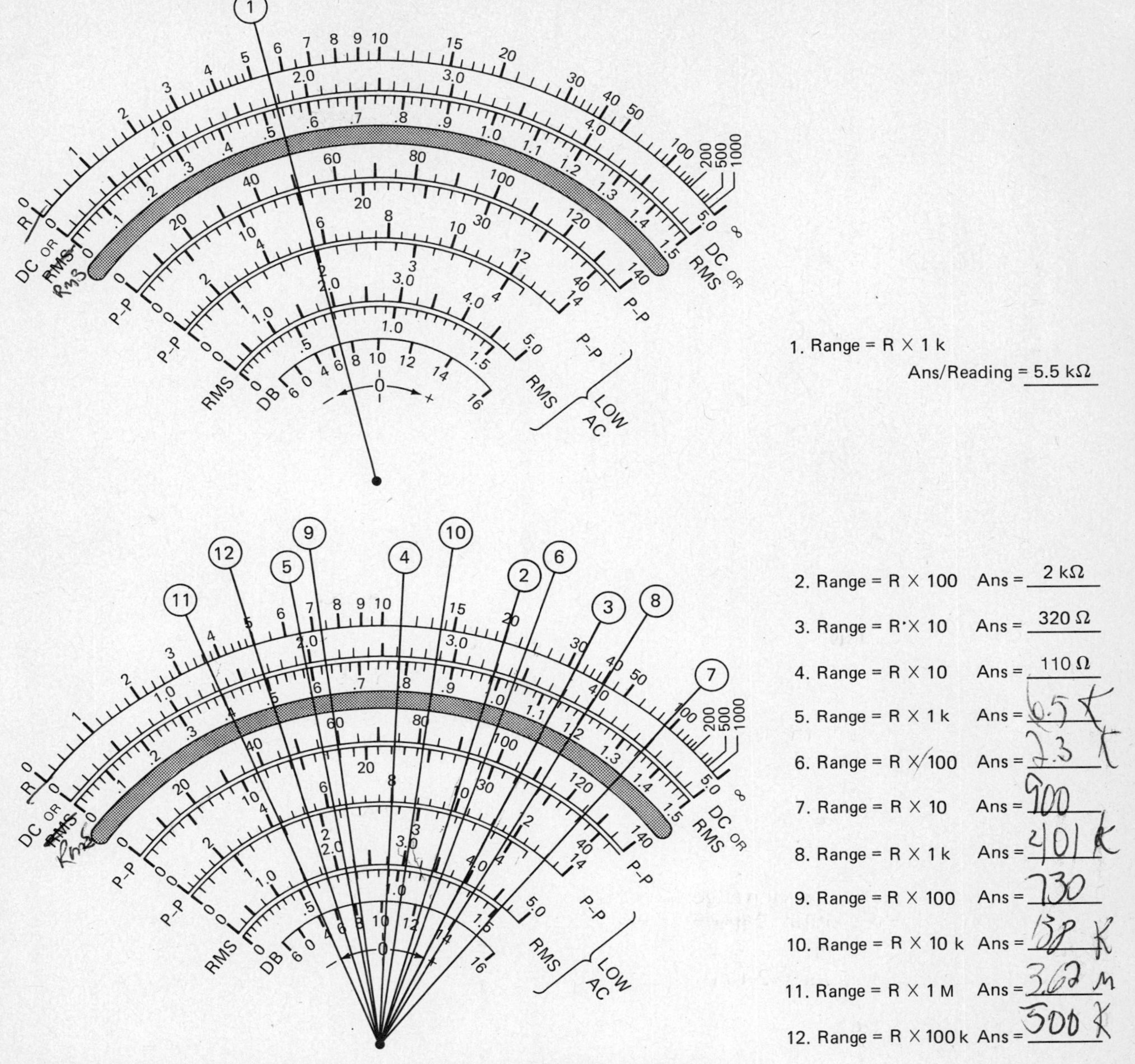

Fig. 2-4. Ohmmeter and voltmeter scales (VTVM type). Record your answers to items 5 to 12 in Table 2-1.

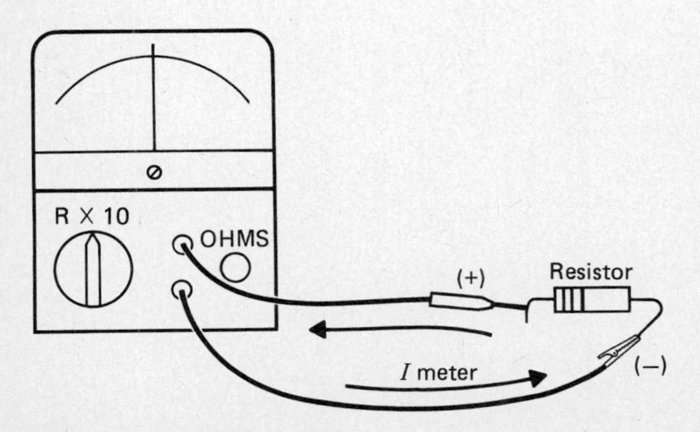

Fig. 2-5. Circuit building aid.

For VTVM/VOM: Always attempt to change ranges so that your measurements fall within the middle of the scale.

Readjust the OHMS (infinity) and ZERO controls each time you change ranges.

Remember that you cannot be entirely exact when reading scales. Do not be overly concerned if your values are not perfect.

NAME ______________________________ DATE ____________

RESULTS FOR EXPERIMENT 2

QUESTIONS

Answer TRUE (T) or FALSE (F) to the following:

T 1. It is always necessary to allow VTVMs to warm up prior to use.

F 2. The VTVM can measure current.

F 3. An ohmmeter will show zero ohms when the leads are not connected together (open circuit).

F 4. Linear scales are used for resistance measurements.

T 5. It is necessary to adjust infinity (∞) and zero ohms whenever changing ranges on an ohmmeter.

T 6. A continuity check gives the value in ohms.

T 7. Shorting the leads together on an ohmmeter results in zero ohms.

T 8. Parallax is an error resulting from reading meter scales from an angular view.

F 9. An ohmmeter cannot be damaged by measuring voltage.

T 10. The range switch is only used for voltage measurements.

REPORT

Turn in the following:

1. Your data tables (Tables 2-1 and 2-2) of resistance measurements.
2. The answers to questions 1 to 10.
3. Refer to Appendix C and write an explanation of the differences between 4-band and 5-band resistors.

TABLE 2–1. Answers to Fig. 2-4

No.	Range	Reading
5	R × 1 k	6.5K
6	R × 100	2.3K
7	R × 10	900 K
8	R × 1 k	40K
9	R × 100	130
10	R × 10 k	138K
11	R × 1 M	3.62M
12	R × 100 k	500K

TABLE 2–2. Resistance Measurements Using the Ohmmeter

Nominal Value, Ω	Measured Value, Ω	Nominal Value, Ω	Measured Value, Ω
270	2.8	3300	3030
150	1.6	4700	4500
180	1.8	3900	308
220	2.2	13000	10025
12K	10.12	6800	6000 (6K)
10K	10	8200	8000 (8K)
820	5.6		
47	4.5		
680	680		
150	180		
820	8.10		
1200	1200		
100	100		
1000	990		
5600	6000		

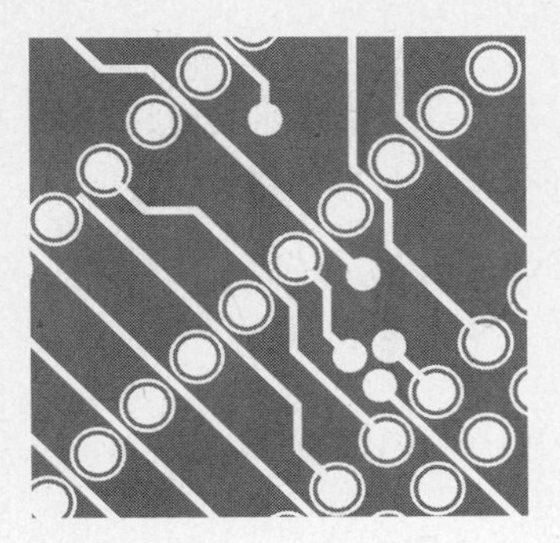

EXPERIMENT 3

VOLTAGE AND CURRENT MEASUREMENTS

OBJECTIVES

At the completion of this experiment, you will be able to:

- Measure voltage with a voltmeter.
- Measure current with an ammeter.
- Use a dc power supply.

SUGGESTED READING

Chapters 1 and 2, *Basic Electronics,* B. Grob, Eighth Edition

INTRODUCTION

Ammeters measure the amount of current (electron flow) in a circuit. Current is measured in units called *amperes*, or *amps*. Ammeters are almost always used in basic electronics lab courses and in physics lab courses because they are excellent for teaching and verifying the flow of current. But they are rarely used by technicians for repair work because ammeters usually measure only direct current (dc) and are not useful where alternating current (ac) is found. In this experiment, you will be inserting the ammeter in simple circuits and measuring small and safe amounts of dc current.

Voltmeters are the most useful tool for testing and troubleshooting dc circuits. They measure the amount of electrical force (charge or a potential difference between two points). The measurement unit is called the *volt.* Wherever there is current, there is also voltage. Most voltmeters measure dc voltage, and many also measure ac voltage, which is covered later. For this experiment, you will be measuring only dc voltage.

Common Values of Current and Voltage

The *milliampere* is a common value of current. The milliampere is one-thousandth of an amp, and that is enough current to do a lot of useful work on a circuit board. Throughout this course, you will mostly be measuring milliamperes and sometimes *microamperes.* In general, any value of current greater than a few amperes is considered high and can present a danger or hazard. Current in the area of 10 amperes and above is high enough to be deadly.

The *millivolt* is also a common value of voltage in dc electronics. It is one-thousandth of a volt. Values of hundreds of millivolts are common on circuit boards, as are values of voltage below 10 or 20 volts (V). Voltage is somewhat different from current, because large amounts of voltage can exist without a lot of current and may not be dangerous if it cannot supply current. However, it is always best to be cautious and safe.

Types of Ammeters and Voltmeters

The most commonly used voltmeters are digital handheld meters with LED (light-emitting diode) displays, often referred to as *DVMs* (*digital voltmeters*) or *DMMs* (*digital multimeters*). However, older meters such as the *VOM* (*volt-ohm-milliammeter*) and the *VTVM* (*vacuum tube voltmeter*) are still used in many places today, especially schools. And some schools even use dedicated single-function ammeters and voltmeters which may have been built especially as teaching tools. For information about the DVM/DMM, VOM, and VTVM, refer to Experiment 2, on resistance measurements, where the meters were shown.

DC Power Supply

A source of dc (direct current) power is essential for activating any circuit. In fact, a battery is the most common source of dc power but it is not a variable type of supply, and it will run out of power if not recharged. For lab work, a variable and constant source of dc power is essential. For that reason, your lab is equipped with a dc power supply that may be capable of supplying 10 or more volts and is also variable. See Fig. 3-1 for a typical dc power supply.

The dc power supply is similar to a battery but is adjustable. Most bench supplies can maintain a constant voltage and, sometimes, a constant current. Such power supplies usually have their ranges or maximum values listed on the face, for example, 0 to 10 V or 0 to 30 V. Also, bench supplies can often

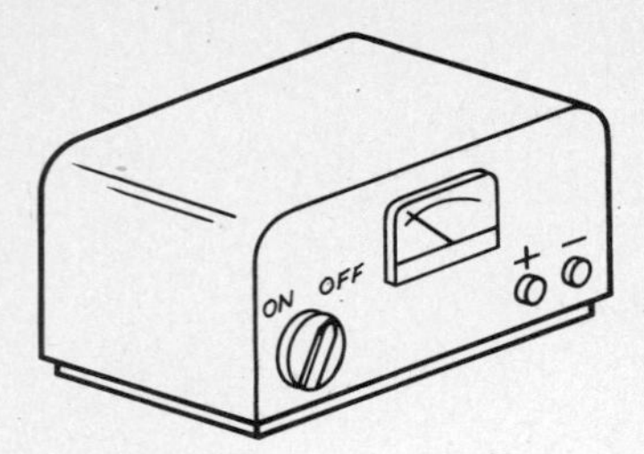

Fig. 3-1. DC power supply.

be adjusted to values less than a volt, including millivolts.

Because every lab has a different type and manufacturer of power supplies, it is necessary to learn how to safely operate the power supply in your situation. One way to do this is to read the manual or simply to look at the controls. The simplest of power supplies may have only positive and negative terminals, a display, and a knob to adjust the voltage. However, there are sophisticated supplies that have both positive and negative voltages, constant or variable current adjustments, and even swept outputs. For this experiment you will need a supply that adjusts between 0 and 10 V.

EQUIPMENT

Voltmeter
Ammeter
DC power supply

COMPONENTS

Resistors (all 0.25 W unless indicated otherwise):

(1) 100 Ω
(1) 1 kΩ
(1) 10 kΩ
(1) 330 Ω
(1) 560 Ω

PROCEDURE

1. Reading simple (linear) voltmeter scales: Refer to Figure 3-2. There are eight typical voltmeter scales shown (*a* to *h*). Notice that each meter face has two scales. Also, notice that the scales are linear, that is, equally divided. Try to read these scales. Remember that it is the range switch that determines which scale is used. For example, meter A is on the 10-V range. Therefore the reading is 6.5 V. If meter A were on the 100-V range, the reading would be 65 V. Be sure you understand that the range indicates the greatest value you can measure on the scale. Fill in the voltage readings for meters *b* through *h*.

2. Setting the Voltmeter

DMM: Digital Meters. Set the function switch to the appropriate VOLTS position. You will be measuring less than 10 V throughout this experiment. Be sure that the leads are properly connected. Digital meters are usually easy to operate and require only a minimal amount of adjustment.

VTVM or VOM: Turn on the meter. Set the function switch to positive (+) dc volts. If you have a probe (VTVM only), set it to dc volts. Adjust the ZERO control to be sure that you start with the needle aligned with the zero volts line.

3. Setting the power supply: Locate the power supply and locate its terminals (+) and (−). These are similar to the ends of a battery. If you are using a power supply with a variable knob, turn it counterclockwise to start at zero. Also, if the power supply has any setttings, be sure to set it for 10 V or less with minimal current.

Turn on the power supply.

4. Measuring power supply voltage: Connect the voltmeter directly to the power supply as shown in Fig. 3-3 (schematic) or Fig. 3-4 (circuit-building aid). First, connect the negative lead or ground side to the negative output of the power supply. This is standard practice. Then connect the positive lead (probe) to the positive (+) side of the power supply.

Note: When a *voltmeter* is shown connected in a schematic, the circled symbol Ⓥ is used.

Adjust the power supply to read 3 V by slowly increasing the voltage control knob. If you are using a digital supply, adjust it in a similar manner. When your voltmeter reads 3 V, stop. Even if the power supply display is a little more or less than the meter reading, it does not matter. The voltmeter is making the measurement, and that is the data you want.

Try increasing and decreasing the power supply in minimal amounts between 0 and 5 V, watching the voltmeter. If you are using a meter movement (needle), be sure never to allow the needle to bump up to full-scale deflection. This may ruin the meter movement or bend the needle pointer. For example, if you are going to measure 10 V, set the meter to a higher scale, such as 20 V.

Obtain any battery less than 9 V and try measuring it with the voltmeter. Because a voltmeter has a very high resistance (millions of ohms), it cannot drain the battery of its current.

5. Measuring resistor voltage: Refer to the circuit in Fig. 3-5, where a 1-kΩ resistor is used in the path of current flow. Notice that the leads of the voltmeter are connected *across* the resistor like a bridge. This

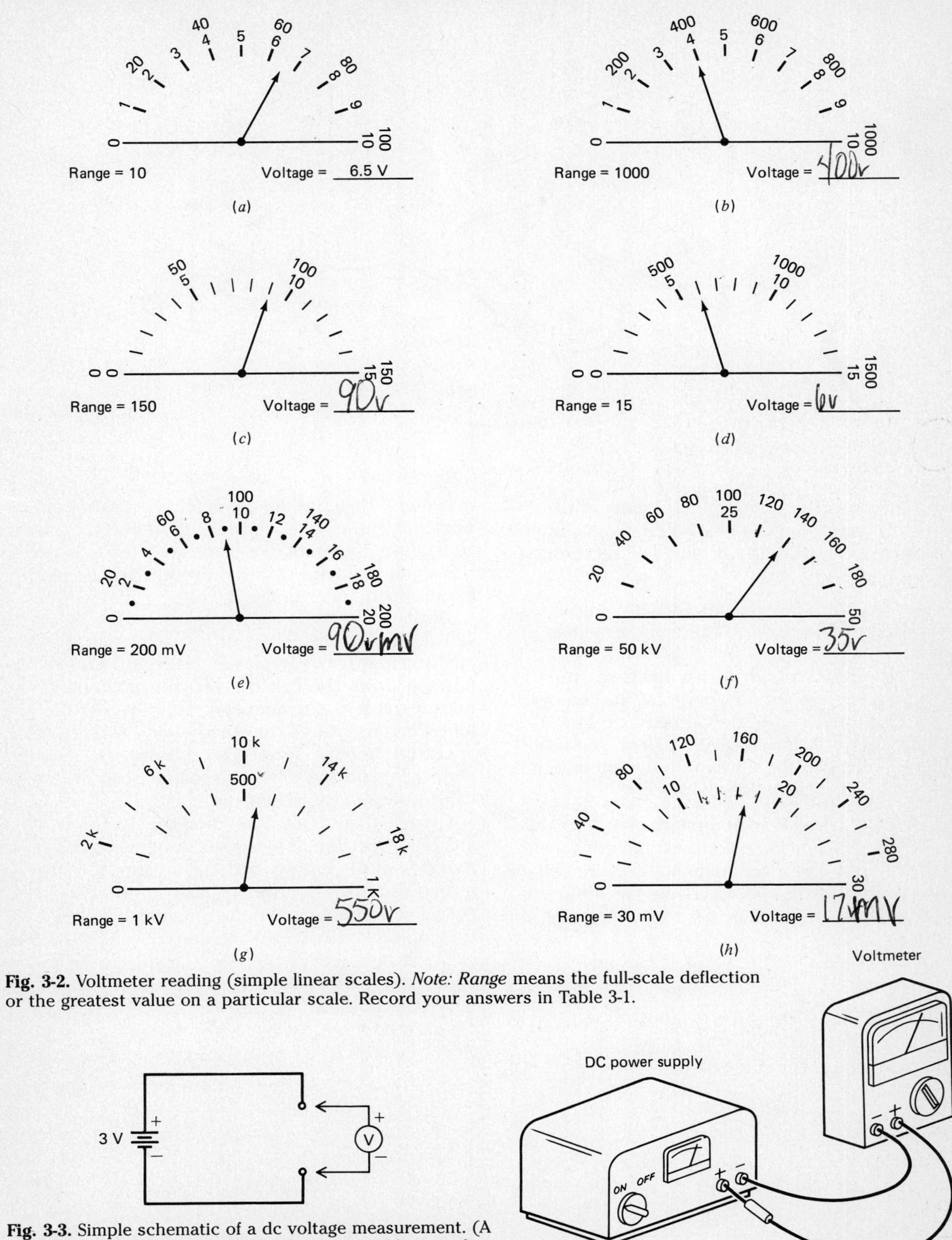

Fig. 3-2. Voltmeter reading (simple linear scales). *Note: Range* means the full-scale deflection or the greatest value on a particular scale. Record your answers in Table 3-1.

Fig. 3-3. Simple schematic of a dc voltage measurement. (A schematic is a type of electronic road map or blueprint.) The 3 V on the left means that the power supply is set at 3 V. The V in a circle on the right indicates a voltmeter (VTVM or VOM).

Fig. 3-4. Circuit building aid. Measuring the output of a dc power supply by using a voltmeter (VTVM or VOM).

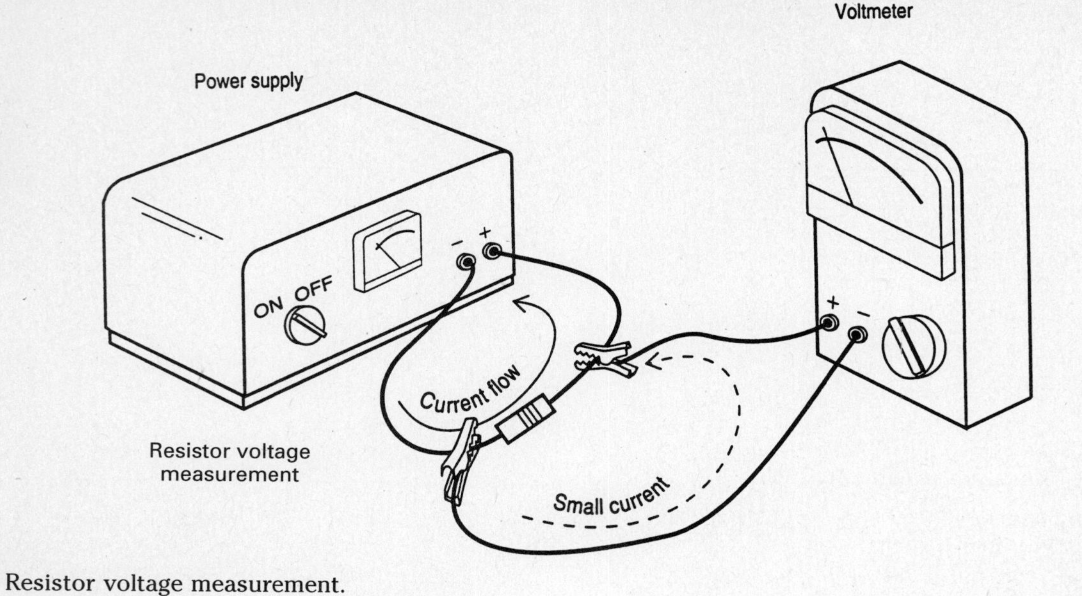

Fig. 3-5. Resistor voltage measurement.

allows a very small (microampere) amount of current to travel into the highly resistive voltmeter to be measured with little or no effect on the rest of the circuit.

Connect the circuit of Fig. 3-5, with 3-V output from the power supply. Record the voltage reading in Table 3-2.

Replace the 1-kΩ resistor with a 100-Ω resistor without adjusting the power supply and record the voltage reading on the voltmeter.

Replace the 100-Ω resistor with a 10-kΩ resistor without adjusting the power supply and record the voltage reading on the voltmeter.

6. Measuring current with an ammeter: You have already learned how to use an ohmmeter to measure resistance and a voltmeter to measure voltage. For both those meters, it was necessary to place the two (+ and −) leads *across* the component you measured. However, an ammeter is actually connected *in* the circuit—in the path of current (electron) flow. Therefore, the leads are used to connect the ammeter into a circuit only after you break the circuit open. Refer to Fig. 3-6.

Notice that the range/function switch is set to 120 mA (full-scale deflection). Also notice that the electron flow (current) leaves the negative side of the battery, flows through the resistor, and enters the negative side of the ammeter. Then it exits the ammeter and returns to the positive side of the battery.

Let us simplify Fig. 3-6 by replacing the ammeter with the symbol *A*. Now, the same circuit of Fig. 3-6 can be seen in the schematic of Fig. 3-7.

Here, it should be understood that to connect the ammeter, the circuit was broken between the positive side of the battery and the resistor. Also, to determine where the polarities are, notice that wherever electron flow enters a component, that side of the component is then considered negative. Where electron flow leaves the component, closer to the positive side of the battery source, it is considered positive. Thus, the resistor and ammeter, in Fig. 3-7, are shown where electron flow determines polarity. Of course, electron flow must enter the common, or

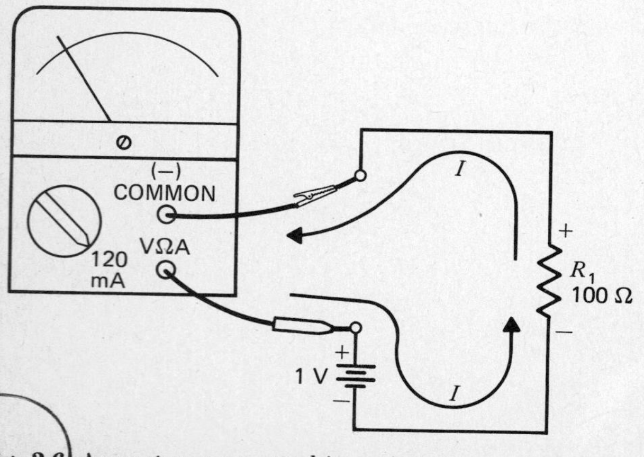

Fig. 3-6. Ammeter connected in a circuit to measure current.

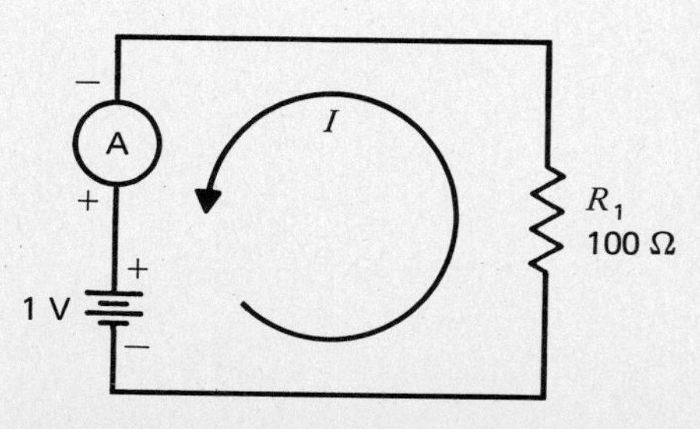

Fig. 3-7. Schematic representation of Fig. 3-6.

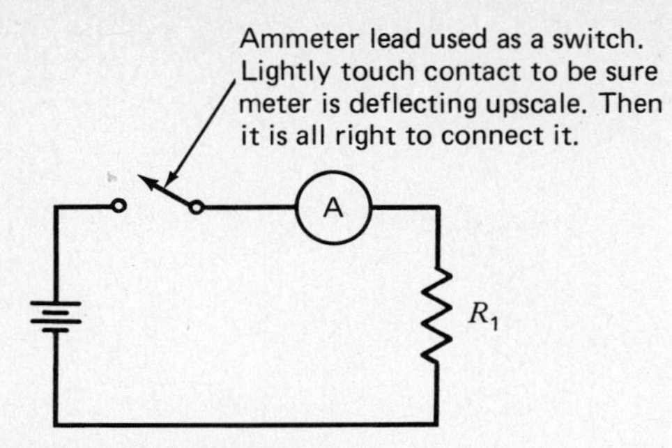

Fig. 3-8. Ammeter in circuit.

negative, side of the ammeter and exit from the positive side.

Be sure that power is turned off before making any connections and then turned on again.

Finally, an easy way to protect an ammeter, or any meter, is to allow one lead (positive, for example) to act as a switch, as shown in Fig. 3-8. Here, the positive lead of the ammeter can be touched lightly to the connection so that you can be sure the proper polarity (meter goes upscale) is there. Lightly tap or touch the positive lead to the place you are going to connect it. Watch the meter needle; it should go upscale without pegging (attempting to go out of range).

Connect the circuit of Fig. 3-7, which is a 100-Ω resistor in the path of current flow with the ammeter but do not turn the power supply on yet.

Slowly adjust the power supply voltage for 1 V across the resistor. You can use a voltmeter to measure the voltage across the resistor and adjust to 1 V if necessary. Note the value of current on the ammeter and record it in Table 3-3.

Replace the 100-Ω resistor with a 330-Ω resistor. The voltage should still be 1 V across the resistor. Note the value of current on the ammeter and record it in Table 3-3.

Replace the 330-Ω resistor with a 560-Ω resistor. The voltage should still be 1 V across the resistor. Note the value of current on the ammeter and record it in Table 3-3.

Turn off the power supply and disconnect the circuit.

NAME ______________________________ DATE ____________

RESULTS FOR EXPERIMENT 3

QUESTION

In your own words, describe the different ways an ohmmeter, an ammeter, and a voltmeter are connected to make measurements. Use drawings to illustrate the three types of measurements. One paragraph and one schematic drawing for each type are required.

REPORT

Turn in the following:

1. Tables 3-1, 3-2, and 3-3.
2. The answer to the question.

TABLE 3–1. Answers to Fig. 3-2

Scale	Reading, V
a	6.5 V
b	400v
c	90v
d	6v
e	90v
f	35v
g	550v
h	17v

TABLE 3–2. Voltage Measurements

Resistor Value	Voltage
1 kΩ	1000v
100 Ω	100v
10 kΩ	10000v

Too high

TABLE 3–3. Current Measurements

Resistor Value	Voltage	Current, I
100 Ω	1 V	10
330 Ω	1 V	3
560 Ω	1 V	1.78

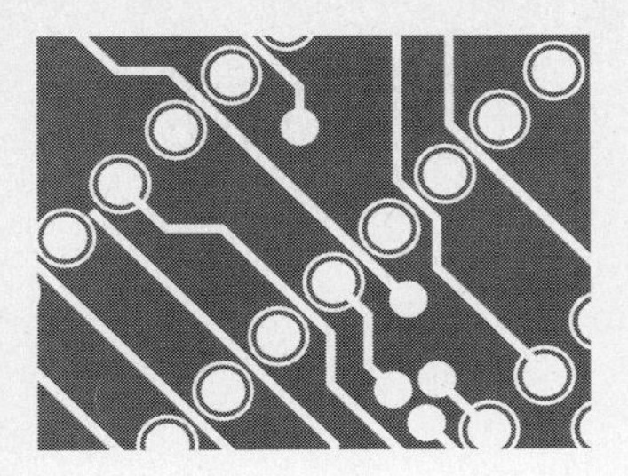

EXPERIMENT 4

OHM'S LAW

OBJECTIVES

At the completion of this experiment, you will be able to:

- Validate the Ohm's law expression, where

$$V = I \times R$$
$$I = \frac{V}{R}$$
$$R = \frac{V}{I}$$

SUGGESTED READING

Chapter 3, *Basic Electronics,* B. Grob, Eighth Edition

INTRODUCTION

Ohm's law is the most widely used principle in the study of basic electronics. In 1828, Georg Simon Ohm experimentally determined that the amount of current I in a circuit depended upon the amount of resistance R and the amount of voltage V. If any two of the factors V, I, or R are known, the third factor can be determined by calculation: $I = V/R$, $V = IR$, and $R = V/I$. Also, the amount of electric power, measured in watts, can be determined indirectly by using Ohm's law:

$$P = \frac{V^2}{R} \qquad \text{or} \qquad P = I^2R$$

Ohm's law is usually represented by the equation $I = V/R$. Because it is a mathematical representation of a physical occurrence, it is important to remember that the relationship between the three factors (I, V, and R) can also be expressed as follows:

Current is directly proportional to voltage if the resistance does not vary.
Current is inversely proportional to resistance if the voltage does not vary.

This experiment provides data that will validate the relationships between current, voltage, and resistance.

EQUIPMENT

Ohmmeter
Voltmeter
Ammeter
Power supply
Connecting leads
Circuit board

COMPONENTS

Resistors (all 0.25 W):

(1) 100 Ω (1) 820 Ω
(1) 330 Ω (1) 1 kΩ
(1) 560 Ω

PROCEDURE

1. Connect the circuit of Fig. 4-1*a* with the power supply turned off. The polarity of the power supply, the voltmeter, and the ammeter must be correct in order to avoid damage to the equipment.

Note: Use the circuit building aid of Fig. 4-1*b* if you have trouble.

2. Refer to Table 4-1. Calculate the current for the first voltage setting (1.5 V, 100 Ω nominal value). Record the value in Table 4-1 under the heading Calculated Current.
3. Check your circuit connection by tracing the path of electron flow. Be sure the ammeter reading is correct for the value of calculated current. Also, be sure the voltmeter range is correct.
4. Before turning the power supply on, turn the voltage adjust knob to zero. Now, turn the power supply on. Use the voltmeter to monitor the power supply and adjust for 1.5 V applied voltage.

Note: The ammeter can also be monitored. Unless you are using a digital meter, the pointer or needle should deflect upscale.

5. Read the value of measured current and record the results in Table 4-1.
6. Repeat procedures 2 to 5 for each value of applied voltage listed in Table 4-1.

Note: It is not necessary to turn the power supply off unless you are disconnecting the circuit in order to change meter ranges.

7. After recording all the measured and calculated values of current for Table 4-1, turn off the power

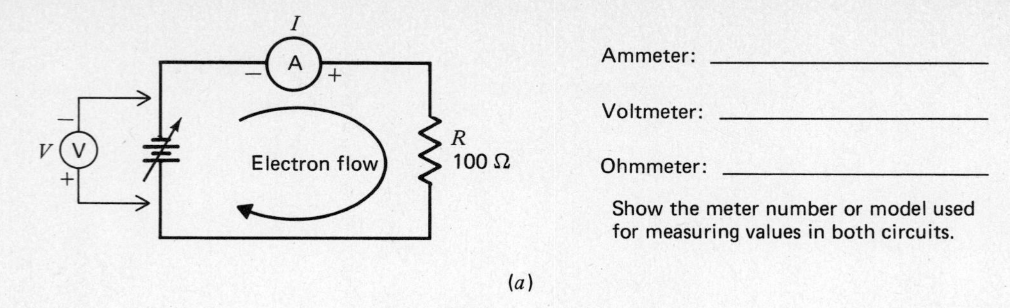

(a)

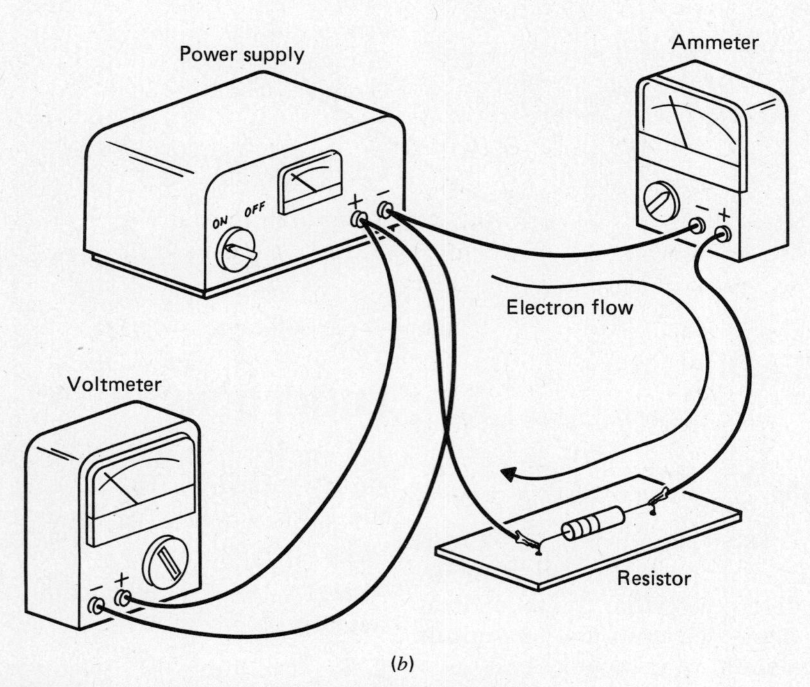

(b)

Fig. 4-1. (*a*) Ohm's law schematic. (*b*) Circuit building aid. (Note that arrows indicate electron flow or current path.)

supply. Be sure that the voltage adjust is set to zero. Disconnect the circuit. The calculated values of power can be done later. Indicate which formula you used.

8. Refer to Table 4-2. Use an ohmmeter to measure and record the values of each resistor listed in Table 4-2.

Note: Remember to adjust the ohmmeter for zero and infinity, depending upon the type you are using.

9. Connect the circuit of Fig. 4-2. Keep the power supply turned off and begin with the first value of resistance in Table 4-2, $R = 1000\ \Omega$ (1 kΩ).

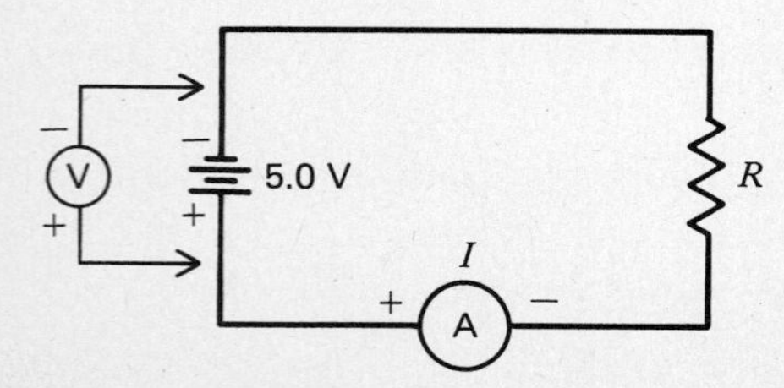

Fig. 4-2. Ohm's law circuit.

Note: This is the same basic circuit as Fig. 4-1. However, the ammeter is located in a different part of the circuit's current path. Use the same precautions as you did with Fig. 4-1.

10. Refer to Table 4-2. Calculate the current for the value of resistance listed in Table 4-2 (5.0 V, 1 kΩ nominal value). Record the calculated value in Table 4-2 under the heading Calculated Current.

11. Check your circuit. Be sure that the ammeter range is correct for the value of calculated current. Also, be sure that the voltmeter range is correct.

12. Turn on the power supply and adjust for 5.0 V applied voltage. Monitor the meters as you did for the circuit of Fig. 4-1.

13. Read the value of measured current and record the results in Table 4-2.

14. Turn the power supply off. Replace the resistor with the next value of resistance listed in Table 4-2.

15. Repeat procedures 10 to 14 for each value of resistance listed in Table 4-2.

16. Turn the power supply off. Disconnect the circuit.

NAME ______________________ DATE ______________

RESULTS FOR EXPERIMENT 4

QUESTIONS

Choose the correct answer.

__C__ **1.** If the circuit of Fig. 4-1 had 10 kΩ of resistance, the amount of applied voltage necessary to produce 1 mA would be:
A. 1000 V **B.** 100 V **C.** 10 V **D.** 1 V

__B__ **2.** In the circuit of Fig. 4-1, if the applied voltage was increased, the amount of power would be:
A. Decreased **B.** Increased **C.** Stayed the same

__C__ **3.** Compared to a voltmeter, the ammeter in Fig. 4-1 is:
A. Drawn differently and connected differently **B.** Drawn the same and connected differently **C.** Drawn differently and connected the same **D.** Drawn the same and connected the same

__A__ **4.** Referring to the circuit of Fig. 4-2, if the voltage was doubled for each step but the resistance was halved, the current (Table 4-2) would:
A. Increase by twice as much **B.** Decrease by one-half **C.** Decrease by one-fourth **D.** Increase by four times as much

__B__ **5.** According to Ohm's law and the data gathered in the experiment:
A. The less resistance, the more current with constant voltage **B.** The more current, the less voltage with constant resistance **C.** The less resistance, the more current with constant voltage **D.** The less current, the more voltage with constant resistance

__D__ **6.** If the terminals (negative and positive) of the power supply in Fig. 4-2 were reversed, it would be necessary to:
A. Reverse the terminals of the ammeter and the resistor **B.** Reverse the terminals of the voltmeter and the ammeter **C.** Reverse the terminals of the voltmeter and the resistor **D.** Reverse the terminals of the resistor only

__C__ **7.** Because the ammeter is connected in the same way as the resistor, would you expect the ammeter's resistance to be:
A. Very large **B.** Very small **C.** Medium value

__C__ **8.** To obtain a current value of 30 mA, the amount of voltage and resistance necessary would be:
A. $V = 100$ V, $R = 333\ \Omega$ **B.** $V = 15$ V, $R = 500\ \Omega$ **C.** $V = 3$ V, $R = 100\ \Omega$
D. A, B, and C

REPORT

Organize your written report in this order. Then turn in your report to the lab instructor.

1. Cover sheet, also called a blank style sheet.
2. Results: Data Tables 4-1 and 4-2.
3. Schematics with the numbers or models of the equipment used.
4. Answers to questions 1 to 8.

Note: Discuss the results after you analyze the data. For this report, discuss voltage, current, and resistance as they are related according to Ohm's law and your data. Write short concise sentences. Remember, the *Discussion* is the most important part of a report; it relates your understanding of the experiment.

The *Purpose* is usually a statement about what you are trying to validate. The *Procedure* is the lab manual title, page number(s) where the procedure is found, and any changes made to the procedure. The *Results* are listed as any data tables or graphs by number. The *Conclusion* is a brief summary of the experiment with respect to the Purpose. Be neat and accurate. Answer the questions assigned, and attach the answers on a separate sheet of lined $8\frac{1}{2} \times 11$ in. paper. Type or write the report in ink (black or blue). A sample report is included in Appendix D.

TABLE 4–1. Ohm's Law

Applied Voltage, V	Nominal Resistance, Ω	Measured Current, mA	Calculated Current,* mA	Calculated Power†
1.5	100	15mA	15mA	22.5mV
2.5	100	25mA	25mA	2.5v
3.5	100	35	35	122.5
4.5	100	45	45	202.5
6.0	100	60	60	360
7.0	100	70	70	490
8.0	100	80	80	640
9.0	100	90	90	810

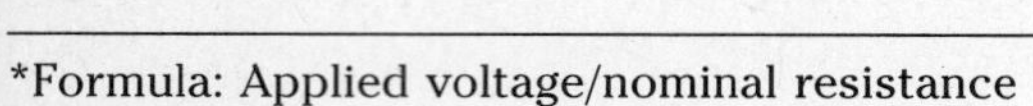

*Formula: Applied voltage/nominal resistance

†Formula: ______________________

TABLE 4–2. Ohm's Law

Applied Voltage, V	Nominal Resistance, Ω	Measured Resistance, Ω	Measured Current, mA	Calculated Current,* mA
5.0	1000	1K	5mA	5
5.0	820	820	6	6.0975
5.0	560	560	9	8.928
5.0	330	330	15	15.151
5.0	100	100	50	50

*Formula: Applied voltage/measured resistance

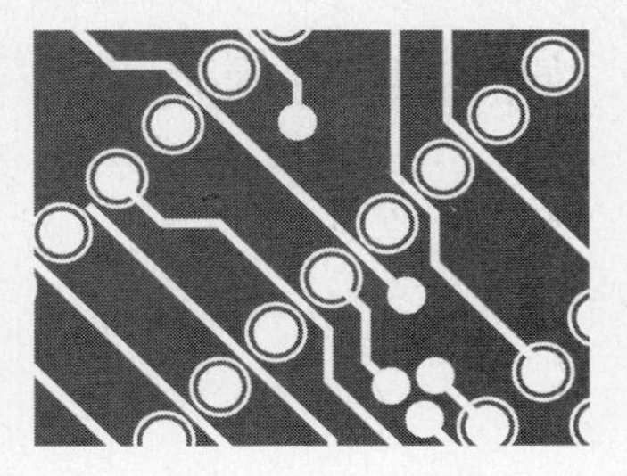

EXPERIMENT 5

APPLYING OHM'S LAW

OBJECTIVES

At the completion of this experiment, you will be able to:

- Calculate V, I, or R from measured values.
- Determine the difference between calculated and measured power.
- Design a simple circuit using Ohm's law.

SUGGESTED READING

Chapter 3, *Basic Electronics,* B. Grob, Eighth Edition

INTRODUCTION

As you already learned in the previous experiment, Ohm's law proves that there is a proportional relationship between voltage, current, and resistance. This law forms the basis for much of the troubleshooting work that technicians do every day. Regardless of the complexity of a circuit, engineers and technicians still use Ohm's law to determine voltage, current, or resistance. This experiment will reinforce your understanding of Ohm's law and show you how to apply it to simple circuits.

Ohm's Law Review

To review, Ohm's law states that:

$V = I/R$	Voltage equals current multiplied by resistance
$I = V/R$	Current equals voltage divided by resistance
$R = V/I$	Resistance equals voltage divided by current

The relationship between V and I is *directly proportional* because as one factor is increased, the other factor is increased at the same rate, but only if R does not change. But the relationship between R and I is *inversely proportional* because as one factor is increased, the other factor is decreased at the same rate, but only if V does not change (fixed value). For example, if the resistance R is increased two times, the current I will decrease by one-half.

In Fig. 5-1, two circuits have the same value of current although the values of V and R are different for each circuit.

Ohm's law can also be used to calculate power using these formulas:

$$P = V \times I$$
$$P = I^2R$$
$$P = V^2/R$$

These relationships are used to calculate the amount of power (in watts) dissipated in a circuit. This is important for protecting circuits from overheating and in determining whether a component is operating within its allowed range or wattage specification. In general, whenever current travels through a resistance, power is used, resulting in heat or light being created. For example, when current passes through a resistor, friction causes heat to be released or dissipated. If too much current passes through a resistor, exceeding its power rating, it may burn or melt the resistor. But most circuits are designed with fuses to prevent excessive current from causing too much damage. By applying Ohm's law, it is easy to determine the levels of current in a circuit.

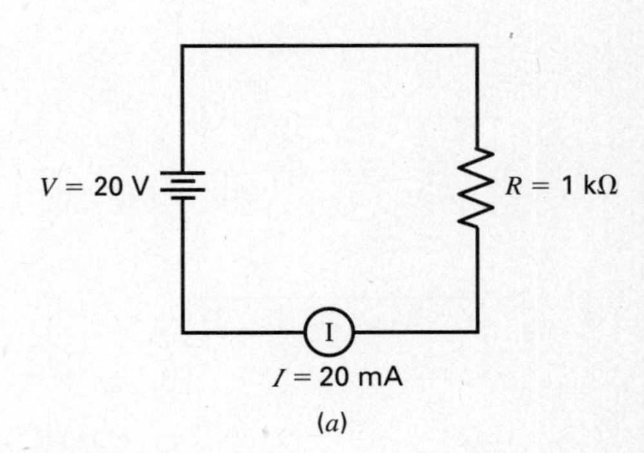

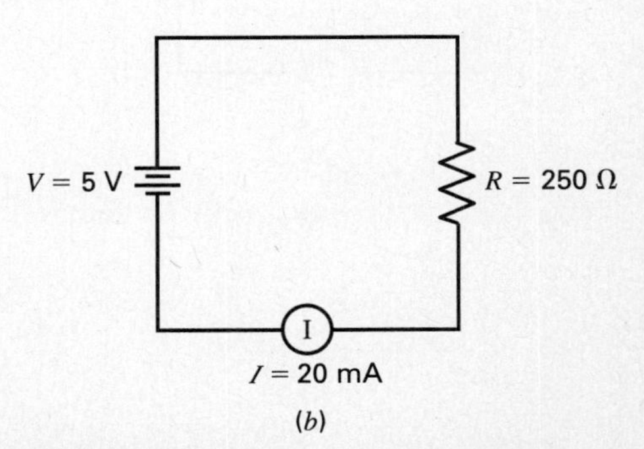

Fig. 5-1. Two circuits with the same current but different values of V and R.

EQUIPMENT

DC power supply
Ohmmeter
Ammeter
Voltmeter

COMPONENTS

Resistors: (1) 330 Ω, (1) 470 Ω, and (1) < 1 kΩ or less for design (step 11)

PROCEDURE

1. Measure the 330-Ω and 470-Ω resistors to be sure that they are in tolerance, and record their values in Table 5-1. Be sure to calibrate (adjust) the ohmmeter for infinity and zero, unless you are using a digital meter. If any resistor is out of tolerance, replace it with a good one.

2. Refer to the circuit schematic of Fig. 5-2*a*. Use Ohm's law to calculate the current in the circuit. Record the value in Table 5-1.

3. Connect the circuit of Fig. 5-2*a*.

4. Measure the voltage across the resistor and the current in the circuit. Record both values, V and I, in Table 5-1.

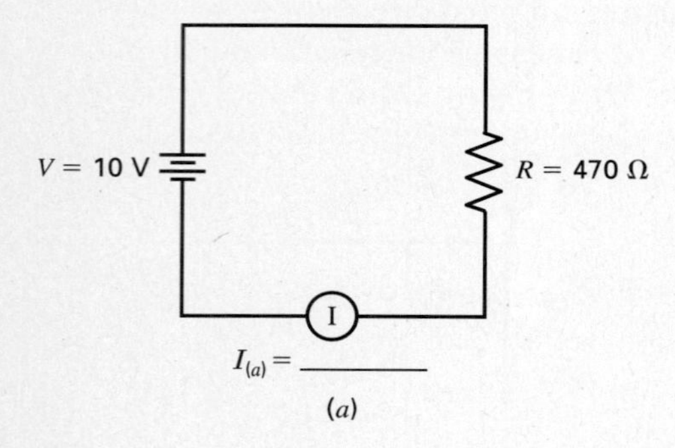

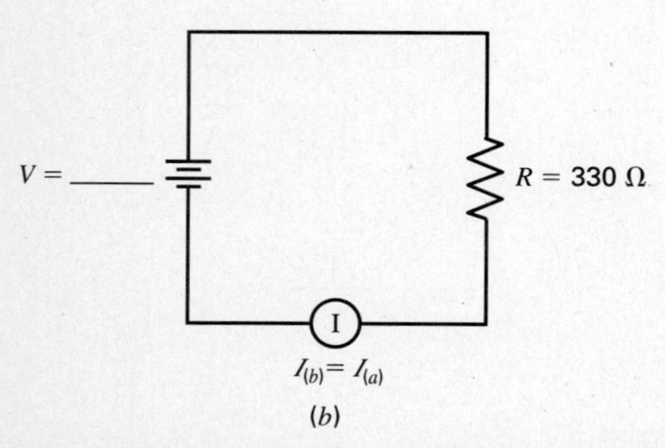

Fig. 5-2. Ohm's law test circuits. (*a*) Given values. (*b*) Unknown values.

5. Calculate the power dissipated, using the nominal values of resistance and voltage and the formula $P = V^2/R$. Record the calculated power dissipation in Table 5-1.

6. Calculate the power dissipated in the resistor, using the measured values of I and R only and the formula $P = I^2/R$.

7. Connect the circuit of Fig. 5-2*b* where $R = 330\ \Omega$ and there is also an ammeter connected in the circuit.

8. Carefully adjust the power supply voltage so that the current in the circuit in Fig. 5-2*b* is approximately equal to the current in the circuit in Fig. 5-2*a*. Record the value of voltage in Table 5-1.

9. Repeat steps 4 through 6 above for the circuit in Fig. 5-2*b*.

10. Percentage of error in power measurments: Calculate the percentage of error between the calculated and measured values of power in Table 5-1. To do this, find the difference between the two values and divide that difference by the calculated value: % error = difference between measured and calculated value ÷ calculated value. It does not matter whether the measured or the calculated value is greater; simply find the difference between them and divide by the calculated value. Record the percentage of error in Table 5-1.

11. Design a circuit that has the approximate value of current (±10 percent) as the circuits of Fig. 5-2*a* and *b* but with the following three specification restrictions: (1) voltage must be between 1 and 15 V; (2) resistance must be less than 1 kΩ; and (3) the resistor used must be a standard value available in your lab (listed in Appendix I).

12. On a separate sheet of paper, draw the schematic for the circuit, showing the design values V, I, and R. Be sure to label all components carefully and show the meter connections. Also, show the design calculations (Ohm's law calculations) you used and be sure to indicate the calculated values of V, I, and R.

13. Measure the resistor you have chosen and record the value in Table 5-2.

14. Repeat steps 4 through 6 above for the circuit you designed. Record all the values in Table 5-2.

Note: You may want to record the values on a separate sheet of paper before recording them in the table in case the design is invalid and you redesign it.

NAME DATE

RESULTS FOR EXPERIMENT 5

QUESTIONS

1. In the circuits of Fig. 5-2*a* and *b*, what aspects of Ohm's law were validated?

2. Describe any difference between the power calculations using the measured values and the calculated values. Refer to the percentage of error values.

3. Explain why you think an ammeter can be connected in the circuit and not affect the flow of current.

4. Explain why the voltage measured across the resistor is the same as the applied voltage.

5. In the circuit you designed, explain how you could reduce the dissipated power by one-half.

REPORT

Turn in the following:

1. The schematic for your design and the calculations.
2. Tables 5-1 and 5-2.
3. The answers to the questions.

TABLE 5-1. Approximate Values Are Acceptable

Circuit	Measured Value, R	Measured Value, V	Measured Value, I	Calculated Value, I	Calculated Value, $P = V^2/R$	Measured Value, $P = I^2R$	% Error, P
a							
b							

TABLE 5-2

Measured Value, R	Measured Value, V	Measured Value, I	Calculated Value, $P = V^2/R$*	Measured Value, $P = I^2R$	% Error P

*Refers to calculated values on separate sheet.

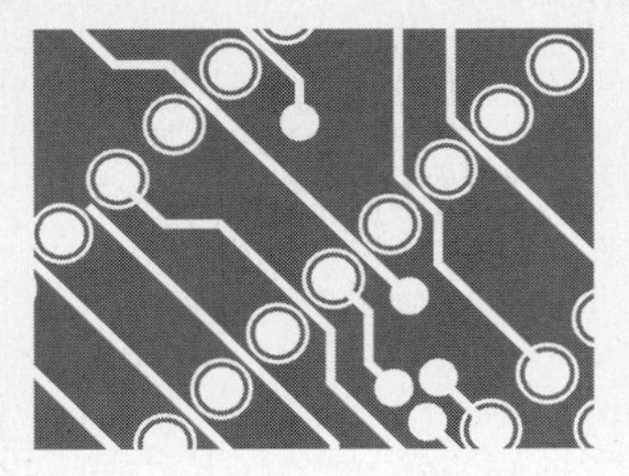

EXPERIMENT 6

SERIES CIRCUITS

OBJECTIVES

At the completion of this experiment, you will be able to:

- Recognize the basic characteristics of series circuits.
- Compare the mathematical relationships existing in a series circuit.
- Compare the mathematical calculations to the measured values of a series circuit.

SUGGESTED READING

Chapter 4, *Basic Electronics,* B. Grob, Eighth Edition

INTRODUCTION

An electric circuit is a complete path through which electrons can flow from the negative terminal of the voltage source, through the connecting wires or conductors, through the load or loads, and back to the positive terminal of the voltage source.

If the circuit is arranged so that the electrons have only one possible path, the circuit is called a *series circuit.* Therefore, a series circuit is defined as a circuit that contains only one path for current flow. Figure 6-1 shows a series circuit with several resistors.

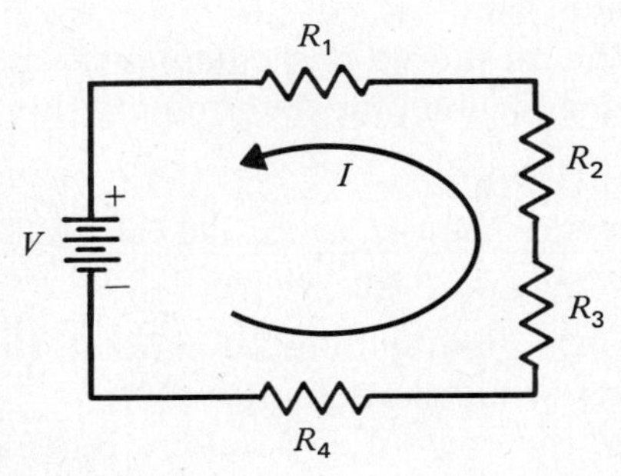

Fig. 6-1. Series circuit.

One of the most important aspects of a series circuit is its relationship to current. Current in a series circuit is determined by Ohm's law, which defines a proportional relation between voltage and the total circuit resistance. This relationship between total voltage and total circuit resistance results in the current being the same value throughout the entire circuit. In other words, the measured current will be the same value at any point in a series circuit.

Figure 6-2 shows a series circuit consisting of a battery and two resistors. The battery is labeled V_t and provides the total voltage across the circuit. The resistors are labeled R_1 and R_2. The resistance values are $R_1 = 100\ \Omega$ and $R_2 = 2.7\ \text{k}\Omega$. The power supply has been adjusted to a level of 20 V.

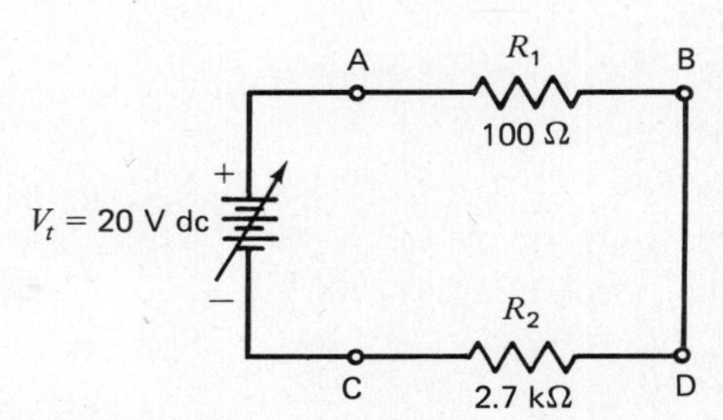

Fig. 6-2. Series circuit for analysis.

Figure 6-2 shows several points labeled A, B, C, and D. These are the points at which current could be measured. To measure the current at these points, it is necessary to break into the circuit and insert an ammeter in series. Remember, in a series circuit the amount of current measured will be the same at each of these points.

The total current, labeled I_T, flowing throughout the series circuit depends upon two factors: the total resistance R_T and the applied total voltage V_T. The applied total voltage was given in Fig. 6-2 such that

$$V_T = 20\ \text{V}$$

To determine the current, the total resistance R_T must be calculated by

$$R_T = R_1 + R_2$$

The total resistance for the circuit shown in Fig. 6-2 is

$$R_T = 100\ \Omega + 2700\ \Omega = 2800\ \Omega$$

For circuits that have three (3) or more series resistors, the above formula may be modified as shown to include the additional resistors:

$$R_T = R_1 + R_2 + R_3 + \cdots$$

When solving for the current I, Ohm's law states that

$$I = \frac{V}{R}$$

When solving for current I_T,

$$I_T = \frac{V_T}{R_T}$$
$$= \frac{20 \text{ V}}{2800 \ \Omega}$$
$$= 0.00714 \text{ A}$$
$$= 7.14 \text{ mA}$$

Applied voltage will be dropped proportionally across individual resistances, depending upon their value of resistance. As shown in Fig. 6-3, the *IR* voltage drops can be solved as follows. The sum of the voltage drops will be the total applied voltage. This is stated by

$$V_T = IR_1 + IR_2$$
$$\text{or} \quad V_T = V_{R_1} + V_{R_2}$$

where

$$V_{R_1} = I_T R_1$$
$$= (7.14 \text{ mA}) (100 \ \Omega)$$
$$= 0.71 \text{ V}$$

and

$$V_{R_2} = I_T R_2$$
$$= (7.14 \text{ mA}) (2700 \ \Omega)$$
$$= 19.27 \text{ V}$$

Therefore,

$$V_T = 0.71 \text{ V} + 19.27 \text{ V}$$
$$= 19.98 \text{ V}$$
$$= 20 \text{ V (approximately)}$$

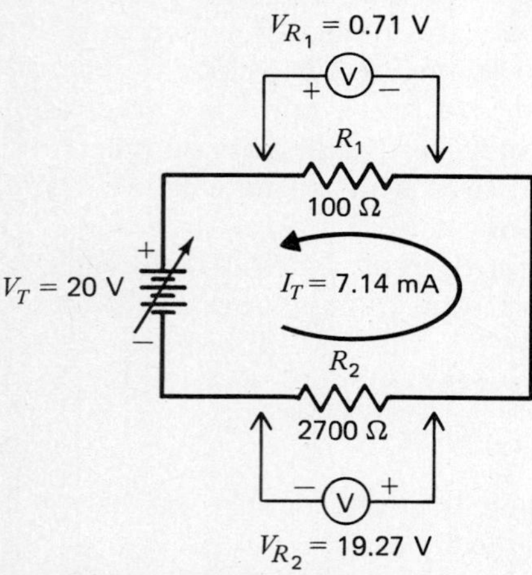

Fig. 6-3. Determining the *IR* (voltage) drops.

EQUIPMENT

Breadboard
DC power supply
Voltmeter
Ammeter
Ohmmeter

COMPONENTS

Resistors (all 0.25 W unless indicated otherwise):

(1) 10 Ω (1) 150 Ω, 1 W
(1) 15 Ω

PROCEDURE

1. With an ohmmeter, measure each resistor value for the resistors required for this experiment. Connect the resistors in series and measure the total resistance R_T. Record the results in Table 6-1.
2. Using the information in the introduction and Fig. 6-4, calculate the total resistance R_T, the series current I_T, and the *IR* voltage drops across R_1, R_2, and R_3. Record the results in Table 6-2.

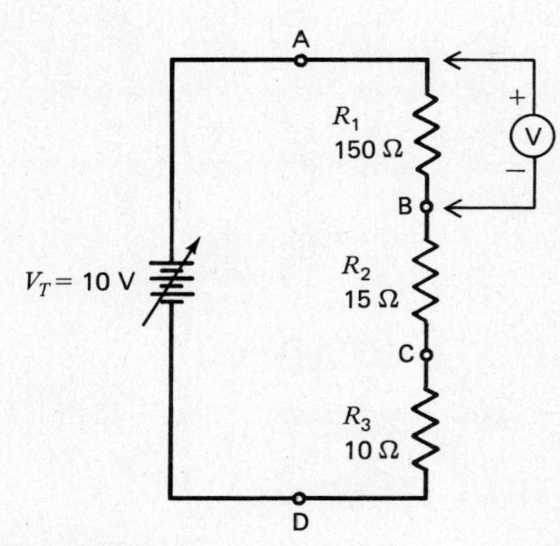

Fig. 6-4. Series circuit.

3. Connect the circuit in Fig. 6-4 and turn on the dc power supply. Using a voltmeter, adjust the power supply level to 10 V dc.
4. Measure the *IR* voltage drops across each resistance as indicated in Fig. 6-4. For example, the voltmeter is shown connected across R_1 to measure V_{R_1}. Record the results in Table 6-2.
5. After recording the measured voltage drops, compare the measured and calculated values. Use the following formula for determining this percentage:

$$\% = \left| \frac{\text{difference between meas. and calc. values}}{\text{calc. values}} \right| \times 100$$

If any error is greater than 20 percent, then repeat calculations or measurements.
6. Measure the current at points A, B, C, and D in Fig. 6-4. Record this information in Table 6-3.

Note 1: To measure current, you must actually break the circuit at these points and insert your ammeter (or current-measuring resistor, if you are not using an ammeter) in accordance with the information presented in the introduction.

Note 2: Check with your instructor in case you need to leave this circuit connected. When all results have been recorded, call your instructor over to your lab station to verify your results.

NAME ______________________________ DATE ____________

RESULTS FOR EXPERIMENT 6

QUESTIONS

Choose the correct answer.

__C__ **1.** In a series circuit, total current I_t is equal to:
A. $R_T \times I_T$ **B.** $V_T \times R_T$ **C.** V_T/R_T **D.** R_T/V_T

__B__ **2.** In a series circuit, the current is:
A. Different through every resistor in series **B.** Always the same through every resistor in series **C.** Calculated by using Ohm's law as $I = V \times R$ **D.** Found only by using the voltmeter

__C__ **3.** The total voltage in a series circuit is:
A. Equal to total resistance **B.** Found by adding the current through each resistor **C.** Equal to the sum of the series *IR* voltage drops **D.** Found by using an ohmmeter

__D__ **4.** In a series circuit with 10 V applied:
A. The greater the total resistance, the greater the total current **B.** The greater the total current, the greater the total resistance **C.** The *IR* voltage drops will each equal 10 V **D.** The sum of the *IR* voltage drops will equal 10 V

__C__ **5.** When an *IR* voltage drop exists in a series circuit:
A. The polarity of the resistor is equal to positive **B.** The polarity of the resistor is equal to negative **C.** The polarity of the resistor is less than the total current on both sides **D.** The polarity of the resistor is positive on one end and negative on the other because of current flowing through it

REPORT

When completing the report, discuss your results by answering the following three questions as the most significant aspects:

1. Does $V_T = I_{R_1} + I_{R_2} + I_{R_3}$?
2. Is the measurement current the same at all parts of the series circuit?
3. Does $R_T = R_1 + R_2 + R_3$?

Write your own conclusion by summarizing the concept of series circuits.

Report Notes

The test circuit (Fig. 6-5) appears along with Tables 6-1 to 6-3. Use them as part of your report. Tear them out here and staple them to your report. You will be responsible for completing the remaining sections of the report.

Note: All necessary paper has been provided for this experiment. The following experiments will gradually include less and less given material until the report becomes your full responsibility.

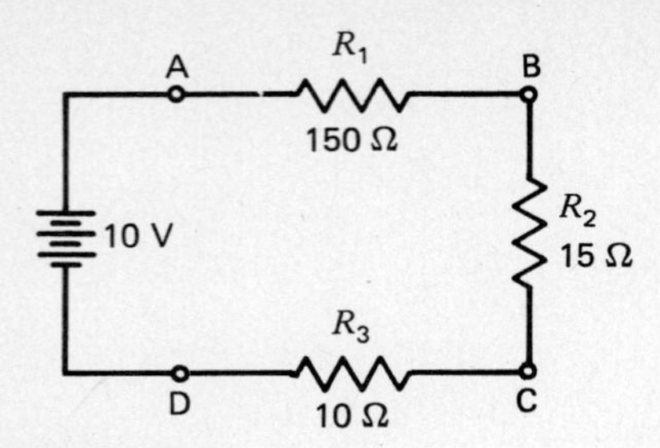

Fig. 6-5. Series circuit.

TABLE 6–1

Nominal Resistance, Ω	Measured, Ω
$R_1 = 150$	9
$R_2 = 15$	14.8
$R_3 = 10$	155
$R_t = 175$	178.8

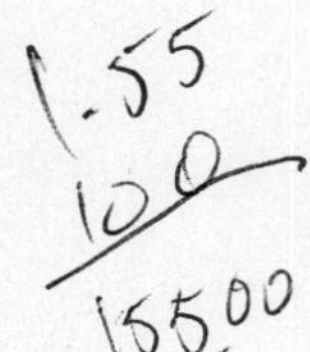

TABLE 6–2

	Calculated	Measured	% Error
R_T	[illegible]	[illegible]	0
I_T	57.1mA	56mA	1.9%
V_{R_1}	8.57mA	8.5v	.82%
V_{R_2}	.857	.83v	3.15%
V_{R_3}	.57	.6	5.08%

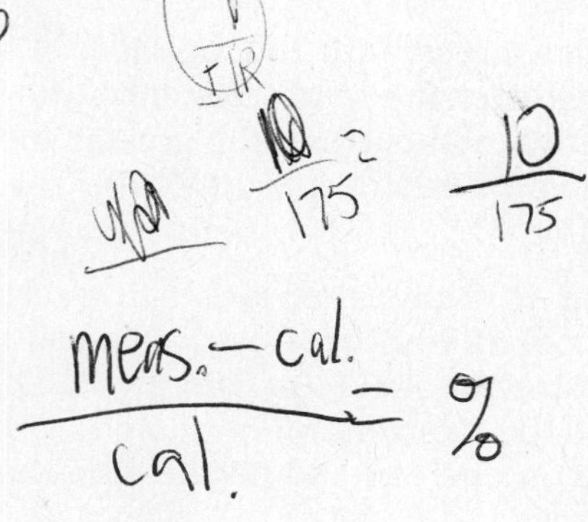

TABLE 6–3

Point	Current, mA
A	56
B	56
C	56
D	56

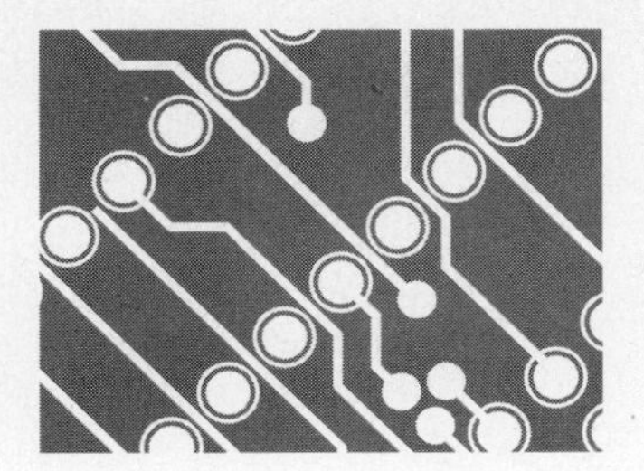

EXPERIMENT 7

SERIES CIRCUITS—RESISTANCE

OBJECTIVES

At the completion of this experiment, you will be able to:

- Recognize the basic characteristics of series circuits; for example, the total resistance R_T of a series string is equal to the sum of the individual resistances.
- Understand that a combination of series resistances is often called a *string* and that the string resistance equals the sum of the individual resistances.
- Compare the mathematical calculations to the measured values of a series circuit and recognize that the amount of current between two points in a circuit equals the potential difference divided by the resistance between these points.

SUGGESTED READING

Chapter 4, *Basic Electronics,* B. Grob, Eighth Edition

INTRODUCTION

When a series circuit is connected across a voltage source, such as a power supply, as shown in Fig. 7-1, the electrons forming the current must pass through all the series resistances. This path is the only way the electrons can return to the power supply. With two or more resistances in the same current path, the total resistance across the voltage source is the total of all individual resistances found in what is referred to as a *series string.* This "total" resistance is referred to as R_T.

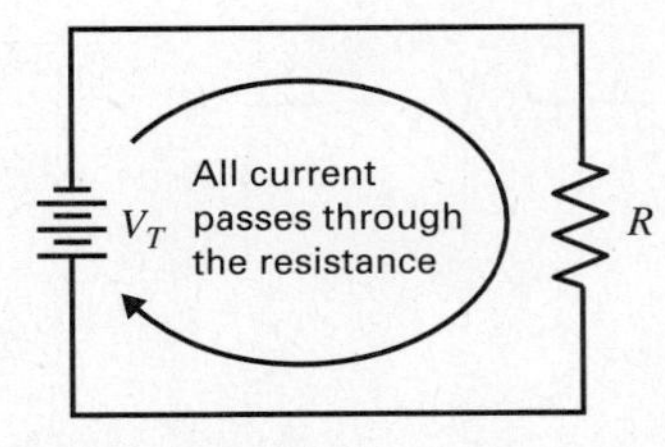

Fig. 7-1. Series resistance.

For example, if the circuit in Fig. 7-2 is analyzed, the total resistance R_T is the sum of the two individual resistances R_1 and R_2. In this case the total resistance would be equal to 1150 Ω (since the string resistance of R_1 (470 Ω) is series added to R_2 (680 Ω).

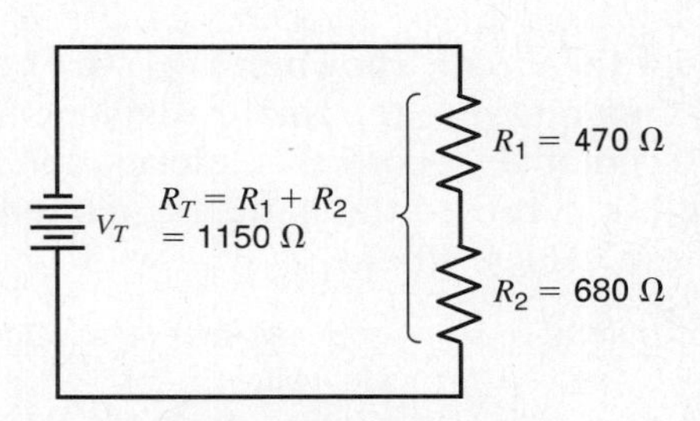

Fig. 7-2. R_T equals the sum of R_1 and R_2.

The total resistive opposition to current flow is the same as if a 1150-Ω resistance were substituted for the two resistors, as shown in Fig. 7-3.

According to Ohm's law, the amount of current between two points in a circuit equals the potential difference divided by the resistance between these points. Since the entire string is connected across the voltage source, the current equals the voltage applied across the entire string divided by the total series resistance of the string (between points A and B in Fig. 7-3). In this case a power supply applies 25 V across 1150 Ω to produce 21.7 mA. This is the same amount of current flow through R_1 and R_2 shown in Fig. 7-2.

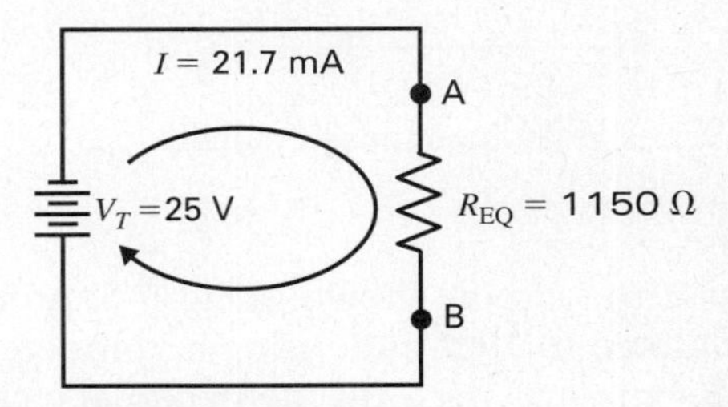

Fig. 7-3. Equivalent series resistance.

EQUIPMENT

Breadboard
DC power supply
VOM/DMM
  Voltmeter
  Ammeter
  Ohmmeter

COMPONENTS

All resistors are 0.25 W unless indicated otherwise:

(1) 100-Ω resistor
(1) 150-Ω resistor

(1) 220-Ω resistor
(1) 390-Ω resistor
(1) 560-Ω resistor

PROCEDURE

1. Measure and record each resistor value for the resistors required in this experiment. Record the results in Table 7-1.

2. Connect the circuit shown in Fig. 7-4. First calculate and then measure the total resistance from point A to point B. Record this information in Table 7-2. In addition, record the percentage of error between these values, where

$$\% \text{ error} = \left| \frac{\text{difference between meas. and calc. values}}{\text{calc. values}} \right| \times 100$$

If the error is greater than 10 percent, repeat the calculations and measurements.

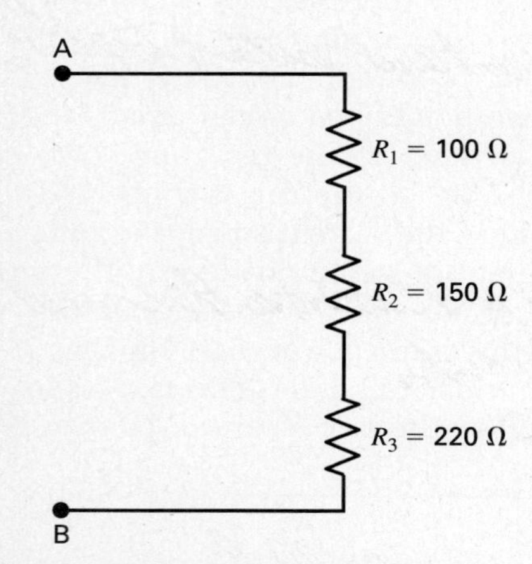

Fig. 7-4. Series resistance measurements.

3. Connect the circuit shown in Fig. 7-5. Adjust the supply voltage to 15 V and, using a voltmeter, take measurements and perform the necessary calculations required to complete Table 7-3.

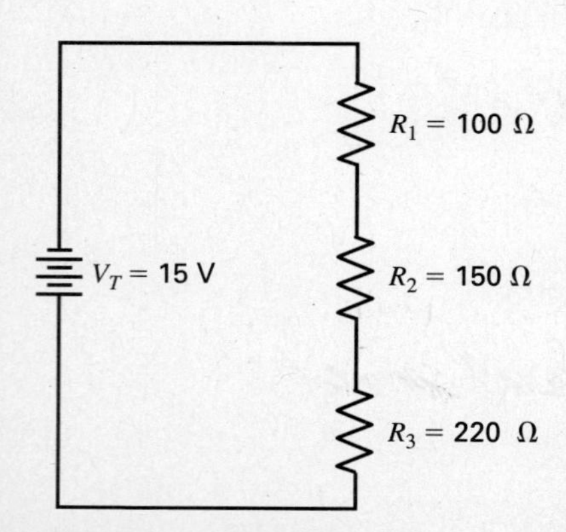

Fig. 7-5. Series string resistance.

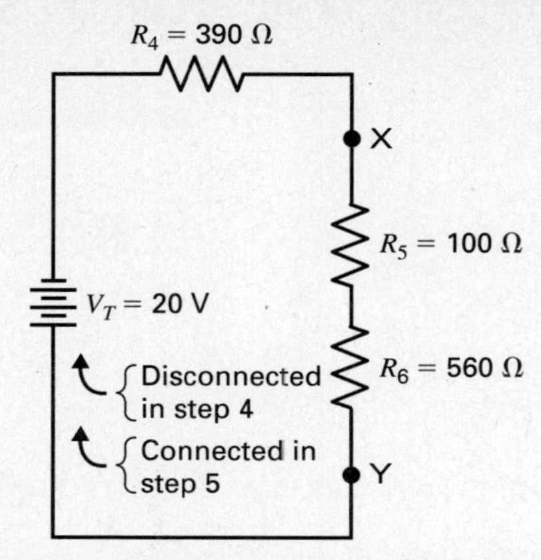

Fig. 7-6. Series resistance with an applied voltage source.

4. Connect the circuit as shown in Fig. 7-6. Calculate the expected resistance between points X and Y and record the results in Table 7-4. With the *power turned off and totally disconnected* from the circuit, measure and record, in Table 7-4, the resistance between X and Y.

5. With the ohmmeter disconnected from the circuit, connect the dc power supply to the circuit in Fig. 7-6 and adjust to 20 V. With an ammeter, measure the current at point Y and record the result in Table 7-4.

Note: It will be necessary to break the circuit at this point and insert the ammeter into the circuit as shown in Fig. 7-7. Based upon the measured resistances and current, first calculate and then measure the voltage across R_5 and R_6.

6. In reviewing step 5, determine the percentage of error and record the result in Table 7-4. The mathematical calculations of the measured values of a series circuit are such that the amount of current between two points in a circuit equals the potential difference divided by the resistance between these points.

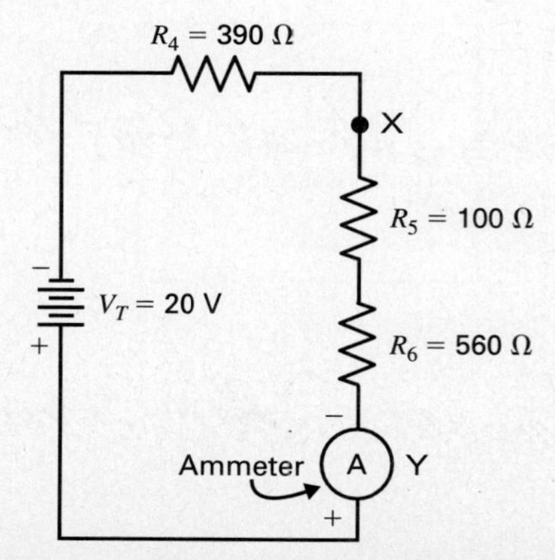

Fig. 7-7. Inserting the ammeter into the circuit.

NAME ____________________ DATE ____________

RESULTS FOR EXPERIMENT 7

QUESTIONS

1. Write the formula that determines the total resistance R_T that is found in a series resistance string.

   $R = V / I$

   $R_T = R_1 + R_2 + R_3 + \ldots$

2. Write the formula that determines the amount of current flow for the circuit shown in Fig. 7-5 if the potential difference is 85 V.

   $I = \frac{V}{R}$ $V = I \cdot R$

3. In your estimation would $V_T = IR_1 + IR_2 + IR_3 + \cdots$, be true for all series resistive strings? Explain.

   Yes. Because you get voltage when multiplying current and resistance together. And by adding them together, you get the total voltage.

4. Do you believe that the measured current is the same at all points of a series resistive string when a potential difference is present across the circuit? Explain. Yes. Since the potential difference is present, and since current in the same at all points, then it would have to have the same current in all points.

5. Could you always expect that $R_T = R_1 + R_2 + R_3 + \cdots$, in a series resistive circuit? Explain.

   Yes because you add up all the resistance before you could figure out the total resistance.

CRITICAL THINKING QUESTIONS

Note: The following questions are designed to help you analyze the previous laboratory experiment in a complete and in-depth fashion. To answer these questions, you should review the related material in Grob, *Basic Electronics,* Eighth Edition.

1. Explain where "sources" of error exist in this experiment. How could these sources of error be reduced?

   By measuring the right items + connecting in the right spot.

2. The purpose of a series circuit is to connect different components that need the same current. After reviewing your results for this experiment, explain how this purpose supports, or agrees with, your findings.

   All components have the same current because they all connect.

3. Explain why the current is the same in all parts of a series circuit.

   Current is the same because, current is going in + out or around the circuit with the same current.

4. Is it the case that the mathematical calculations of the measured values of a series circuit are such that the amount of current between two points in a circuit equals the potential difference divided by the resistance between these points? Explain.

5. Explain what is meant by the term *series string.*

REPORT

Turn in a complete report.

TABLE 7–1. Individual Resistor Values

Resistors	Measured	% Tolerance
100	100	0
150	150	0
220	220	0
390	380	2.56%
560	550	1.78%

TABLE 7–2. Total Resistance R_T and Percentage of Error

	Calculated	Measured	% Error
Total Resistance	1KW	1380	2.1

TABLE 7–3. Series Circuit Measurements

Resistors	Value	Measured*	Measured Voltage	Calculated Current
R_1	100	100	3.2	32 mA
R_2	150	180	4.82	32.1mA
R_3	220	220	6.85	31.1 mA

*Values from previous table.

TABLE 7–4. Series Circuit Measurements and Percentage of Error

Resistance	Expected	Measured	Measured Voltage	Calculated Current	% Error
X to Y	660	650			
Current Y		18.8mA			
R_5			2v	20mA	6%
R_6			10.5v	18.75mA	.27%

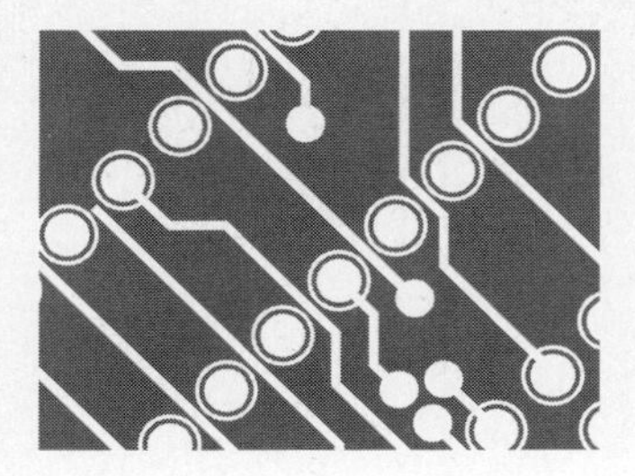

EXPERIMENT 8

SERIES CIRCUITS—ANALYSIS

OBJECTIVES

At the completion of this experiment, you will be able to:

- Recognize that, when you know the current *I* for one component connected into a series circuit, this value is used for the current *I* in all components, since the current is the same in all parts of a series circuit.
- Determine that, in order to calculate *I*, the total V_T can be divided by the total R_T, or an individual *IR* drop can be divided by its resistance.
- Compare the mathematical calculations to the measured values of a series circuit to the extent that, when the individual voltage drops around the series circuit are known, they can be added to equal the applied V_T. Further, you will demonstrate that a known voltage drop can be subtracted from the total V_T to find the remaining voltage drop.

SUGGESTED READING

Chapter 4, *Basic Electronics*, B. Grob, Eighth Edition

INTRODUCTION

It is useful to remember general methods for analyzing series circuits. For example, when analyzing series resistive circuits, if the circuit current for one component is known, you can use this value for currents in all the remaining series components, since the current is the same in all parts of a series circuit.

In order to calculate the circuit current *I*, the total applied voltage V_T can be divided by the total circuit resistance R_T, or the voltage drops (*IR* drops) of an individual component can be divided by its resistance *R*.

When the individual voltage drops around a circuit are known, they can be added to equal the applied voltage V_T. This also means that a known voltage drop can be subtracted from the total applied voltage in order to find the remaining voltage drop.

A common application of series circuits is to use a resistance to drop the voltage from the voltage source to a lower value, as shown in Fig. 8-1. The load resistance represented here is a transistor amplifier

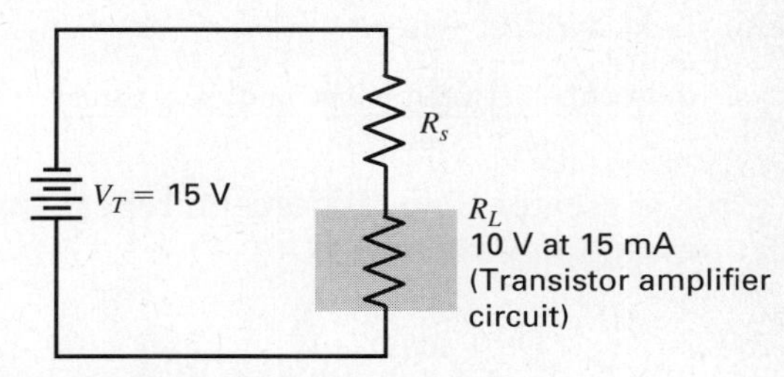

Fig. 8-1. Series dropping resistor.

which would normally operate at 10 V_{dc} with a constant dc load current of 15 mA. The load requirements are 10 V_{dc} at 15 mA. The available voltage source can be lowered only to 15 V_{dc} minimum. A suitable series voltage-dropping resistor R_s must be designed so that the voltage-dropping resistor is inserted in series to provide a voltage drop V_s that will make V_L equal to 10 V_{dc}. The required voltage drop across V_s is the difference between V_L and the higher V_T. For example:

$$V_s = V_T - V_L = 15 - 10 = 5 \text{ V}$$

This voltage drop of 5 V must be provided with a current of 15 mA, because the current is the same through R_s and R_L. To calculate R_s:

$$R_s = 5 \text{ V}/15 \text{ mA} = 333.33\ \Omega$$

EQUIPMENT

Breadboard
DC power supply
VOM/DMM
  Voltmeter
  Ammeter
  Ohmmeter

COMPONENTS

All resistors can be 0.25 W or 0.5 W unless indicated otherwise:

(1) 100-Ω resistor
(1) 150-Ω resistor
(1) 220-Ω resistor
(1) 390-Ω resistor
(1) 560-Ω resistor

PROCEDURE

1. Measure and record each resistor value for the resistors required in this experiment. Record the results in Table 8-1.
2. Connect the circuit shown in Fig. 8-2. First calculate and then measure the total resistance from point A to point B. Record this information in Table 8-2. In addition, record the percentage of error between these values, where

$$\% \text{ error} = \left| \frac{\text{difference between meas. and calc. values}}{\text{calc. values}} \right| \times 100$$

If the error is greater than 10 percent, repeat the calculations and measurements.

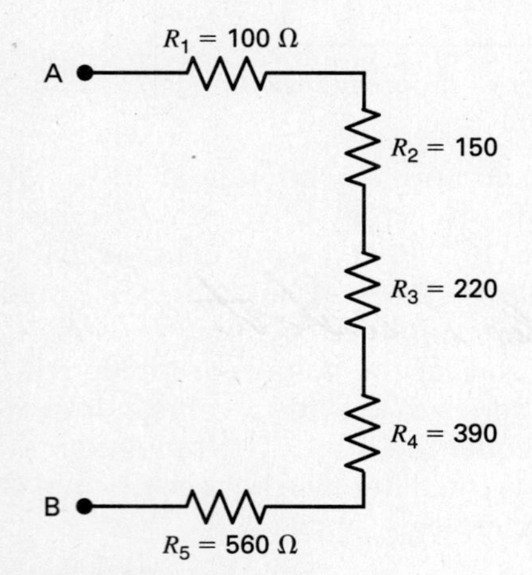

Fig. 8-2. Series resistive circuit.

3. Connect the circuit as shown in Fig. 8-3 and apply 20 V_{dc}. With the supply voltage on, open the circuit at point A and, using an ammeter, measure and record the current in Table 8-3. Disconnect the ammeter and reconnect the circuit.

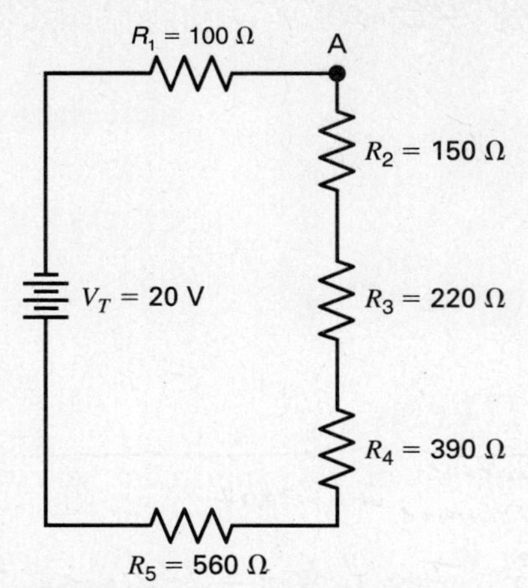

Fig. 8-3. Voltage applied to the series resistive circuit.

4. Using a voltmeter, measure the *IR* voltage drop across the resistors R_1, R_2, R_3, and R_4, and record this information in Table 8-3.
5. By mathematical calculation, record the current in Table 8-3. If the series current *I* is known for one component, this value is the current *I* found in all components in series.
6. Subtract the *IR* voltage drops of R_1, R_2, R_3, and R_4 from the total applied voltage and record the results in Table 8-4 as IR_5.
7. Complete Table 8-4. Use the formula shown in step 2 in determining the percentage of error. If the error is greater than 10 percent, repeat the calculations and measurements.
8. Using a voltmeter, measure and record, in Table 8-4, the *IR* voltage drop across R_5. Does this step demonstrate that a known voltage drop can be subtracted from the total V_T to find the remaining voltage drop? Explain in Table 8-5.

DATE

ETS FOR EXPERIMENT 8

QUESTIONS

1. Explain the significance of the following statement: In a series resistive circuit, in order to calculate I, the total V_T can be divided by the total R_T, or an individual IR drop can be divided by its resistance.

$I = \frac{V}{R}$ voltage / resistance = current

$V_T = I_T \cdot R_T$ Total Voltage → Total Current · Total Resistance

2. Describe what a zero voltage drop could be.

Having no kind of voltage or zero voltage.

3. Describe the nature of the IR drop and current value of a component which displays the characteristics of a short.

It gives out the voltage value and current value in a short.

4. In a series circuit, if the IR voltage drop is measured to be the same across two resistors, what can be said about these two resistors?

That both resistors hold the same voltage drop.

5. In a series circuit, if the current is measured to be 0 mA and is the same in all resistances, what would you suspect is taking place in this circuit?

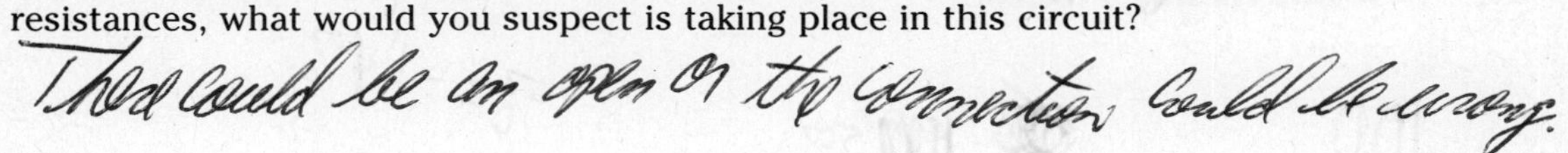

CRITICAL THINKING QUESTIONS

Note: The following questions are designed to help you analyze the previous laboratory experiment in a complete and in-depth fashion. To answer these questions, you should review the related material in Grob, *Basic Electronics,* Eighth Edition.

1. As described in the introduction of this experiment, a common application of series circuits is to use a resistance to drop the voltage from the voltage source to a lower value. Design a series-dropping resistor R_s, so that the load requires 5 V at 50 mA, while the supply voltage is limited to 14 V_{dc}.

2. Determine the resistor's wattage rating for the design problem as described in critical thinking question 1. Using manufacturer's specification sheets and/or supplier catalogs, select a resistor that closely matches your component design. Using this value, and assuming that your design is not a perfect match, how will the voltage drops and circuit current values be affected? Explain.

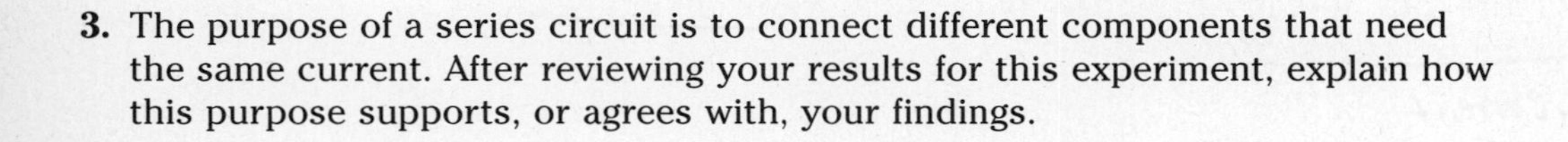

3. The purpose of a series circuit is to connect different components that need the same current. After reviewing your results for this experiment, explain how this purpose supports, or agrees with, your findings.

4. Explain why the current is the same in all parts of a series circuit.

5. Explain where the sources of errors exist within this experiment. How could these sources of error be reduced?

A 150 220 390 B 560

%err. = diff between meas. − calc. measure / calc. ×100

% = 1400−1420 / 1420 ×100

% = −1.4%

REPORT

Turn in a complete report.

TABLE 8–1. Individual Resistor Values

Resistors	Measured	% Tolerance
100	100	5%
150	150	5%
220	220	5%
390	390	2.5
560	560	1.78

TABLE 8–2. Total Resistance R_T and Percentage of Error

	Calculated	Measured	% Error
Total Resistance	1420	1400	−1.4%

TABLE 8–3. Current and Voltage Measurements

Current = V/R

Point A Resistors	Value	Measured*	Measured Voltage	Calculated Current
R_1	100	100	1.7	V/R = 1.7/150 = .011
R_2	150	150	2.3	2.3/150 = .015
R_3	220	220	5.8	5.8/220 = .026
R_4	390	390	5.6	5.6/390 = .014
			V_t 15.4	

*Values from previous table.

TABLE 8–4. The Total Voltage *IR* Drops and Percentage of Error

Voltage Applied = 20v

	Measured *IR* Drops	Calculated *IR* Drops*	% Error
IR_1	1.7	1.1	%54.5
IR_2	2.3	2.25	%4.5
IR_3	5.8	5.72	%7.2
IR_4	5.6	5.46	%2.5
Sum of *IR* Drops	15.1		
V_T − sum = IR_5	4.6		

$\frac{1.7 - 1.1}{1.1} \times 100 = \%$

*Values from previous table.

TABLE 8–5. Analyzing *IR* Drops

Calculated IR_5*: 4.6 — Explain: Used 20v - Calculated IR Drops.

Measured IR_5: 4.6

*Use value of IR_5 from Table 8-4.

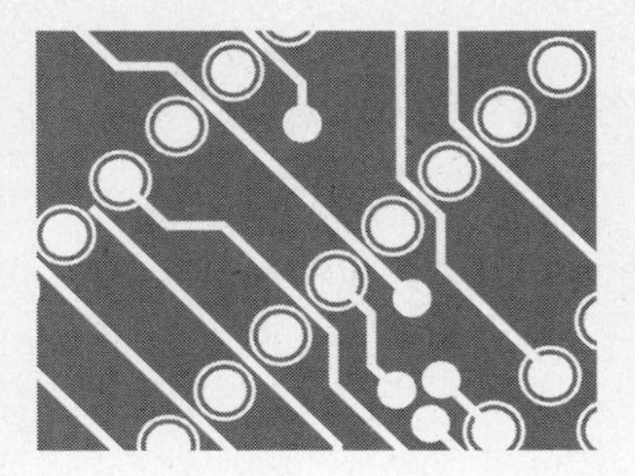

EXPERIMENT 9

SERIES CIRCUITS—WITH OPENS

OBJECTIVES

At the completion of this experiment, you will be able to:

- Recognize that an open circuit is a break in the current path and since the current is the same in all parts of a series circuit, an open in any part results in no current flow for the entire circuit.
- Understand that the resistance of an open circuit path is very high because an insulator such as air takes the place of the conducting path of the circuit.
- Verify that at the point of open in a series circuit, the value of current is practically zero, although the supply voltage is considered maximum.

SUGGESTED READING

Chapter 4, *Basic Electronics,* B. Grob, Eighth Edition

INTRODUCTION

An open circuit is a break in the current path. The resistance of the open path is very high because an insulator, in this case air, takes the place of a conducting part of the circuit. Since the current is the same in all parts of a series circuit, as shown in Fig. 9-1*a*, an open in any part results in no current throughout the entire circuit. This is illustrated in Fig. 9-1*b*. The open which exists between points A and B provides an infinite resistance to the series circuit. Since the open circuit resistance at this point is extremely large when compared to the resistances of R_1 and R_2, and since the supply voltage remains unchanged, the resulting current flow is considered to be zero. The current flow in Fig. 9-1*b* is zero and therefore results in there being no *IR* voltage drop across any of the series resistances.

It is extremely important to note, however, that even though there is no current flow in an open series circuit and therefore no *IR* drops, the voltage source still maintains its output voltage and can be a potential shock hazard for the technician working on such open circuits.

EQUIPMENT

Breadboard
DC power supply
VOM/DMM
  Voltmeter
  Ammeter
  Ohmmeter

COMPONENTS

All resistors can be 0.25 W or 0.5 W unless indicated otherwise:

(1) 100-Ω resistor
(1) 150-Ω resistor
(1) 220-Ω resistor
(1) 390-Ω resistor

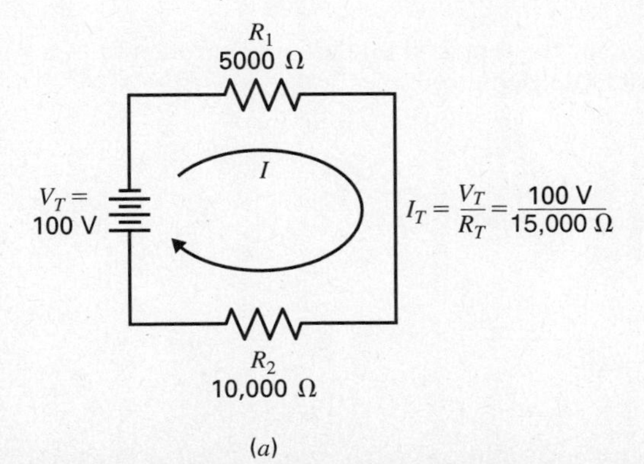

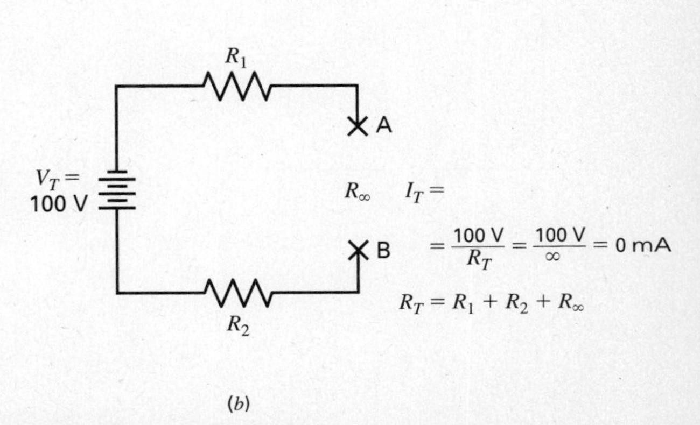

Fig. 9-1. Series resistive circuits. (*a*) Series circuit with a complete path for current flow. (*b*) Series circuit with an open that establishes an infinite series resistance.

PROCEDURE

1. Measure and record each resistor value for the resistors required in this experiment. Record the results in Table 9-1.

2. Connect the circuit shown in Fig. 9-2. First calculate and then measure the total resistance from point A to point B. Record this information in Table 9-2. In addition, record the percentage of error between these values, where

$$\% \text{ error} = \left| \frac{\text{difference between meas. and calc. values}}{\text{calc. values}} \right| \times 100$$

If the error is greater than 10 percent, repeat the calculations and measurements.

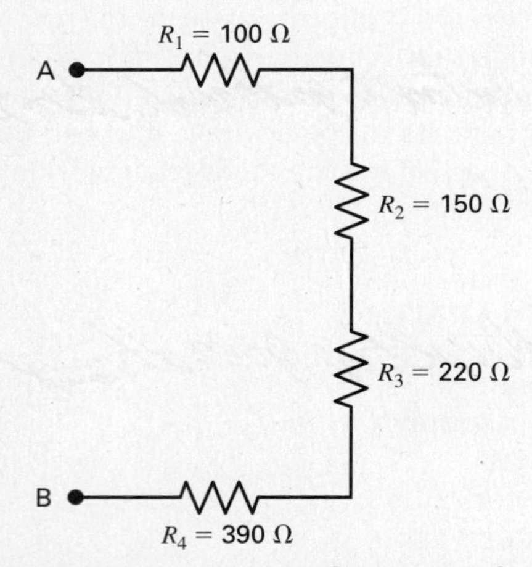

Fig. 9-2. Series resistive circuit without a supply voltage.

3. Connect the supply voltage to the circuit as shown in Fig. 9-3. Adjust this voltage to 20 V_{dc}.

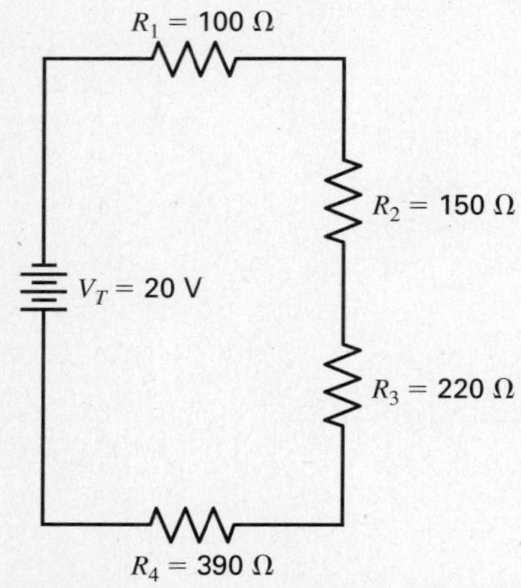

Fig. 9-3. Series resistive circuit with the supply voltage connected.

4. Using a voltmeter, measure and record, in Table 9-3, the voltage drops across each of the series resistances.

5. Using an ammeter and with the supply voltage on, open the circuit at each of the points, as shown in Fig. 9-4, and measure and record the currents in Table 9-3.

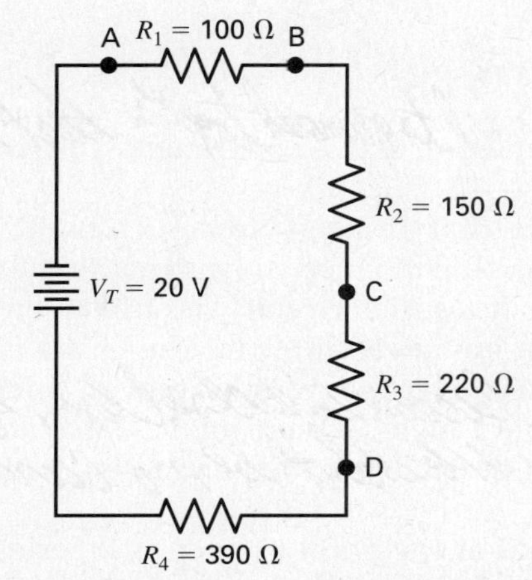

Fig. 9-4. Current and voltage measurements in a series resistive circuit.

6. With the supply voltage on, open the circuit as shown in Fig. 9-5, and repeat steps 4 and 5. Again, record your measurements in Table 9-3.

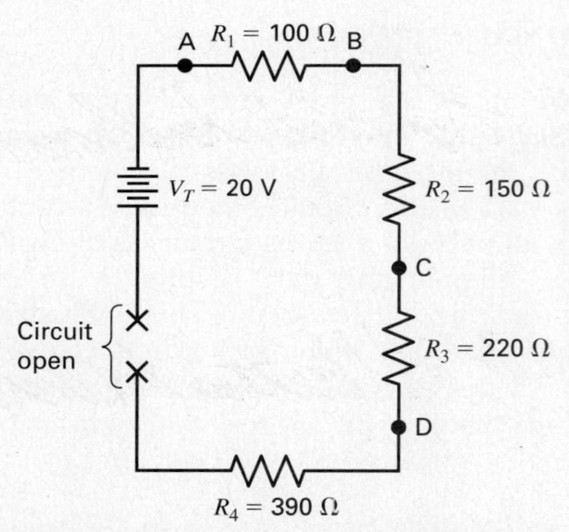

Fig. 9-5. Current and voltage measurements in a series resistive open circuit.

DATE 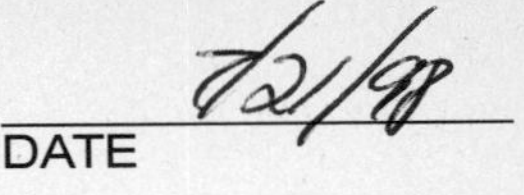

ERIMENT 9

what the unique characteristics of a series resistive

together that in a closed loop.

2. Describe what happens to the current in a series resistive circuit if an open in the circuit path occurs.

   Because in a closed loop, if there were no voltage to go through, then there wouldn't be no current.

3. Describe what happens to the voltage drops in a series resistive circuit if an open in the circuit path occurs.

   When there's open in a closed loop. No voltage goes through. No voltage in any resistor too.

4. In a series resistive circuit that provides a given amount of current flow, when the resistors are compared why does the resistor with a higher ohmic value also have a larger voltage drop across it? Is this also true for a circuit with an open?

   Larger resistor handle more voltage.

5. Give an application of a series circuit.

   An old Christmas tree lights

CRITICAL THINKING QUESTIONS

Note: The following questions are designed to help you analyze the previous laboratory experiment in a complete and in-depth fashion. To answer these questions, you should review the related material in Grob, *Basic Electronics,* Eighth Edition.

1. Explain where the sources of error exist in this experiment. How could these sources of error be reduced?

2. How could the idea of open circuits apply to the 120-V_{ac} voltage from the power line in your home?

3. Explain why the current is the same in all parts of a series circuit describe why the IR drops are zero in an open series resistive circ

4. Demonstrate mathematically why the current of an open circuit is pract zero.

5. Why is the source voltage in an open series resistive circuit present with or without current flow in the external circuit?

REPORT

Turn in a complete report.

TABLE 9–1. Individual Resistor Values

Resistors	Measured	% Tolerance
100	100	0
150	150	0
220	210	4.5
390	380	2.8

TABLE 9–2. Total Resistance R_T and Percentage of Error

	Calculated	Measured	% Error
Total Resistance	860	850	1.18

TABLE 9-3. Current and Voltage Measurements

	Circuit without Open			Circuit with Open		
Resistor Values	Measured Voltage	Circuit Points	Measured Current	Measured Voltage	Circuit Points	Measured Current
R_1	2.4	A	24	0	A	0
R_2	3.6	B	24	0	B	0
R_3	5	C	24	0	C	0
R_4	9	D	24	0	D	0

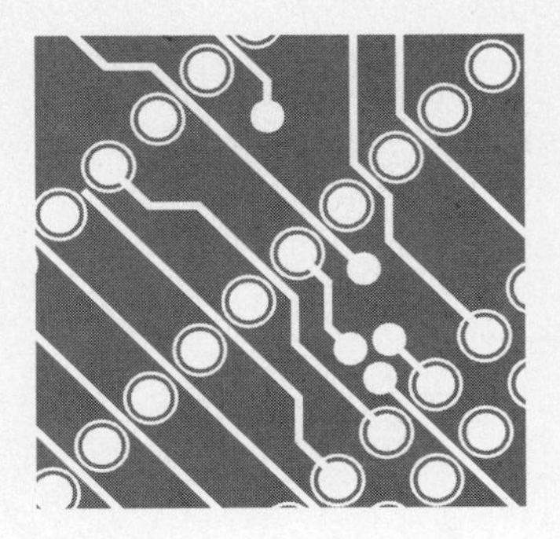

EXPERIMENT 10

SERIES-AIDING AND SERIES-OPPOSING VOLTAGES

OBJECTIVES

At the completion of this experiment, you will be able to:

- Define the terms series-aiding and series-opposing.
- Construct a series-aiding and a series-opposing circuit.
- Measure current and voltage and anticipate correct polarity connections.

SUGGESTED READING

Chapter 4, *Basic Electronics,* B. Grob, Eighth Edition

INTRODUCTION

In many practical applications, a circuit may contain more than one voltage source. Voltage sources that cause current to flow in the same direction are considered to be *series-aiding,* and their voltages add. Voltage sources that tend to force current in opposite directions are said to be *series-opposing,* and the effective voltage source is the difference between the opposing voltages. When two opposing sources are inserted into a circuit, current flow would be in a direction determined by the larger source. Examples of series-aiding and series-opposing sources are shown in Fig. 10-1*a* and *b*.

Series-aiding voltages are connected such that the currents of the sources add, as shown in Fig. 10-1*a*. The 10 V of V_1 produces 1 A of current flow through the 10-Ω resistance of R_1. Also, the voltage source V_2, of 5 V, creates 0.5 A of current flowing through the 10-Ω resistance of R_1: The total current would then be additive and be 1.5 A.

When voltage sources are connected in a series-aiding fashion, where the negative terminal of one source is connected to the positive terminal of the next, voltages V_1 and V_2 are added to find the total voltage.

$$V_T = 5\text{ V} + 10\text{ V} = 15\text{ V}$$

The total current can then be determined by

$$I_T = 15\text{ V}/10\Omega = 1.5\text{ A}$$

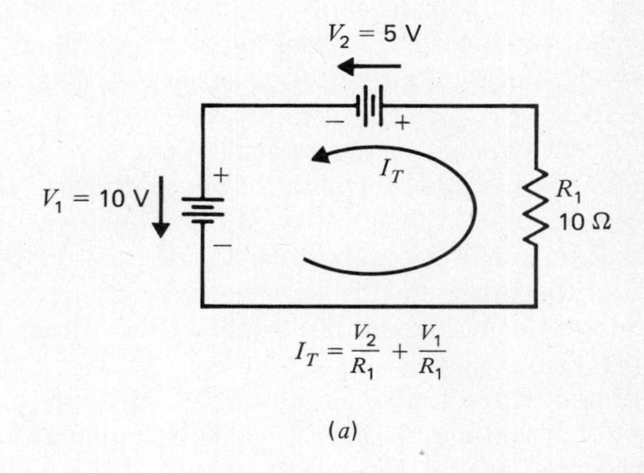

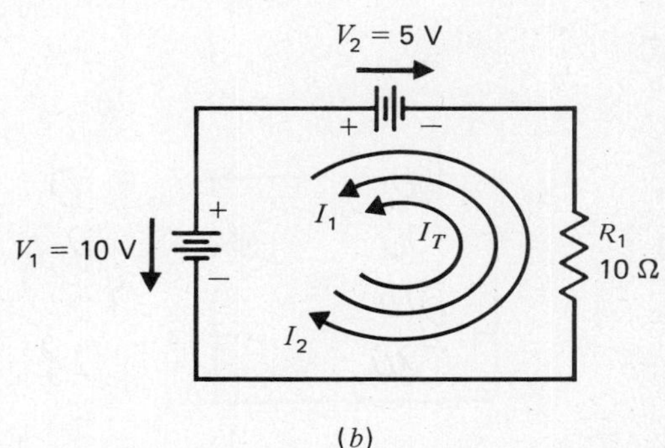

Fig. 10-1. (*a*) Series-aiding voltages. (*b*) Series-opposing voltages.

Series-opposing voltages can be subtracted, as shown in Fig. 10-1*b*. The currents that are generated are opposing each other. These voltages can still be algebraically added, keeping in mind their algebraic sign. Here, V_2 is smaller than V_1, and the difference between them is +5 V, resulting in an I_T of 0.5 A.

EQUIPMENT

VOM
Test leads

COMPONENTS

(4) D cells (1.5-V batteries)

PROCEDURE

1. Connect the negative lead of the meter to the negative terminal of the battery, and connect the positive lead of the meter to the positive terminal of the battery. Identify and number each battery 1 through 4. Measure and record in Table 10-1 the voltage of each of the dry cells supplied to you.
2. Connect batteries 1 and 2 as series-aiding. Measure and record in Table 10-2 their total voltage.
3. Connect batteries 1, 2, and 3 as series-aiding. Measure and record in Table 10-2 their total voltage.
4. Repeat this process, measuring and recording the voltages of the four batteries as series-aiding, in Table 10-2.
5. Connect two batteries in parallel. (Be sure to connect the negative terminal of one battery to the negative terminal of the other, and connect the positive terminal of one battery to the positive terminal of the other. In this way, we have connected them together.) Measure and record this voltage in Table 10-3.
6. Connect three batteries in parallel. Measure and record this voltage in Table 10-3. Then connect four batteries in parallel. Measure and record this voltage in Table 10-3 also.

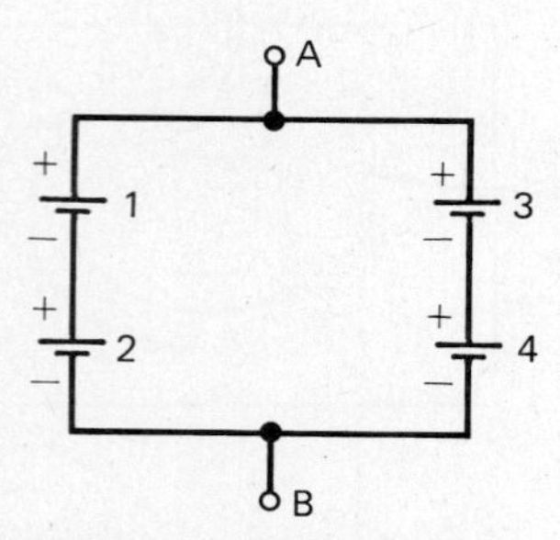

Fig. 10-2. Series-parallel batteries.

7. Connect the batteries in a series-parallel arrangement as shown in Fig. 10-2. Measure and record in Table 10-4 the voltage from point A to point B.

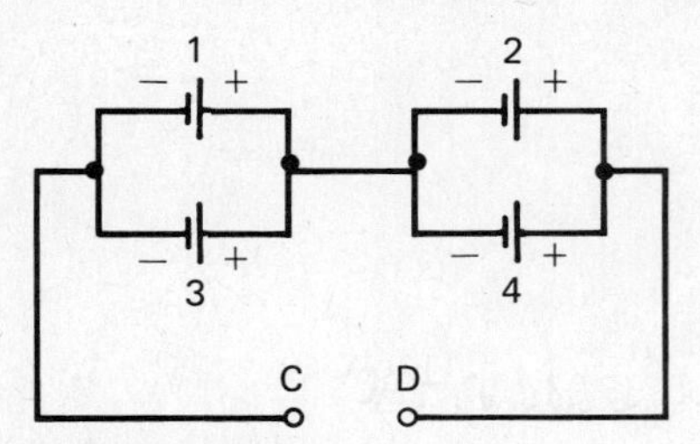

Fig. 10-3. Series-aiding circuit.

8. Connect the circuit as shown in Fig. 10-3. Measure and record in Table 10-4 the voltage from point C to point D.
9. Connect the series-aiding–series-opposing arrangements shown in Fig. 10-4*a* to *c*. Measure and record in Table 10-5 the voltage across each circuit. Before connecting the voltmeter, determine which are the probable positive and negative terminals.

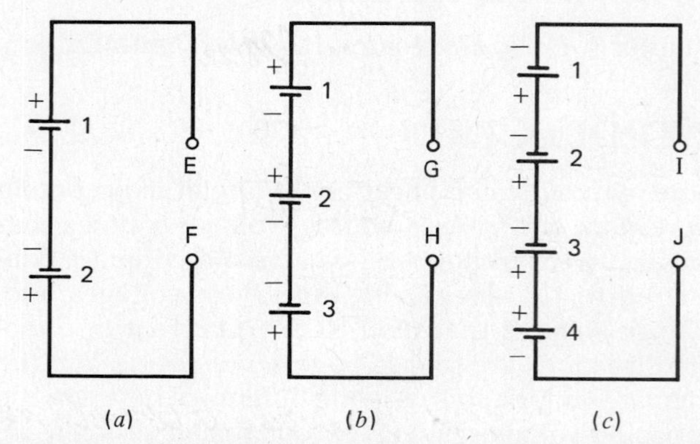

Fig. 10-4. (*a*) Series-opposing circuit. (*b*) Series-aiding and -opposing circuit. (*c*) Series-aiding and -opposing circuit.

NAME ______________________ DATE ____________

RESULTS FOR EXPERIMENT 10

QUESTIONS

1. Name four precautions which must be observed in measuring voltages.

Doesn't add voltage
All positive + negative ends are together.

2. What would happen to a dry cell or battery if the positive and negative terminals were short-circuited?

They may not give the power desired.

3. What arrangement of six dry cells gives the maximum voltage?

In series

4. Draw a practical arrangement of ten 1.5-V dry cells to give a battery of 7.5 V.

+ 1.5 | 1.5 | 1.5 | 1.5 | 1.5 − = 7.5v

5. Explain the difference in connection between two dry cells connected in series-aiding and in series-opposing.

In series, they would be connected next to eachother
In series opposing, they would be connected in parallel.

REPORT

Write a complete report. Describe how combinations of positive and negative voltages add and oppose each other.

TABLE 10–1

Battery	Measured Voltages
1	1.56
2	1.56
3	1.56
4	1.56

TABLE 10–2

Series-Aiding Battery	Measured Voltages
1 + 2	3.05v
1 + 2 + 3	4.6v
1 + 2 + 3 + 4	6.09v

TABLE 10–3

Parallel-Arrangement Battery	Measured Voltages
1 + 2	1.56
1 + 2 + 3	1.56
1 + 2 + 3 + 4	1.56

TABLE 10–4

Circuit	Voltages	Terminals
Fig. 10-2	3.01	A to B
Fig. 10-3	3.01	C to D

TABLE 10–5

Circuit	Voltages	Terminals
Fig. 10-4*a*	0	E to F
Fig. 10-4*b*	1.05	G to H
Fig. 10-4*c*	0	I to J

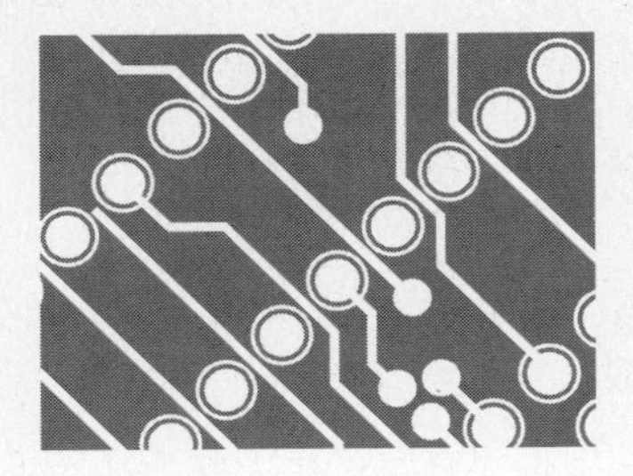

EXPERIMENT 11

PARALLEL CIRCUITS

OBJECTIVES

At the completion of this experiment, you will be able to:

- Identify a parallel circuit.
- Accurately measure current in a parallel circuit.
- Use Ohm's law to verify measurements taken in a parallel circuit.

SUGGESTED READING

Chapter 5, *Basic Electronics,* B. Grob, Eighth Edition

INTRODUCTION

A parallel circuit is defined as one having more than one current path connected to a common voltage source. Parallel circuits, therefore, must contain two or more load resistances which are not connected in series. Study the parallel circuit shown in Fig. 11-1.

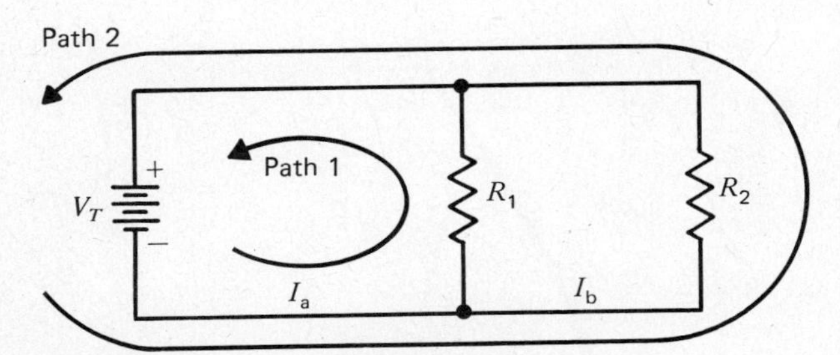

Fig. 11-1. Parallel circuit with two branches.

Beginning at the voltage source V_T and tracing counterclockwise around the circuit, two complete and separate paths can be identified in which current can flow. One path is traced from the source through resistance R_1 and back to the source; the other is traced from the source through resistance R_2 and back to the source.

The source voltage in a series circuit divides proportionately across each resistor in the circuit. In a parallel circuit, the same voltage is present across all the resistors of a parallel bank. In other words,

$$V_T = V_{R_1} = V_{R_2} = \cdots$$

The current in a circuit is inversely proportional to the circuit resistance. This fact, obtained from Ohm's law, establishes the relationship upon which the following discussion is developed. A single current flows in a series circuit.

In summary, when two or more electronic components are connected across a single voltage source, they are said to be *in parallel.* The voltage across each component is the same. The current through each component, or branch, is determined by the resistance of that branch and voltage across the bank of branches. Adding a parallel resistance of any value increases the total current. The total resistance of a circuit (R_T) can be found by dividing the total voltage applied (V_T) by the total current (I_T).

When measuring currents and resistances in the following procedure, some important precautions should be observed. When measuring currents, be sure to install the ammeter in a series configuration, with the ammeter connected in series with the individual branch resistances through which the current is flowing. Also, before measuring branch resistances, be sure to turn off all voltage sources.

EQUIPMENT

DC power supply, 0–10 V
Ammeter
Voltmeter
Protoboard or springboard
Test leads

COMPONENTS

Resistors (all 0.25 W):

(2) 1 kΩ (1) 2.2 kΩ

PROCEDURE

1. Measure the resistance values of R_1, R_2, and R_3 and record in the required locations of Tables 11-1 to 11-3, where the nominal values are:

$$R_1 = 1.0\ \text{k}\Omega$$
$$R_2 = 1.0\ \text{k}\Omega$$
$$R_3 = 2.2\ \text{k}\Omega$$

2. Connect the circuit as shown with R_1 only in Fig. 11-2. Adjust the power supply voltage to 10 V.

3. Using an ammeter, measure and record in Table 11-1 the current through points a and b.

4. Using a voltmeter, measure and record in Table 11-1 the voltage across R_1.

5. To this circuit, add R_2 across (meaning that R_2 is

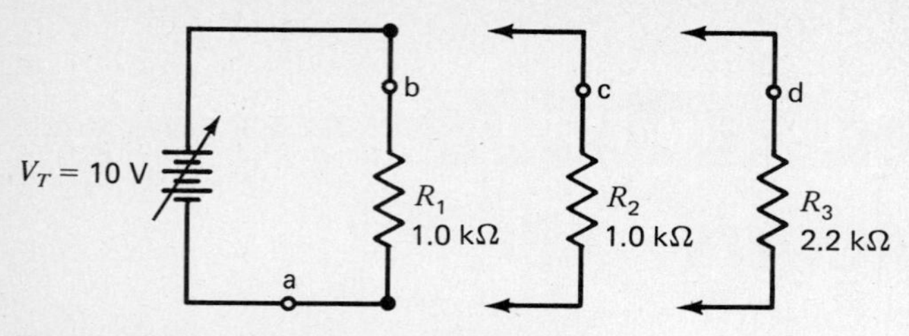

Fig. 11-2. Three-branch parallel circuit.

connected in parallel) R_1. With an ammeter, measure and record in Table 11-2 the current through points a, b, and c.

6. Using a voltmeter, measure and record in Table 11-2 the voltages across R_1 and R_2.
7. Finally, add R_3 across R_2. With an ammeter, measure and record in Table 11-3 the current through points a, b, c, and d.
8. Using a voltmeter, measure and record in Table 11-3 the voltages across R_1, R_2, and R_3.
9. Calculate the total resistances and the current for each of the three previous circuits and record this information in Tables 11-1 to 11-3.

NAME

DATE

RESULTS FOR EXPERIMENT 11

QUESTIONS

1. What is a parallel circuit? What circuit characteristics indicate that a parallel circuit condition exists?

2. In the circuit of Fig. 11-2, determine the power being dissipated by each resistor using the values of current determined in procedure step 7. Use the formula I^2R = power (watts).

3. Are the voltages the same across each resistor in a parallel circuit?

4. Are the currents the same through each resistor in a parallel circuit?

5. Suppose in procedure step 7 that R_3 developed a short-circuited condition. How would the current flowing through each resistor change? Would the voltage drops across each resistor change? How?

REPORT

Write a complete report. Describe the three most significant aspects of the experiment.

TABLE 11–1

	Measured	Calculated
R_1	______	
R_T		______
V_{R_1}	______	
I_a	______	______
I_b	______	______

TABLE 11–2

	Measured	Calculated
R_1	______	
R_2	______	
R_T		______
V_{R_1}	______	
V_{R_2}	______	
I_a	______	______
I_b	______	______
I_c	______	______

TABLE 11–3

	Measured	Calculated
R_1	______	
R_2	______	
R_3	______	
R_T		______
V_{R_1}	______	
V_{R_2}	______	
V_{R_3}	______	
I_a	______	______
I_b	______	______
I_c	______	______
I_d	______	______

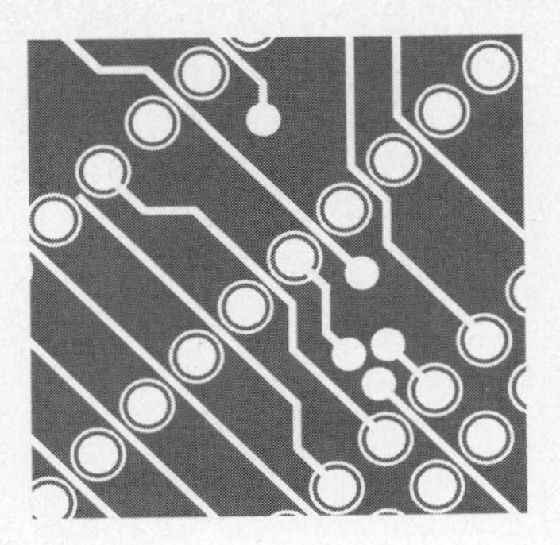

EXPERIMENT 12

PARALLEL CIRCUITS—RESISTANCE BRANCHES

OBJECTIVES

At the completion of this experiment, you will be able to:

- Recognize the basic characteristics of a parallel branch circuit. For example, the parallel circuit arrangement is used to connect components that require the same voltage.
- Compare the mathematical calculations to the measured values of a parallel branch circuit.
- Recognize that for a parallel resistor circuit each branch current equals the applied voltage divided by the branch resistance.
- Recognize that with a parallel circuit arrangement, any branch that has less resistance allows more current to flow.
- Determine that current can have different values in different parts of parallel circuits.

SUGGESTED READING

Chapter 5, *Basic Electronics,* B. Grob, Eighth Edition

INTRODUCTION

A parallel circuit is formed when two or more components, or resistances, are connected across a voltage source, as shown in Fig. 12-1. In this figure, R_1, R_2, R_3, and R_4 are in parallel with each other and the 10-V supply source. This figure can be redrawn, as shown in Fig. 12-2, to readily show that each component connection is really equivalent to a direct connection at the terminals of the battery, because the connecting wires exhibit almost no resistance. Since R_1, R_2, R_3, and R_4 are connected directly across the two terminals of the battery, all resistances must

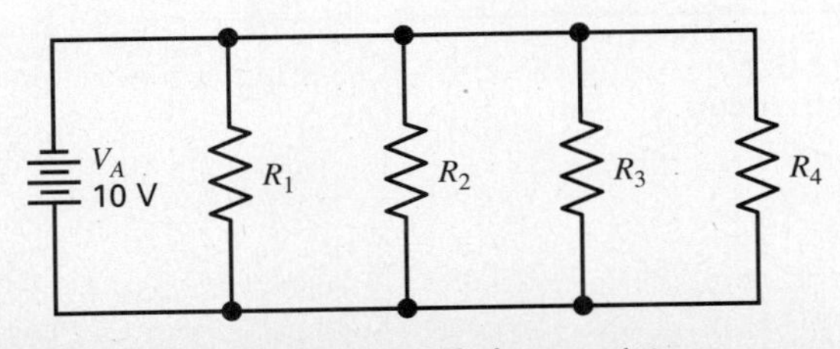

Fig. 12-1. A parallel circuit with four resistors.

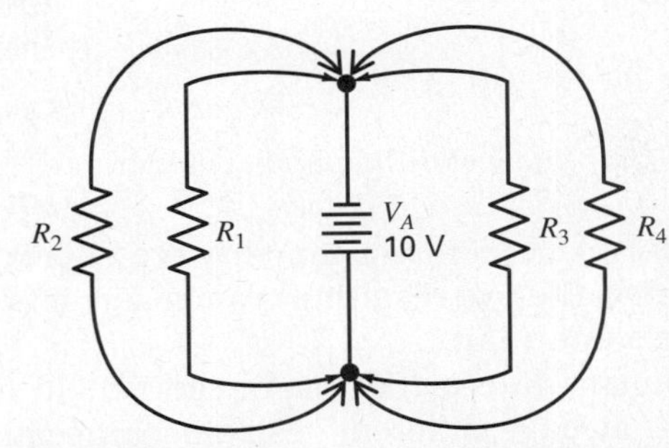

Fig. 12-2. Reconfiguration of a parallel circuit with four resistors.

have the same potential differences as the battery. It therefore follows that the voltage is the same across each of the components that are connected in a parallel fashion. The parallel circuit arrangement is used, therefore, to connect components that require the same voltage from a common supply voltage.

Again, with reference to Fig. 12-1, R_1, R_2, R_3, and R_4 can be referred to as *branch* resistances. Although the voltage is the same across each branch resistance, the current divides into branches according to Ohm's law.

In each branch circuit the amount of branch current is equivalent to the applied voltage divided by the individual branch resistor. In other words, when Ohm's law is applied to the parallel circuit, the current equals the voltage applied across the circuit divided by the resistance between the two points at which that voltage is applied. As shown in Fig. 12-3, a 15-V source is applied across the 3900-Ω resistor (R_3). This results in a calculated current flow of 0.0038 A (3.8 mA) between points E and F. The battery voltage is *also* applied across the parallel resistance of R_2, which applies 15 V across a 2200-Ω resistor. This results in a calculated current of 0.0068 A (6.8 mA) between points C and D. This current provides a different value through R_1 with the same applied voltage, because the resistance is different. Remember that the current in each parallel branch equals the applied voltage divided by each individual branch resistance.

Further, as in a circuit with just one resistance, any branch that has less resistance allows more current

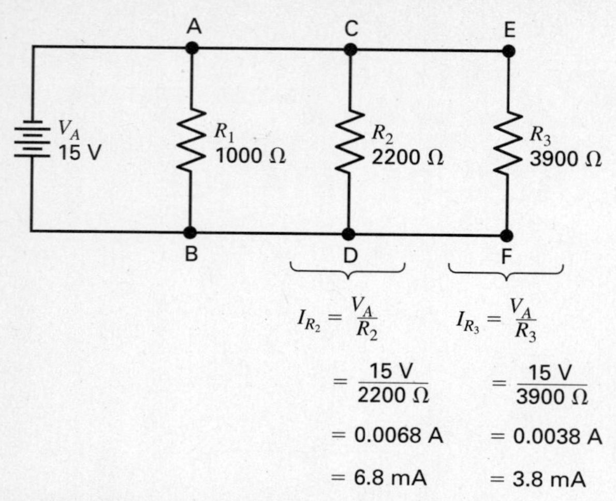

Fig. 12-3. Ohm's law and the parallel circuit.

to flow. If two branch resistances were equivalent in ohmic value, the two resulting branch currents would be of the same value.

In summary, the current can be different in parallel circuits that have different resistances because the applied voltage is the same across all branches. How much current is in each separate path depends on the amount of resistance in each branch.

EQUIPMENT

Breadboard
DC power supply
VOM/DMM
  Voltmeter
  Ammeter
  Ohmmeter

COMPONENTS

All resistors are 0.25 W unless indicated otherwise:

(1) 390 Ω
(1) 1 kΩ
(1) 1.2 kΩ
(1) 2.2 kΩ
(1) 3.9 kΩ

PROCEDURE

1. Measure and record each resistor value for the resistors required in this experiment. Record the results in Table 12-1.

2. Connect the circuit shown in Fig. 12-4. First calculate and then measure the total resistance from point A to point B. Record this information in Table 12-2. In addition, record the percentage of error between these values, where:

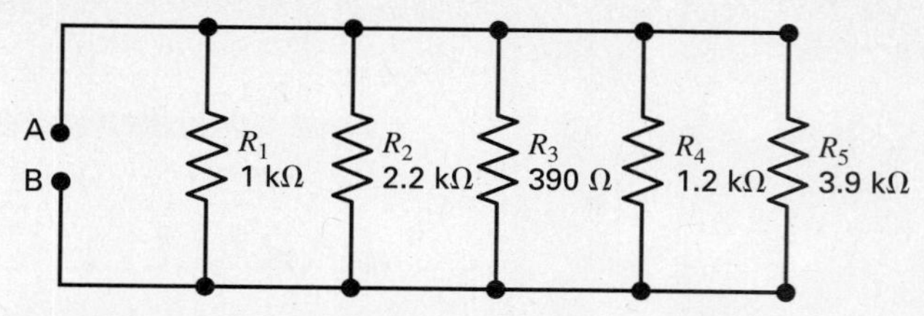

Fig. 12-4. Calculate and measure the total circuit resistance.

$$\%\ \text{error} = \left| \frac{\text{difference between meas. and calc. values}}{\text{calc. values}} \right| \times 100$$

If the error is greater than 10 percent, repeat the calculations and measurements.

3. Connect the circuit shown in Fig. 12-5. Adjust the supply voltage to 15 V and, using a voltmeter, take measurements required to complete Table 12-3 (Part A).

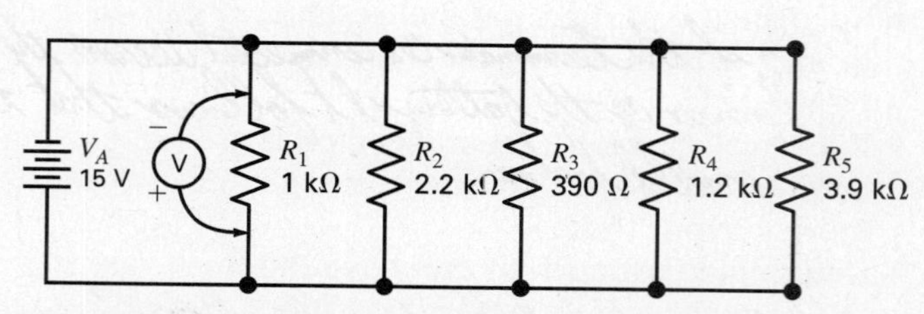

Fig. 12-5. Measuring the voltage existing in a parallel branch circuit.

4. Referring to Fig. 12-6, adjust the supply voltage to 15 V and, using an ammeter, take the current measurements at points A through F and perform the necessary calculations required to complete Table 12-3 (Part B).

5. Using the formula as shown in step 3, record in Table 12-3 (Part C) the percentage of error between the calculated and measured currents.

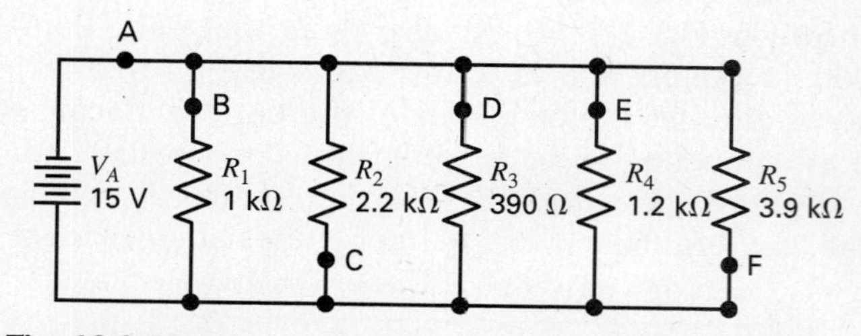

Fig. 12-6. Measuring the current existing in a parallel branch circuit.

NAME ____________________ DATE ____________

RESULTS FOR EXPERIMENT 12

QUESTIONS

1. Write the formula that determines the total resistance R_T of the circuit depicted in Fig. 12-3.

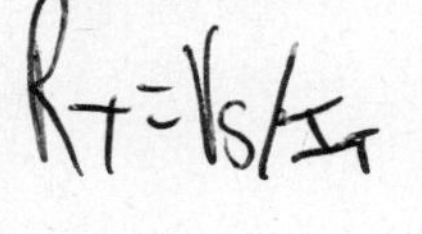

2. Mathematically determine the branch current passing through R_1, as shown in Fig. 12-3. Show all calculations.

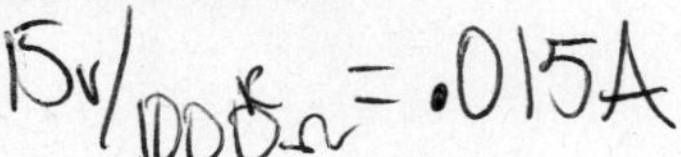

3. In your estimation would $V_T = IR_1 = IR_2 = IR_3 = \cdots$, be true for all parallel resistive branches? Explain.

Only if the terminals are connected across the battery, all resistances must have the same potential difference as the battery. It follows that the voltage is the same across each of the components in a parallel fashion.

4. In a parallel circuit, the amount of current in each separate branch depends upon what factor?

The current is different in parallel circuits that have different resistances because the applied voltage is the same across all branches. Current is in each separate path + depends on the amount of resistance in each branch.

5. Could you always expect that $R_T = R_1 + R_2 + R_3 + \cdots$, in a series resistive circuit? Explain.

Yes. Because all resistors that are in series add up together.

CRITICAL THINKING QUESTIONS

Note: The following questions are designed to help you analyze the previous laboratory experiment in a complete and in-depth fashion. To answer these questions, you should review the related material in Grob, *Basic Electronics,* Eighth Edition.

1. Explain where the sources of errors exist in this experiment. How could these sources of error be reduced?

2. The purpose of a parallel circuit is to connect different components that need the same voltage. After reviewing your results for this experiment, explain how this purpose supports, or agrees with, your findings. Explain.

3. Explain why the voltage is the same across all branches in a parallel circuit.

4. Explain why, for a parallel resistive circuit, each branch current equals the applied voltage divided by the branch resistance.

5. How is it possible for current to be different in various parts of parallel circuits when the applied voltage is found to be the same across all branches?

REPORT

Turn in a complete report.

TABLE 12–1. Individual Resistor Values

	Nominal Value	Measured Value
R_1 =	1 kΩ	9.60K
R_2 =	2.2 kΩ	2.1K
R_3 =	390 Ω	390
R_4 =	1.2 kΩ	1.2K
R_5 =	3.9 kΩ	3.9K

TABLE 12–2. Total Resistance R_T and Percentage of Error

	Nominal Calculated Total Resistance $R_1 \parallel R_2 \parallel R_3 \parallel R_4 \parallel R_5$	Total Resistance Measured	% Error
R_T =	399.6K		

TABLE 12-3. Recording Voltage, Current, and Error Measurements

Part A				Part B				Part C
	Measured Voltage		Tables 12-1 and 12-2, Measured Resistance		Calculated, $I = V/R$		Measured, I	% Error
V_A	15.1	R_T	200	I_T		Point A	77	
V_{R_1}	15.1	R_1	1K	I_{R_1}		Point B	15	
V_{R_2}	15.1	R_2	2.2K	I_{R_2}		Point C	2	
V_{R_3}	15.1	R_3	390	I_{R_3}		Point D	38	
V_{R_4}	15.1	R_4	1.2K	I_{R_4}		Point E	12	
V_{R_5}	15.1	R_5	3.9K	I_{R_5}		Point F	37	

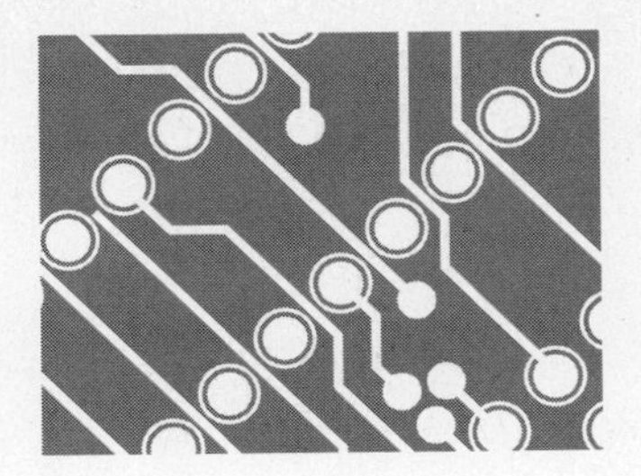

EXPERIMENT 13

PARALLEL CIRCUITS—ANALYSIS

OBJECTIVES

At the completion of this experiment, you will be able to:

- Recognize that, for a parallel circuit, the main-line total current equals the sum of the individual branch currents.
- Use the formula $I_T = I_1 + I_2 + I_3 + I_4 + \cdots$, applied to any number of parallel branches, regardless of whether the individual branch resistances are equal or unequal.
- Recognize that a circuit's equivalent resistance across a common voltage source is found by dividing the common voltage by the total current of all the branches.

SUGGESTED READING

Chapter 5, *Basic Electronics,* B. Grob, Eighth Edition

INTRODUCTION

Components connected in parallel are usually wired directly across each other so that the entire parallel combination is connected across the voltage source, as shown in Fig. 13-1. A combination of parallel branches is often called a *bank*, and a bank may contain two or more parallel resistors. The connecting wires provide no resistance and have almost no effect on circuit operation. One advantage of having circuits wired in parallel is that since only one pair of connecting leads is attached to the voltage source, less wire is used. It is common to find a pair of leads connecting all the branches to the terminals of the voltage source.

The main-line current is also known as the *total circuit current* and is equivalent to the sum of the individual branch currents. In Fig. 13-2, the supply voltage is 35 V and each of the three resistors establishes an independent current flow according to Ohm's law. The sum of the three currents is equivalent to the total (main-line) current, as demonstrated by the formula $I_T = I_1 + I_2 + I_3$. This formula applies for any number of parallel branches, whether the resistances are equal or unequal.

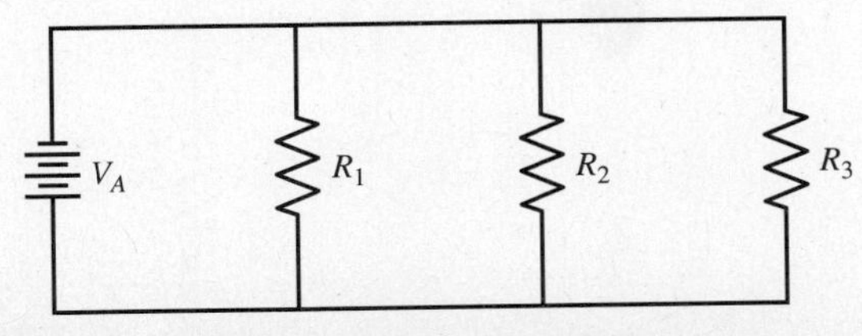

Fig. 13-1. A parallel circuit with three resistors.

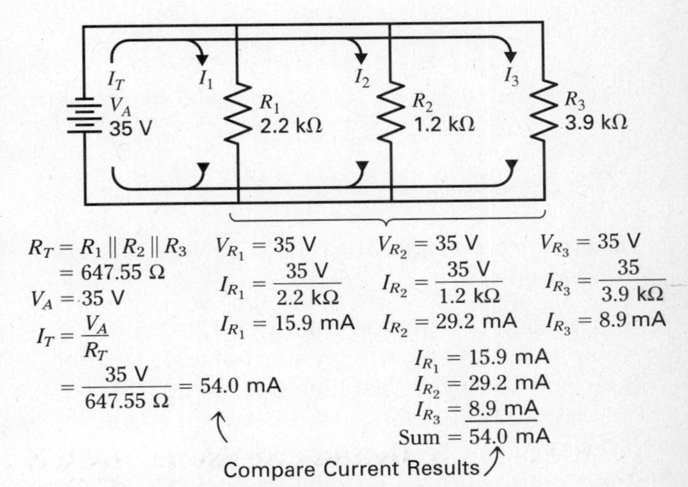

Fig. 13-2. A parallel circuit with three resistors.

The main-line current is equal to the total of the branch currents. All current in the circuit must originate from one side of the voltage source and return to its opposite side in order to form a complete path. Therefore, the main-line current I_T equals the sum of the branch currents.

Analysis of the parallel resistive circuit reveals that the combined equivalent resistance across the supply voltage can be found by Ohm's law, so that the common voltage across the parallel resistances is divided by the total current of all the branches. Again referring to Fig. 13-2, note that the parallel equivalent resistance of R_1, R_2, and R_3 is 648 Ω and results in an opposition to the total current flow in the main line.

Two techniques are used to determine the equivalent resistance of a parallel circuit. These are referred to as the *reciprocal resistance formula* and the *total-current method* (see Fig. 13-3).

There are unique occasions when the resistance is equal in all branches. At those times, the combined equivalent resistance equals the value of one branch resistance divided by the number of branches.

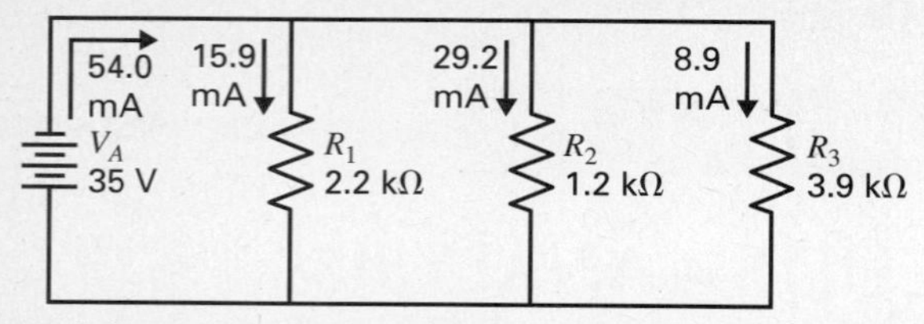

Determining equivalent resistance by the reciprocal resistance formula:

$$\frac{1}{R_{EQ}} = \frac{1}{R_1} + \frac{1}{R_2} + \frac{1}{R_3}$$

$$= \frac{1}{2.2\ \text{k}\Omega} + \frac{1}{1.2\ \text{k}\Omega} + \frac{1}{3.9\ \text{k}\Omega}$$

$$R_{EQ} = 647.55\ \Omega \cong 648\ \Omega\ \text{(rounded)}$$

Determining equivalent resistance by the total-current method:

$$R_{EQ} = \frac{V_A}{I_T} = \frac{35\ \text{V}}{54.0\ \text{mA}} = 648.1481\ \Omega \cong 648\ \Omega\ \text{(rounded)}$$

Fig. 13-3. Determining an equivalent resistance.

In summary, consider the following when analyzing parallel circuits:

1. When a circuit provides more current with the same applied voltage, the greater value of current corresponds to less resistance because of the Ohm's law inverse relationship between current and resistance.
2. The combination of parallel resistances for a parallel bank is always less than the smallest individual branch resistance.

EQUIPMENT

Breadboard
DC power supply
VOM/DMM
  Voltmeter
  Ammeter
  Ohmmeter

COMPONENTS

All resistors are 0.25 W unless indicated otherwise:

(1) 680 Ω (1) 1.2 kΩ
(1) 1.0 kΩ (1) 22 kΩ

PROCEDURE

1. Measure and record each resistor value for the 680-Ω, 1.0-kΩ, and 1.2-kΩ resistors required in the first part of this experiment. Record the results in Table 13-1.
2. Connect the circuit shown in Fig. 13-4. First calculate and then measure the total resistance from point A to point B. Record this information in Table 13-1. In addition, record the percentage of error between these values, where:

$$\%\ \text{error} = \left| \frac{\text{difference between meas. and calc. values}}{\text{calc. values}} \right| \times 100$$

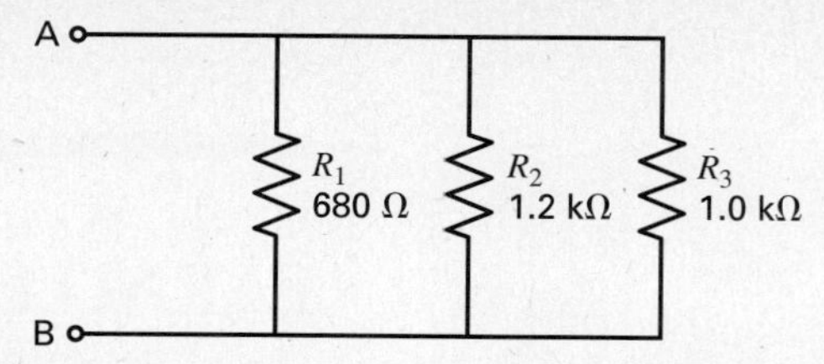

Fig. 13-4. Finding the total resistance and percentage of error.

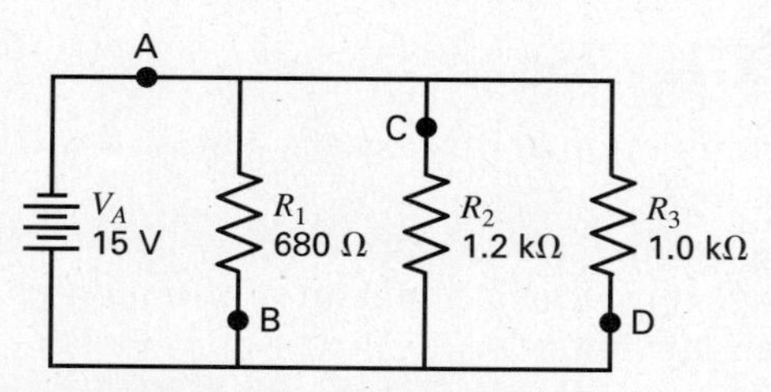

Fig. 13-5. Main-line and branch current.

If the error is greater than 10 percent, repeat the calculations and measurements.
3. Connect the circuit shown in Fig. 13-5. Adjust the supply voltage to 15 V and, using a voltmeter, make voltage measurements across the supply voltage and the individual resistors. Record this information in Table 13-2.
4. Again referring to Fig. 13-5, while the voltage is connected and turned on, break the circuit at point A and, with an ammeter, measure the current passing through this point. Record this information in Table 13-2.
5. Repeat step 4 and make current measurements at points B, C, and D. Record this information in Table 13-2.
6. Complete all calculations required in Table 13-3. Be certain that you use the measured resistance values from Table 13-1 in all calculations. Determine the percentage of error between the calculated and measured currents and record the results in Table 13-3.
7. Connect the circuit in Fig. 13-6. Measure and record, in Table 13-4, each individual resistance value as well as the total resistance from points A and B.
8. Complete and record the calculations required for Table 13-4. Explain in the table how the measured and calculated values compare.

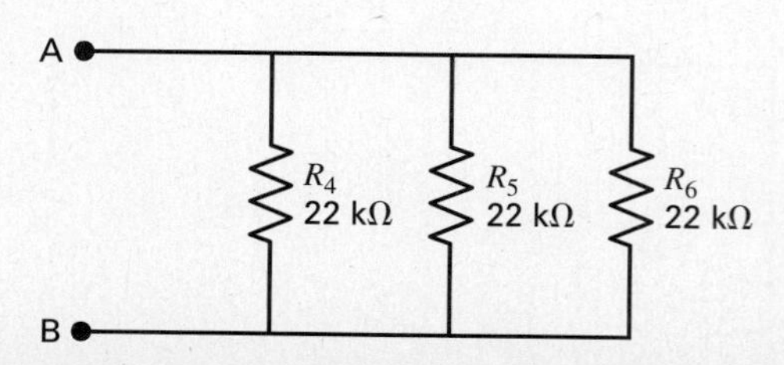

Fig. 13-6. Three equal resistances in parallel.

NAME DATE

RESULTS FOR EXPERIMENT 13

QUESTIONS

1. Why is it true that the combined resistance of a parallel branch circuit equals the value of one branch resistance divided by the number of branches?

2. Define the term *bank* with regard to the parallel resistive circuit.

3. In your estimation would $V_T = I_{R1} = I_{R2} = I_{R3} = \cdots$, be true for all parallel resistive branches? Explain.

4. Does the formula $I_T = I_1 + I_2 + I_3 + I_4 + \cdots$, apply for any number of parallel branches? What if the individual branch resistances were equal or unequal? Explain.

5. What is meant by the *total-current method*?

CRITICAL THINKING QUESTIONS

Note: The following questions are designed to help you analyze the previous laboratory experiment in a complete and in-depth fashion. To answer these questions, you should review the related material in Grob, *Basic Electronics,* Eighth Edition.

1. Explain where the sources of errors exist in this experiment. How could these sources of error be reduced?

2. One purpose of this experiment is to validate that the formula for the total current I_T in the main line of a parallel resistive circuit is $I_T = I_1 + I_2 + I_3 + I_4 + \cdots$. After reviewing your results for this experiment, explain how this purpose supports, or agrees with, your findings.

3. Explain why the voltage is the same across all branches in a parallel circuit.

4. Describe the two methods of analyzing main-line current flow as demonstrated in Fig. 13-2.

5. Explain what is meant by the statement "When a circuit provides more current with the same applied voltage, the greater value of current corresponds to less resistance because of the Ohm's law inverse relationship between current and resistance." Show an example of this statement.

REPORT

Turn in a complete report.

TABLE 13–1. Individual Resistor Values

	Nominal Value	Measured Value	% Error
R_1 =	680 Ω	680	0%
R_2 =	1.2 kΩ	1200	0%
R_3 =	1.0 kΩ	1000	0%
		Step 1	Step 2

		Sum Measured	% Error
Sum =	302.7 Ω	301	56%
		Step 2	

TABLE 13–2. Voltage Measurements

	Step 3		Step 4
V_A	15	I_A	51
V_{R_1}	15.1	I_B	23
V_{R_2}	15.1	I_C	15
V_{R_3}	15.1	I_D	16

TABLE 13–3. Comparison of Calculated and Measured Currents

	Voltage Measurements from Table 13-2		Resistance Measurements from Table 13-1		Calculated Currents Columns 1 and 2		Measured Currents from Table 13-2	Current % Error
V_{R_1}	13.1	R_1	680	I_1	22.3	I_1	23	3.6%
V_{R_2}	13.1	R_2	1200	I_2	15mA	I_2	13	4 %
V_{R_3}	13.1	R_3	1000	I_3	15mA	I_3	15	.66%

TABLE 13–4. Tabulations for Three Equal Resistances in Parallel

	Nominal Values	Measured Values	Calculated by Reciprocal Method	Calculated by Other Method Described in Introduction
$R_4 =$	22 kΩ	2200		
$R_5 =$	22 kΩ	2200		
$R_6 =$	22 kΩ	2200		
		$R_T =$ 7000	$R_T =$ 7333	$R_T =$ 737

Explain: How Do Calculated and Measured Values Compare?

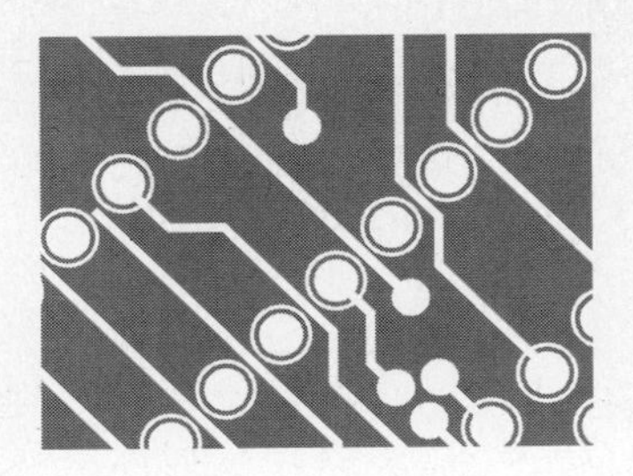

EXPERIMENT 14

PARALLEL CIRCUITS—OPENS AND SHORTS

OBJECTIVES

At the completion of this experiment, you will be able to:

- Validate that an open in a parallel circuit results in an infinite resistance that allows no current to flow, whereas the effect of a short circuit is excessive current flow.
- Recognize that short-circuited components are typically not damaged, since they do not have greater than normal current passing through them.
- Recognize that the amount of current resulting from a short circuit is limited by the small resistance of the wire conductors.

SUGGESTED READING

Chapter 5, *Basic Electronics,* B. Grob, Eighth Edition

INTRODUCTION

Parallel Open Circuits: An open in any circuit creates an infinite resistance that permits no current to flow. However, in parallel circuits there is a difference between an open circuit in the main line and an open circuit in a parallel branch, as shown in Fig. 14-1. An open circuit in the main line prevents any electrons from flowing in the main line or in any branch. An open in a branch results in no current flow in that particular branch. The current in all the other parallel branches remains the same, because each is connected directly to the voltage source. However, the total main-line current will change, since the total resistance of the circuit changes because one of the branches is open.

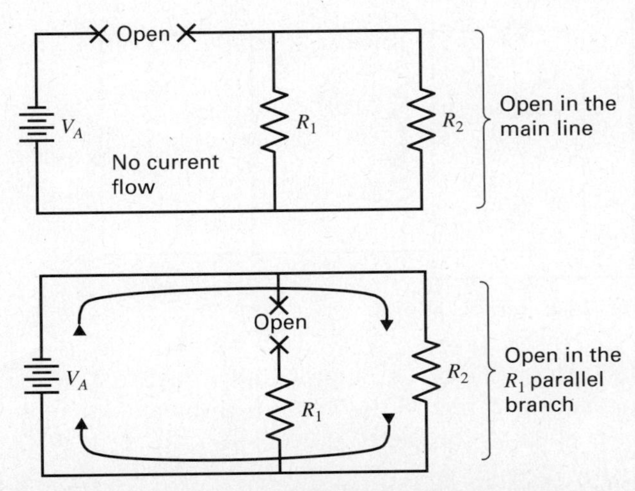

Fig. 14-1. An open in the main line versus an open in a branch.

One advantage of wiring circuits in parallel is that an open in one component will open only that branch, allowing the other parallel branches to operate with normal voltages and currents.

Parallel Short Circuits: A short circuit has almost a zero resistance level. Its effect, therefore, is to allow excessive current to flow in the shorted circuit, as shown in Fig. 14-2. If a wire conductor were connected across a component, the effective resistance would be essentially zero and the current would be extremely high. This high amount of current is limited by the current-carrying capability of the wire.

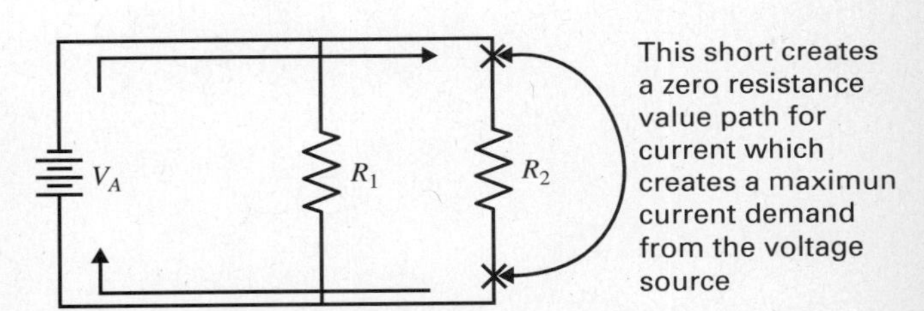

Fig. 14-2. A short circuit and excessive current flow.

Typically, in circuits which develop a shorted component, the voltage source cannot usually maintain its voltage level while at the same time providing the excessive current demand to the shorted component. The amount of current flowing can be dangerously high to the extent that wire can become hot enough to burn insulation and other components. To prevent the damaging effects of excessively high current flow, fuses are installed. A *fuse* is a component that intentionally burns open when there is too high a level of current demand from the supply voltage.

Short-circuited components, such as resistors, have no current passing through them. This is because the short circuit is a parallel path with almost no resistance. When this is the case, all current flows in this path, as shown in Fig. 14-3. In this figure the short bypasses the parallel resistances, and these resistances are referred to as being *shorted out.*

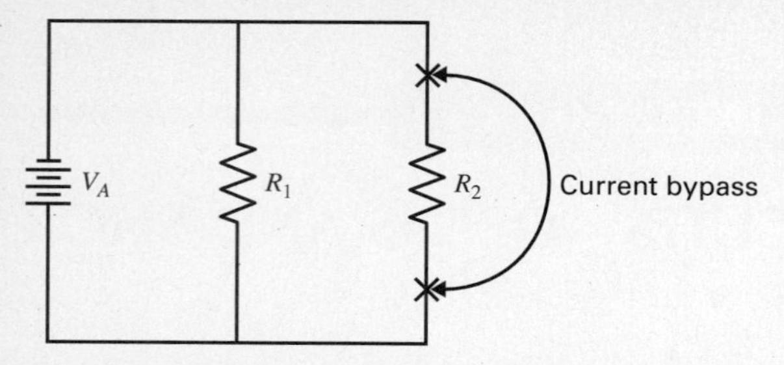

Fig. 14-3. A shorted component's current is bypassed.

When a parallel branch circuit is analyzed, if any individual resistor or component is shorted, all resistive branches are also shorted. This idea can be extended to a short existing across the voltage source; in this case the entire circuit is shorted as well.

Short-circuited components are not usually damaged, since the current passing through the actual component is less than it is under normal operating conditions. If the short circuit does not damage the voltage source and the associated wiring for the circuit, the components will function again when the short is removed and the circuit is restored to normal.

EQUIPMENT

Breadboard
DC power supply
VOM/DMM
  Voltmeter
  Ammeter
  Ohmmeter

COMPONENTS

All resistors are 0.25 W unless indicated otherwise:

(1) 1000 Ω
(1) 1500 Ω
(1) 2200 Ω
(1) 3900 Ω
(1) 5600 Ω

For Critical Thinking Question 1:

(1) Clear glass functioning fuse (any current rating)
(1) Clear glass nonfunctioning fuse (any current rating)

PROCEDURE

1. Measure and record each resistor value for the resistors required in this experiment. Record the results in Table 14-1.
2. Connect the circuit shown in Fig. 14-4. First calculate and then measure the total resistance from point A to point B. Record the results in Table 14-2.

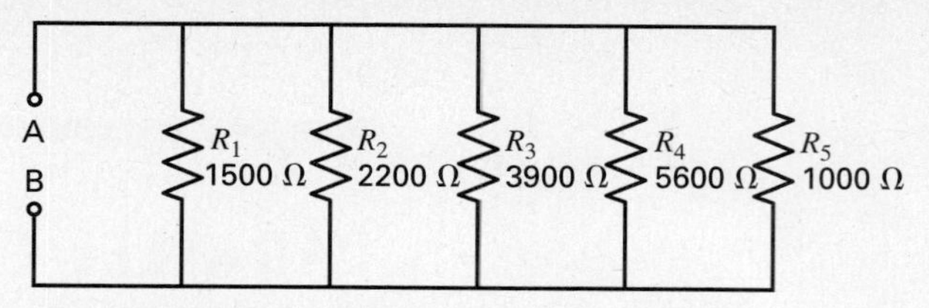

Fig. 14-4. Determining the total resistance.

In addition, record the percentage of error between these values, where:

$$\% \text{ error} = \left| \frac{\text{difference between meas. and calc. values}}{\text{calc. values}} \right| \times 100$$

If the error is greater than 10 percent, repeat the calculations and measurements.

Short Circuit

3. Connect the circuit shown in Fig. 14-5, but *do not* turn on the power supply. When constructing this circuit, notice that this configuration uses a resistor in series with the supply voltage. This is done so that there will always be a reference level of current being maintained from the power supply. For example, if in this circuit a short exists across the entire parallel branch arrangement, this series resistance will maintain a minimal circuit resistance and a maximum circuit current. This is necessary because if the entire parallel branch arrangement were shorted and there were no series resistance, a theoretically infinite amount of current could be demanded from the power supply. Actually, the power supply that you will be using cannot provide an infinite amount of current, and if a short were provided across the supply, the internal circuitry would be damaged or a fuse opened or a circuit breaker tripped (opened).

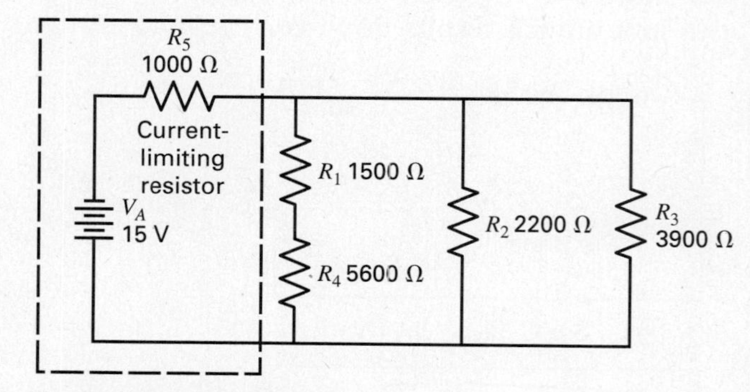

Fig. 14-5. Parallel shorts.

4. Turn on the power supply and adjust to 15 V_{dc}. Measure and record the voltage drops and currents as needed to complete Table 14-3.
5. Using a clip lead of a small piece of wire, place a short across resistance (R_1, R_2, R_3, and R_4) one at a time, and retake voltage and current measurements

necessary to complete Table 14-4. Be sure to answer the questions in Table 14-4.

Open Circuit

6. Connect the circuit shown in Fig. 14-6, but *do not* turn on the power supply. Refer to step 3 and notice that, when the *previous* circuit was constructed, this configuration used a resistor in series with the supply voltage. This was done so that there would always be a reference level of current maintained from the power supply. In the analysis of open circuits it is *not* necessary to include a series resistor in the test circuit. This is because, when an open occurs in a parallel resistive circuit, the parallel branch resistance becomes practically infinite. If the open occurs in the main line of the power supply, the total resistance becomes infinite as well. The addition of infinite resistances does not harm the power supply. Because of Ohm's law, an infinitely large resistance creates an infinitely small current in relation to the constant voltage provided by the power supply.

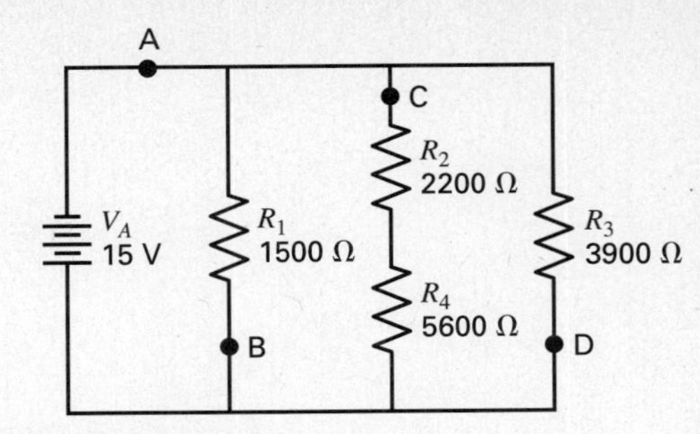

Fig. 14-6. Parallel opens.

7. Turn on the power supply and adjust it to 15 V_{dc}. Measure and record the voltage drops and currents as needed to complete Table 14-5.

8. Open the circuit at the identified points (A, B, C, and D). Retake voltage and current measurements and complete Table 14-6. Be sure to answer the question that appears in Table 14-6.

NAME

DATE

RESULTS FOR EXPERIMENT 14

QUESTIONS

1. What is the result of an open circuit? Explain what happens to the levels of voltage and current in a basic parallel branch circuit.

2. How will an open in a parallel branch affect the main-line current?

3. What is the main advantage of wiring a circuit in a parallel fashion?

4. Why does a short display practically no resistance? Provide a schematic drawing explaining your answer.

5. What limits the current resulting from a short?

CRITICAL THINKING QUESTIONS

Note: The following questions are designed to help you analyze the previous laboratory experiment in a complete and in-depth fashion. To answer these questions, you should review the related material in Grob, *Basic Electronics,* Eighth Edition.

1. Ask your laboratory instructor for two fuses, one that functions and one that does not. After studying these components, describe how they are similar and how they are different. Explain in your own words how you think these components operate.

2. Explain in your own words why short-circuited components are rarely damaged.

3. If any individual resistor is shorted in a parallel circuit, why are all other resistive branches shorted as well?

4. Explain what is meant by the term *bypass* with reference to a shorted circuit.

5. When a parallel circuit develops a shorted component, the voltage source cannot usually maintain its voltage level. Explain.

REPORT

Turn in a complete report.

TABLE 14–1. Individual Resistor Values

		Nominal Resistance	Measured Resistance
Step 1	R_1	1500 Ω	________
	R_2	2200 Ω	________
	R_3	3900 Ω	________
	R_4	5600 Ω	________
	R_5	1000 Ω	________

TABLE 14–2. Total Resistance R_T and Percentage of Error

		Calculated	Measured	% Error
Step 2	R_T	________	________	________

TABLE 14–3. Voltage Drops and Current Measurements

	Measured R Values from Table 14-1	Measured Voltage Drop	Current Measured through Resistor
R_1	______	______	______
R_2	______	______	______
R_3	______	______	______
R_4	______	______	______

TABLE 14–4. Voltage Drops and Current Measurements with Shorted Components

With Only R_1 Shorted		With Only R_2 Shorted		With Only R_3 Shorted		With Only R_4 Shorted	
V_{R_1} ______	I_1 ______	V_{R_1} ______	I_1 ______	V_{R_1} ______	I_1 ______	V_{R_1} ______	I_1 ______
V_{R_2} ______	I_2 ______	V_{R_2} ______	I_2 ______	V_{R_2} ______	I_2 ______	V_{R_2} ______	I_2 ______
V_{R_3} ______	I_3 ______	V_{R_3} ______	I_3 ______	V_{R_3} ______	I_3 ______	V_{R_3} ______	I_3 ______
V_{R_4} ______	I_4 ______	V_{R_4} ______	I_4 ______	V_{R_4} ______	I_4 ______	V_{R_4} ______	I_4 ______

How Do the Above Measurements Reinforce the Characteristics of a Short?

For Extra Credit: Verify by Calculations the Expected Voltages and Currents for This Circuit when R_2 Is Shorted

TABLE 14–5. Voltage Drops and Current Measurements

	Measured R Values from Table 14-1	Measured Voltage Drop	Current Measured through Resistor
R_1			
R_2			
R_3			
R_4			

TABLE 14-6. Voltage Drops and Current Measurements with Opens

Point A Open		Point B Open		Point C Open		Point D Open	
V_{R_1} ______	I_1 ______	V_{R_1} ______	I_1 ______	V_{R_1} ______	I_1 ______	V_{R_1} ______	I_1 ______
V_{R_2} ______	I_2 ______	V_{R_2} ______	I_2 ______	V_{R_2} ______	I_2 ______	V_{R_2} ______	I_2 ______
V_{R_3} ______	I_3 ______	V_{R_3} ______	I_3 ______	V_{R_3} ______	I_3 ______	V_{R_3} ______	I_3 ______
V_{R_4} ______	I_4 ______	V_{R_4} ______	I_4 ______	V_{R_4} ______	I_4 ______	V_{R_4} ______	I_4 ______

How Do the Above Measurements Validate the Characteristics of an Open Circuit?

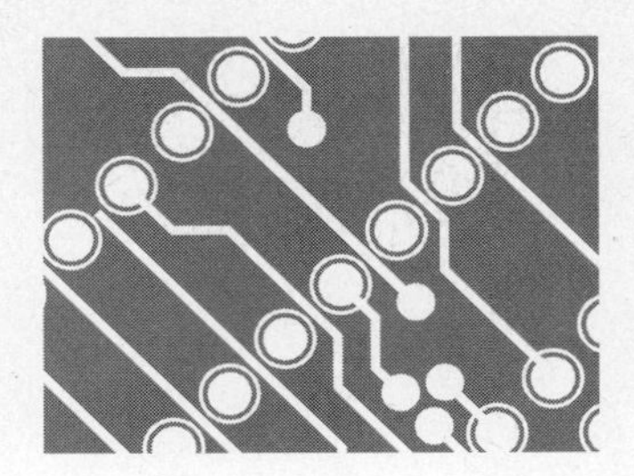

EXPERIMENT 15

SERIES-PARALLEL CIRCUITS

OBJECTIVES

At the completion of this experiment, you will be able to:

- Identify a series-parallel circuit.
- Accurately measure voltages and current present in a series-parallel circuit.

SUGGESTED READING

Chapter 6, *Basic Electronics,* B. Grob, Eighth Edition

INTRODUCTION

Consider the circuit shown in Fig. 15-1. Resistors connected together as shown are often called a *resistor network.* In this network, resistors R_2 and R_3 are considered to be in a parallel arrangement. Also, this parallel arrangement is in series with R_1. To calculate the total resistance R_T, the equivalent resistance of R_2 and R_3 must be determined, where

$$R_{eq} = \frac{R_2 \times R_3}{R_2 + R_3}$$
$$= 150\ \Omega \text{ (approx.)}$$

Therefore, the equivalent resistance of this parallel arrangement is approximately equal to 150 Ω.

The total resistance is now easily found by adding the two resistances R_1 and R_{eq}, where

$$R_T = R_1 + R_{eq}$$

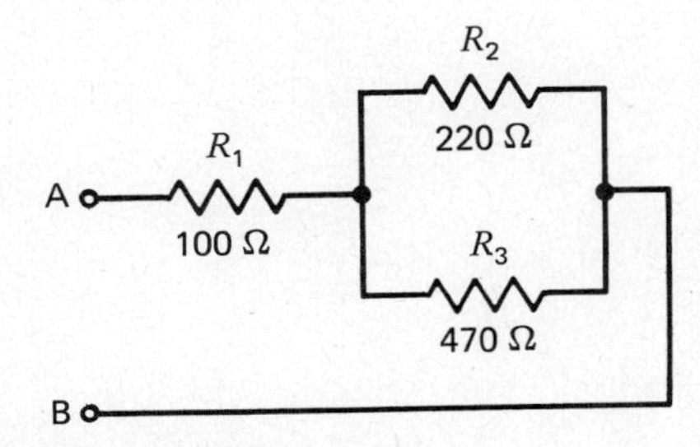

Fig. 15-1. Series-parallel circuit.

EQUIPMENT

Ohmmeter
DC power supply
Ammeter
Voltmeter
Protoboard or springboard
Leads

COMPONENTS

Resistors (all 0.25 W unless indicated otherwise):

(1) 68 Ω	(2) 150 Ω
(3) 100 Ω	(1) 220 Ω
(1) 120 Ω	(1) 470 Ω
(1) 150 Ω/1 W	

PROCEDURE

1. Measure and record the actual resistance values shown in Table 15-1.

2. Connect the circuit shown in Fig. 15-2, where $V = 10$ V, $R_1 = 100\ \Omega$, $R_2 = 220\ \Omega$, and $R_3 = 470\ \Omega$.

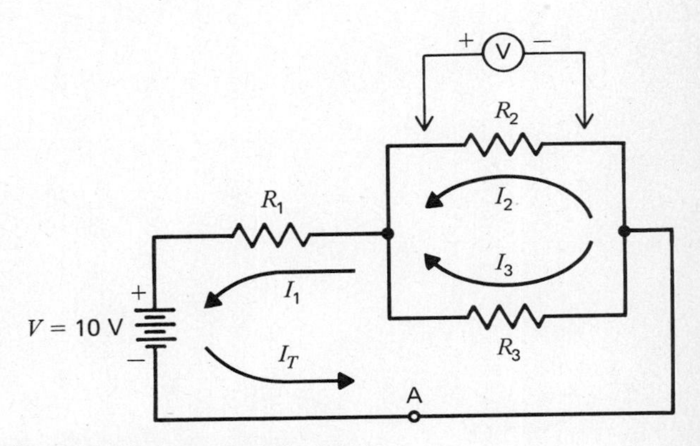

Fig. 15-2. Series-parallel circuit.

3. Calculate, measure, and record V_1, V_2, V_3, I_1, I_2, I_3, and I_T (at point A) in Table 15-2.

4. Measure and record in Table 15-2 the total applied voltage.

5. With the voltage source removed, measure, calculate, and record R_T in Table 15-2.

6. Calculate the percentage of error for Table 15-2.

7. Construct the circuit shown in Fig. 15-3, where

$V_T = 10$ V	$R_4 = 120\ \Omega$
$R_1 = 150\ \Omega/1$ W	$R_5 = 150\ \Omega$
$R_2 = 100\ \Omega$	$R_6 = 100\ \Omega$
$R_3 = 100\ \Omega$	$R_7 = 68\ \Omega$

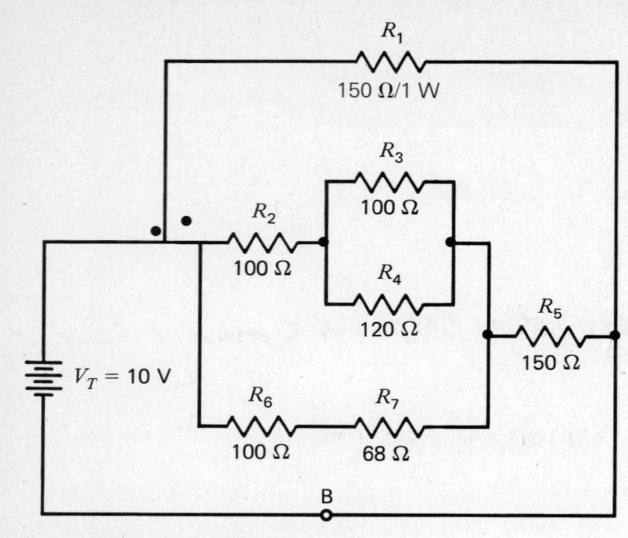

Fig. 15-3. Series-parallel circuit.

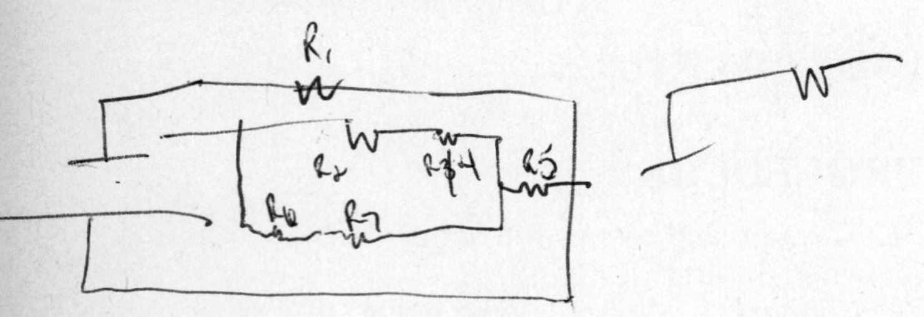

8. Calculate, measure, and record V_1, V_2, V_3, V_4, V_5, V_6, V_7, I_1, I_2, I_3, I_4, I_5, I_6, I_7, and I_T (at point B) in Table 15-3.

9. Measure and record in Table 15-3 the total applied voltage V_T.

10. With the voltage source removed, measure, calculate, and record R_T in Table 15-3.

11. Calculate the percentage of error for Table 15-3.

NAME ______________________ DATE ____________

RESULTS FOR EXPERIMENT 15

QUESTIONS

1. In your own words, explain what a series-parallel circuit is.

In a circuit. You will have series + parallel all together. With one voltage source to provide amount of voltage current for components.

2. In the circuit shown in Fig. 15-2, determine the power being dissipated by each resistor. Use the formula VI = power (watts).

$P_1 = 160$ $P_3 = 78mW$

$P_2 = 162$

3. In Fig. 15-2, are the voltages the same across each resistor?

NO

4. In Fig. 15-2, are the currents the same through each resistor?

NO

5. Suppose in Fig. 15-3 that R_3 developed a short-circuited condition. How would the current flowing through each resistor change? Would the voltage drop across each resistor change? How?

With R_3 shorted. Current will increase. Voltage drop will increase. There was more current flow through each resistor which provide voltage drop in each resistor.

REPORT

Write a complete report. Discuss how Ohm's law applies, and compare the calculated and measured data. Write a conclusion that summarizes the circuit operation.

TABLE 15–1 (values for Fig. 15-3)

Nominal Resistance	Measured Resistance
$R_1 = 150\ \Omega$	150
$R_2 = 100\ \Omega$	100
$R_3 = 100\ \Omega$	100
$R_4 = 120\ \Omega$	120
$R_5 = 150\ \Omega$	150
$R_6 = 100\ \Omega$	100
$R_7 = 68\ \Omega$	68

V=I·R

TABLE 15–2

	Calculated	Measured	% Error
V_1	4.0023	4v	.06%
V_2	5.9977	6v	.04%
V_3	5.9997	6v	.04%
V_T		10v	
I_1	40.023	40mA	.06%
I_2	27.262	27mA	.97%
I_3	12.761	13mA	1.84%
I_T	40.023	40mA	.06%
R_T	249.855	235	5.94%

TABLE 15–3

	Calculated	Measured	% Error
V_1	10v	10v	0
V_2	2.24	2.3v	2.8
V_3	1.26	1.3v	3.1
V_4	1.26	1.3	0
V_5	6.8	6.8	0
V_6	2.2v	2.1	3.8
V_7	1.5v	1.4	6.6
V_T		10v	
I_1	66.6	66	1.1
I_2	12.4	12	2.6
I_3	12.6	13	3.1
I_4	10.5	10	4.7
I_5	3.3mA	43.8	1.1
I_6	22.4	21	6.25
I_7	22.4	21	6.25
I_T	110	110	0%
R_T	90.86	90	.95

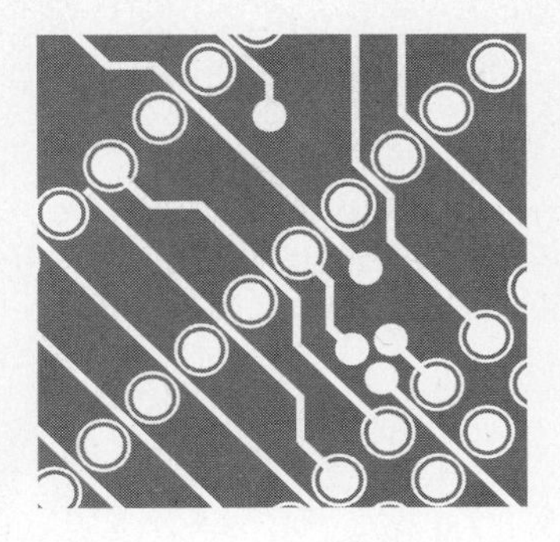

EXPERIMENT 16

SERIES-PARALLEL CIRCUITS—RESISTANCE

OBJECTIVES

At the completion of this experiment, you will be able to:

- Recognize the basic characteristics of series-parallel resistive circuits.
- Confirm that, within a series-parallel circuit, main-line currents are the same through series resistances.
- Confirm that voltage drops across parallel resistive components in a series-parallel circuit are equivalent.

SUGGESTED READING

Chapter 6, *Basic Electronics,* B. Grob, Eighth Edition.

INTRODUCTION

All components in a parallel configuration with the voltage supply have the same voltage drop shown in Fig. 16-1. However, if there is a need to have a voltage less than what is created across one of the parallel resistance branches, an additional resistor can be placed in series within one of the branches, as shown in Fig. 16-2.

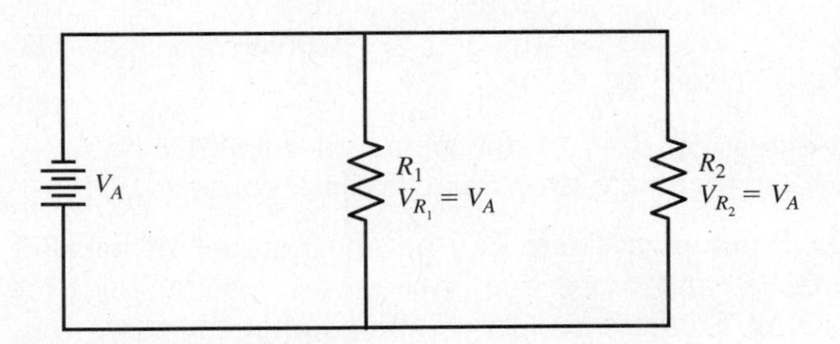

Fig. 16-1. Parallel circuit.

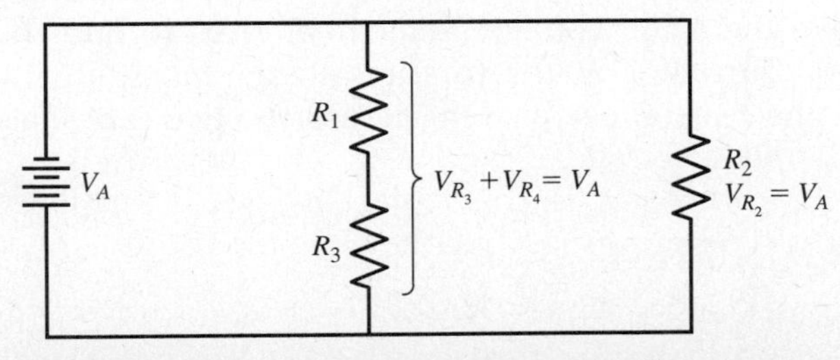

Fig. 16-2. Adding a series resistor to a parallel circuit.

Components in series have the same level of current passing through them. If there is a need to have a component with the same voltage level, another component can be placed across (or in parallel with) one of the series resistors.

Series-parallel circuits are used when it is necessary to provide different amounts of voltage and current from components that use only one source of supply voltage.

Finding R_T: Fig. 16-3 depicts a series-parallel circuit. In order to determine the total resistance (R_T) of this combination, it is necessary to follow the current from the negative side of the supply voltage, through the resistor network and back to the power supply. When this series-parallel circuit is analyzed in this fashion, it is seen that all the current is passing through both R_1 and R_2, and because of this, R_1 and R_2 are seen in series with each other. From this series arrangement, the current then divides at junction point A. At this point, some of the current will pass through R_3, and the remainder through R_4. The amount of current that will pass will depend upon Ohm's law, and since at this junction point there is current division, resistors R_3 and R_4 are in parallel with each other. The divided currents will reunite at junction joint B and pass through R_5. In this case, all the current will pass through resistor R_5, and because of this fact, R_5 is seen to be in series with the parallel combination of R_3 and R_4, and then in series with R_1 and R_2. Expressed as a formula, total resistance R_T is:

$$R_T = R_1 + R_2 + R_3 \parallel R_4 + R_5$$

$$= 1 \text{ k}\Omega + 1.5 \text{ k}\Omega + \frac{1}{1/680\ \Omega + 1/1.2\text{ k}\Omega} + 3.9 \text{ k}\Omega$$

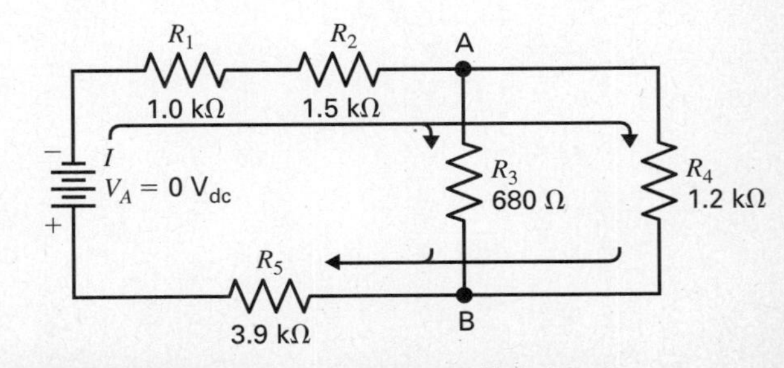

Fig. 16-3. Analysis of a series-parallel circuit.

$$= 1\ k\Omega + 1.5\ k\Omega + 434\ \Omega + 3.9\ k\Omega$$
$$= 6834\ \Omega$$

Total Current: The total current can be calculated if the level of the supply voltage is known. If the power supply in Fig. 16-3 were adjusted to 50 V_{dc}, the current could be calculated by Ohm's law to be approximately 7.3 mA. There is 7.3 mA of main-line current present, as determined by:

$$R_T = 6834\ \Omega$$
$$V_T = 50\ V_{dc}$$
$$I_T = \frac{V_T}{R_T} = \frac{50\ V}{6834\ \Omega} \approx 0.0073\ A = 7.3\ mA$$

Current and Voltage Calculations: Now that the main-line current is known, it is seen that it passes through R_1 and R_2. The current passing through these resistors creates a voltage drop of 7.3 V and 10.95 V, respectively. This is determined as:

$$I_T = 7.3\ mA = 0.0073\ A$$
$$I_{R_1} = 0.0073\ A$$
$$I_{R_2} = 0.0073\ A$$
$$V_{R_1} = I_T \times R_1 = 0.0073\ A \times 1000\ \Omega = 7.3\ V$$
$$V_{R_2} = I_T \times R_2 = 0.0073\ A \times 1500\ \Omega = 10.95\ V$$

When the 7.3 mA enters junction A, the current divides through R_4 and R_5. Since R_4 and R_5 are in parallel, the voltage drop is the same across each of these parallel resistors. From the above, the equivalent resistance R_{eq} of R_3 and R_4 was determined to be 434 Ω. The total main-line current of 7.3 mA passes through this equivalent resistance and creates a voltage drop of 3.17 V. Again, since R_3 and R_4 are in parallel, the voltage drop across R_3 is 3.17 V and the voltage drop across R_4 is the same (3.17 V). These calculations are as follows:

$$R_{eq(R_3\|R_4)} = 434\ \Omega$$
$$I_T = 7.3\ mA = 0.0073\ A$$
$$V_{eq(R_3\|R_4)} = I_T \times R_{eq(R_3\|R_4)} = 0.0073\ A \times 434\ \Omega = 3.1628\ V \cong 3.17\ V$$
$$V_{R_3} \cong 3.17\ V$$
$$V_{R_4} \cong 3.17\ V$$
$$I_3 = \frac{V_{R_3}}{R_3} = \frac{3.17\ V}{680\ \Omega} = 0.0047\ A \cong 4.7\ mA$$
$$I_4 = \frac{V_{R4}}{R_4} = \frac{3.17\ V}{1.2\ k\Omega} = 0.0026\ A \cong 2.6\ mA$$

At junction B the two currents from R_3 and R_4 are reunited, and this 7.3 mA passes through R_5. The voltage drop on R_5 is 28.6 V. This is determined as follows:

$$I_3 + I_4 = 0.0047\ A + 0.0026\ A$$
$$I_5 = 0.0073\ A = 7.3\ mA$$
$$V_{R_5} = I_5 \times R_5 = 0.0073\ A \times 3900\ \Omega = 28.47\ V$$

Note that:

$$V_T \cong V_{R_1} + V_{R_2} + V_{eq(R_3\|R_4)} + V_{R_5}$$
$$50\ V \cong 50\ V$$

Power demands of each component can now also be determined, since the resistance values, voltage drops, and currents are all known. The wattage dissipation needs of the components are determined as follows:

$$P_{R_1} = I_1 \times V_{R_1} = 0.0073\ A \times 7.3\ V = 0.0533\ W = 53.3\ mW$$
$$P_{R_2} = I_2 \times V_{R_2} = 0.0073\ A \times 10.95\ V = 0.0799\ W = 79.9\ mW$$
$$P_{R_3} = I_3 \times V_{R_3} = 0.0047\ A \times 3.17\ V = 0.0149\ W = 14.9\ mW$$
$$P_{R_4} = I_4 \times V_{R_4} = 0.0026\ A \times 3.17\ V = 0.0082\ W = 8.2\ mW$$
$$P_{R_5} = I_5 \times V_{R_5} = 0.0073\ A \times 28.47\ V = 0.2080\ W \approx 208\ mW$$
$$P_T = P_1 + P_2 + P_3 + P_4 + P_5 = 0.0533\ W + 0.0799\ W + 0.0149\ W + 0.0082\ W + 0.2078\ W = 0.3641\ W \approx 364.1\ mW$$

Review Fig. 16-4 to determine all current paths and resistor voltage drops as calculated above.

In Summary: There can be any number of parallel strings and more than two series resistances in a string. Still, Ohm's law can be used in the same way for the series and parallel parts of the circuit. The series parts have the same current; the parallel parts have the same voltage. Remember that, to find the total current *V/R*, the total resistance must include all the resistances present across the two terminals of applied voltage.

EQUIPMENT

Breadboard
DC power supply

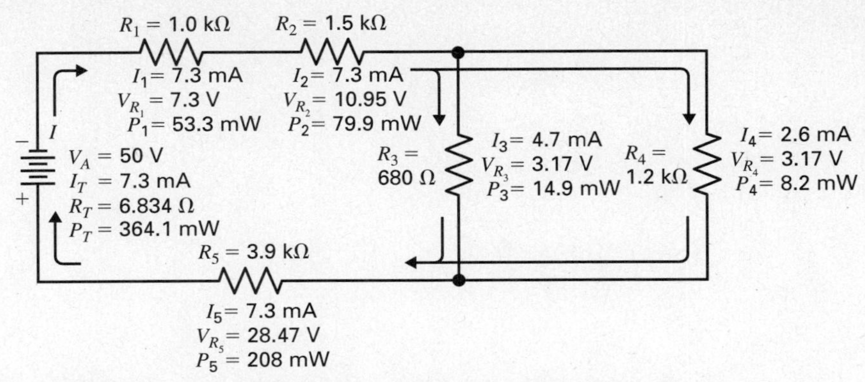

Fig. 16-4. Voltage drops, currents, and power dissipations of a series-parallel circuit.

VOM/DMM
- Voltmeter
- Ammeter
- Ohmmeter

COMPONENTS

All resistors are 0.25 W unless indicated otherwise:

- (1) 100 Ω
- (1) 150 Ω
- (1) 220 Ω
- (1) 390 Ω
- (1) 560 Ω

PROCEDURE

1. Measure and record each resistor value for the resistors required in this experiment. Record the results in Table 16-1.

2. Connect the circuit shown in Fig. 16-5. First calculate and then measure the total resistance from point A to point B. Record this information in Table 16-2. In addition, record the percentage of error between these values, where:

$$\% \text{ error} = \left| \frac{\text{difference between meas. and calc. values}}{\text{calc. values}} \right| \times 100$$

If the error is greater than 10 percent, repeat the calculations and measurements.

3. Connect the circuit shown in Fig. 16-6. Perform the necessary calculations as required in Table 16-2.

4. For the circuit shown in Fig. 16-6, adjust the supply voltage to 15 V and, using a voltmeter, take voltage measurements as required in Table 16-2.

5. Again, for the circuit shown in Fig. 16-6, and with the power supply adjusted to 15 V, use an ammeter and, by breaking the current path at the identified points, measure the current and record your results in Table 16-2.

6. Using the formula described in step 2, calculate the percentages of error between your calculations and voltage and current measurements, as required in Table 16-2.

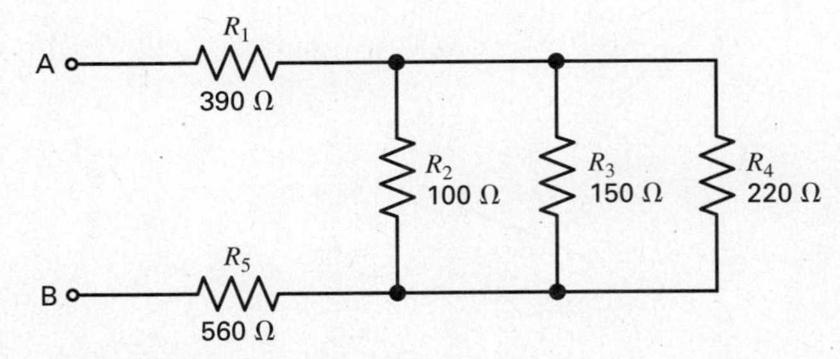

Fig. 16-5. Finding the total resistance.

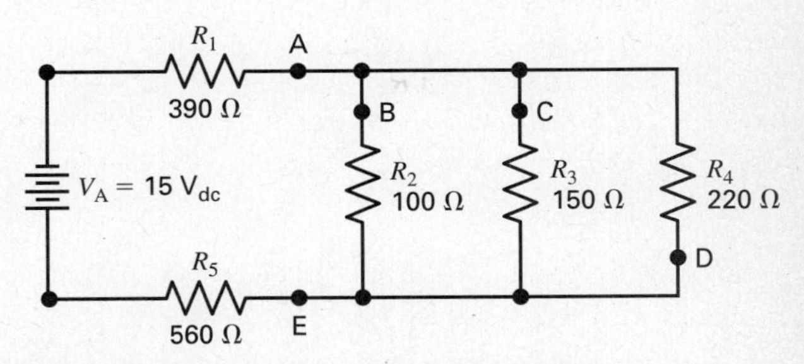

Fig. 16-6. Series-parallel circuit under analysis.

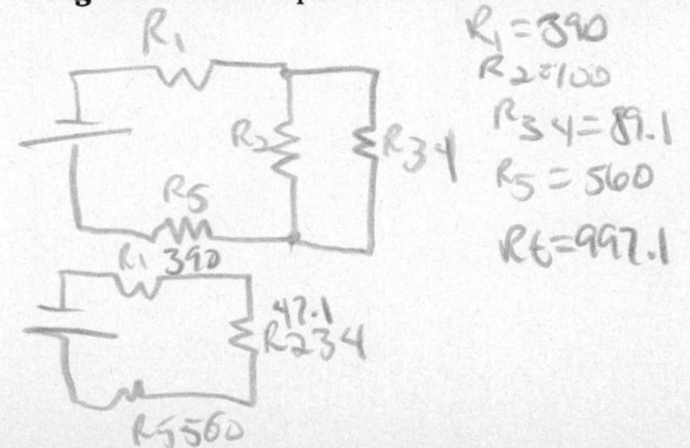

NAME ______________________ DATE ______________

RESULTS FOR EXPERIMENT 16

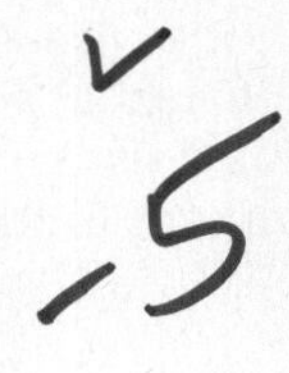

QUESTIONS

1. Write the formula that correctly determines the total resistance of the circuit in Fig. 16-6.

   Rt=R1+R5+R2||R3||R4

2. With reference to Fig. 16-6, which resistors are parallel to, or in series with, R_3? Why?

   R3+4 || R3
   Req of R2-4 series
   R2R3+R4 have junction points.

3. If in Fig. 16-1, the voltage across R_1 was determined to be 20 V, what would the circuit supply voltage be? Explain.

4. If in Fig. 16-4, the current measured through R_5 was 20 mA, what would be the current through R_1? Why?

   R1 series R5

5. Write the formula that would give the equivalent resistance of five 22-kΩ resistors connected in parallel. Applying your formula, determine this resistive value.

   Req=R1||R2||R3||R4||R5   Req=4.4K

CRITICAL THINKING QUESTIONS

Note: The following questions are designed to help you analyze the previous laboratory experiment in a complete and in-depth fashion. To answer these questions, you should review the related material in Grob, *Basic Electronics,* Eighth Edition.

1. In analyzing series-parallel circuits, it is believed that with a parallel string across the main line, the branch currents and the total current can be found without knowing the total resistance. Explain how this principle can be true.

2. In analyzing series-parallel circuits, it is believed that when parallel strings have series resistances in the main line, the total resistance must be calculated to

find the total current, assuming no branch currents are known. Explain how this principle can be true.

3. In analyzing series-parallel circuits, if the source voltage is applied across the total resistance of the entire circuit, a total current will be produced that will be found in the main line. Explain how this principle can be true.

4. In analyzing series-parallel circuits, it is believed that any individual series resistance has its own voltage drop that is less than the total applied voltage. Explain how this principle can be true.

5. In analyzing series-parallel circuits, it is believed that any individual branch current must be less than the total main-line current. Explain how this principle can be true.

REPORT

Turn in a complete report.

TABLE 16–1. Individual Resistor Values

	Nominal Resistance	Measured Value
R_1	390 Ω	390 Ω
R_2	100 Ω	100 Ω
R_3	150 Ω	150 Ω
R_4	220 Ω	220 Ω
R_5	560 Ω	550 Ω

TABLE 16–2. Measurements and Calculations for Resistance, Voltage, and Current

Step		Calculated	Measured	% Error
Step 2	R_T	997.4 Ω	1K	2.7%
Step 4	V_{R_1}	5.8656	5.6	4.5
	V_{R_2}	.712	.7	1.6
	V_{R_3}	.712	.7	1.6
	V_{R_4}	.712	.7	1.6
	V_{R_5}	8.4224	8.3	1.4
Step 5	I_1 (Point A)	15.04	15	.20%
	I_2 (Point B)	7.12	7	1.6
	I_3 (Point C)	4.74	5	5.5
	I_4 (Point D)	3.24	2.9	10.2%
	I_5 (Point E)	15.04	15	0.2%

Step 6 (% Error column)

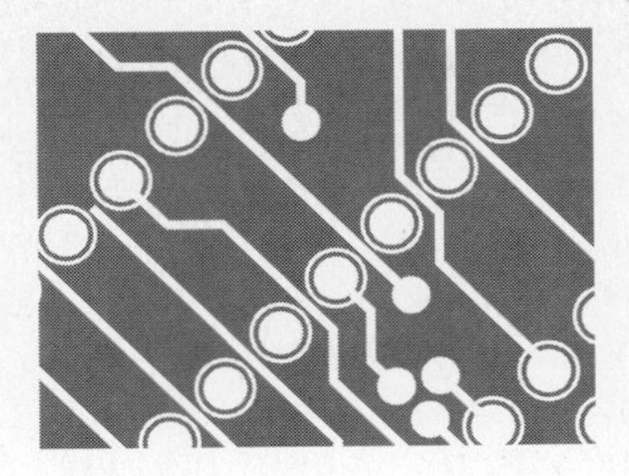

EXPERIMENT 17

SERIES-PARALLEL CIRCUITS—ANALYSIS

OBJECTIVES

At the completion of this experiment, you will be able to:

- Recognize the basic characteristics of series-parallel resistive banks that are in series with other components.
- Determine that, within a series-parallel circuit, main-line currents are the same through series resistances.
- Confirm that voltage drops across parallel resistive components in a series-parallel circuit are equivalent.

SUGGESTED READING

Chapter 6, *Basic Electronics,* B. Grob, Eighth Edition

INTRODUCTION

Another way to analyze complex series-parallel circuits is to consider resistance banks in series with other resistors. Figure 17-1 depicts such a circuit. Here R_1 is in series with a parallel combination of R_2 and R_3. From this point R_4 is seen to be in a series relationship with the parallel combination of R_5 and R_6, leaving R_7 as a series component. If the main-line current from the supply voltage is followed throughout this circuit, we can see that currents are equivalent through series components and that the voltage drops across parallel components are also equivalent. This is demonstrated by the following calculations.

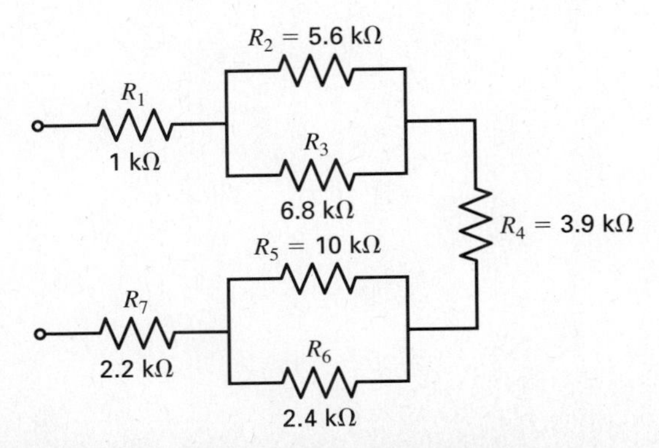

Fig. 17-1. Series-parallel circuit for analysis.

$$\begin{aligned}R_T &= R_1 + R_2 \parallel R_3 + R_4 + R_5 \parallel R_6 + R_7\\ &= 1\text{ k}\Omega + 5.6\text{ k}\Omega \parallel 6.8\text{ k}\Omega + 3.9\text{ k}\Omega + 10\text{ k}\Omega \parallel 2.4\text{ k}\Omega + 2.2\text{ k}\Omega\\ &= 1\text{ k}\Omega + 3070.97\ \Omega + 3.9\text{ k}\Omega + 1935.48\ \Omega + 2.2\text{ k}\Omega\\ &= 12{,}106.45\ \Omega\end{aligned}$$

Figure 17-2 shows the equivalent total resistance for Fig. 17-1. This total resistance, with an applied voltage of 100 V_{dc}, will create a current of 8.3 mA, as shown below:

$$\begin{aligned}I_T &= V_A/R_T\\ &= 80\text{ V}/12{,}106\ \Omega\\ &= 0.0033\text{ A} = 8.3\text{ mA}\end{aligned}$$

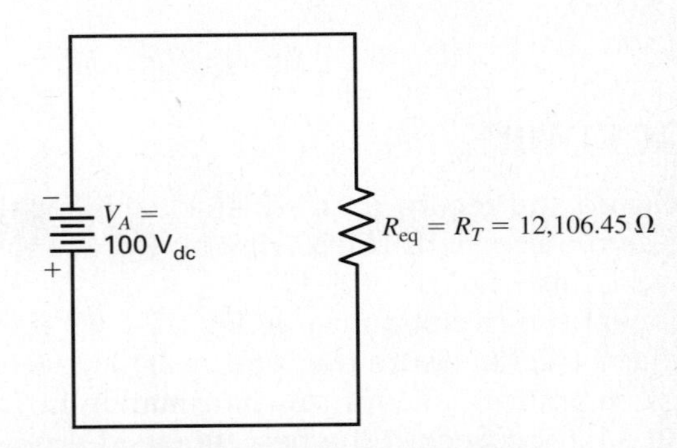

Fig. 17-2. The equivalent total resistance.

The values from all calculations for the circuit shown in Fig. 17-1 are shown in Fig. 17-3.

In summary, there can be more than two parallel resistances in a bank and any number of banks in series. Still, Ohm's law can be applied in the same way to the series and parallel parts of the circuit. The general procedures for circuits of this type is to find

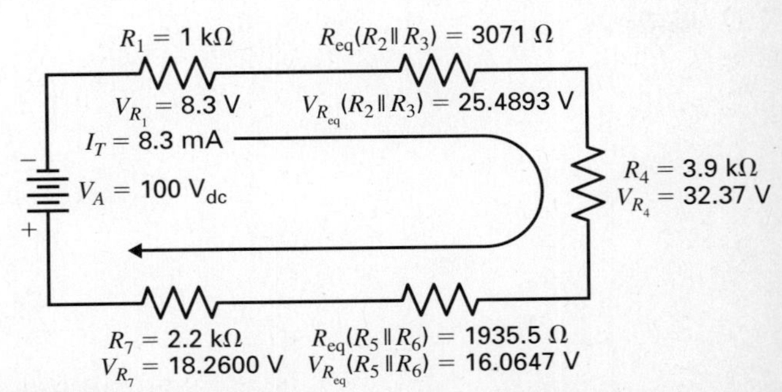

Fig. 17-3. Determining the equivalent resistance of a series-parallel circuit.

the equivalent resistance of each bank and then add all the series resistances.

Again, as in the previous experiment, the most important facts to know are which components are in series with each other and which parts of the circuit are in parallel.

EQUIPMENT

Breadboard
DC power supply
VOM/DMM
- Voltmeter
- Ammeter
- Ohmmeter

COMPONENTS

All resistors are 0.25 W unless indicated otherwise:

(1) 100 Ω
(1) 150 Ω
(1) 220 Ω
(1) 390 Ω
(1) 560 Ω
(1) 820 Ω

PROCEDURE

1. Measure and record each resistor value for the resistors required in this experiment. Record the results in Table 17-1.
2. Connect the circuit shown in Fig. 17-4. First, calculate and then measure the total resistance from point A to point B. Record this information in Table 17-2. In addition, record the percentage of error between these values, where:

$$\% \text{ error} = \left| \frac{\text{difference between meas. and calc. values}}{\text{calc. values}} \right| \times 100$$

If the error is greater than 10 percent, repeat the calculations and measurements.
3. Connect the circuit shown in Fig. 17-5. Adjust the supply voltage to 15 V. Using a voltmeter, take the required measurements to complete Table 17-3.
4. With 15 V applied to the circuit, as shown in Fig. 17-5, determine with an ammeter the current flowing at each identified point and record this measurement in Table 17-3.
5. Perform all calculations required to complete Table 17-3.

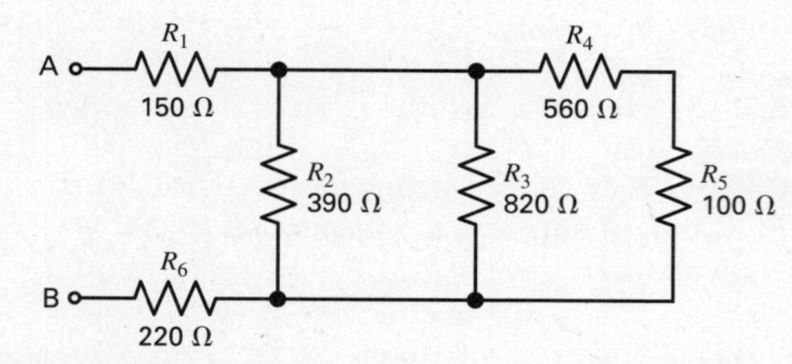

Fig. 17-4. Determining the equivalent resistance of the complex circuit.

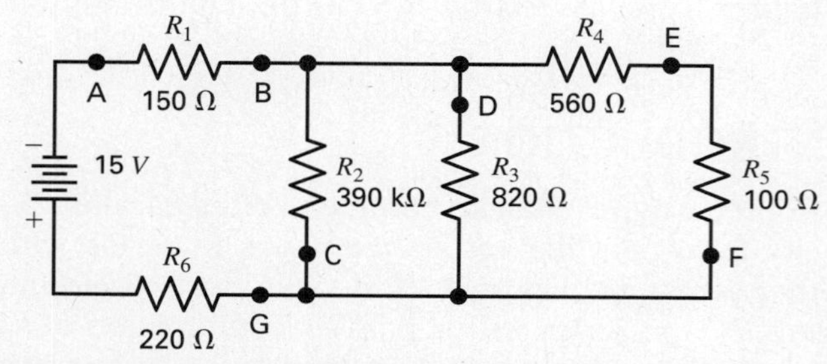

Fig. 17-5. Complex series-parallel circuit analysis.

NAME DATE

RESULTS FOR EXPERIMENT 17

QUESTIONS

1. Draw a diagram showing three resistors in a bank that is in series with three resistors.

2. From Fig. 17-4, describe which resistors are in a parallel circuit arrangement.

3. From your readings in Grob, *Basic Electronics,* Eighth Edition, describe three of the six characteristics of a parallel resistor circuit.

4. From your readings in Grob, *Basic Electronics,* Eighth Edition, describe three of the five characteristics of a series resistor circuit.

5. In Fig. 17-5, explain how you would know which resistors are in parallel with each other and which are in series.

CRITICAL THINKING QUESTIONS

Note: The following questions are designed to help you analyze the previous laboratory experiment in a complete and in-depth fashion. To answer these questions, you should review the related material in Grob, *Basic Electronics,* Eighth Edition.

1. Determine all circuit calculations (voltage drops and currents) for the circuit shown in Fig. 17-5, where the applied voltage is changed to 15 V_{dc}. Determine the power dissipation required for each resistor. If the voltage were increased to 15 V_{dc}, would the 0.25-W power rating of the resistors recommended for use in this experiment be adequate?

2. Determine the total resistance R_T for Fig. 17-3. Show all calculations.

3. Determine the power dissipation required for each resistor shown in Fig. 17-3. Show all calculations.

4. Determine the total resistance R_T for Fig. 17-5. Show all calculations.

5. Determine the power dissipation required for each resistor shown in Fig. 17-5. Show all calculations.

REPORT

Turn in a complete report.

TABLE 17–1. Individual Resistor Values

	Nominal Values	Measured Values
R_1	150 Ω	______
R_2	390 Ω	______
R_3	820 Ω	______
R_4	560 Ω	______
R_5	100 Ω	______
R_6	220 Ω	______

TABLE 17–2. Total Resistance R_T and Percentage of Error

	Measured	Calculated	% Error
Step 2 { R_T	______	______	______

TABLE 17–3. Voltage, Current Measurements, and Percentage of Error

		Measured	Calculated	% Error
Step 3	V_{R_1}	______	______	______
	V_{R_2}	______	______	______
	V_{R_3}	______	______	______
	V_{R_4}	______	______	______
	V_{R_5}	______	______	______
	V_{R_6}	______	______	______
Step 4	I_T (Point A)	______	______	______
	I_{R_1} (Point B)	______	______	______
	I_{R_2} (Point C)	______	______	______
	I_{R_3} (Point D)	______	______	______
	I_{R_4} (Point E)	______	______	______
	I_{R_5} (Point F)	______	______	______
	I_{R_6} (Point G)	______	______	______
				Step 5

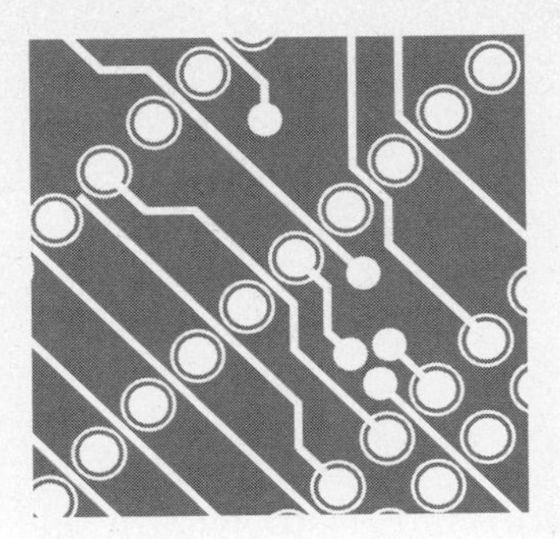

EXPERIMENT 18

SERIES-PARALLEL CIRCUITS—OPENS AND SHORTS

OBJECTIVES

At the completion of this experiment, you will be able to:

- Confirm the basic characteristics of series-parallel resistive circuits.
- Identify the characteristics and effects of opens in a series-parallel resistive circuit.
- Identify the characteristics and effects of shorts in a series-parallel resistive circuit.

SUGGESTED READING

Chapter 6, *Basic Electronics,* B. Grob, Eighth Edition

INTRODUCTION

The purpose of this experiment is to learn about the characteristics of electrical opens and shorts and how they affect currents and voltages. In this experiment we will see how a series-parallel circuit is affected.

The Short Circuit: A short circuit has practically zero resistance. Its effect, therefore, is to allow excessive current to flow. An open circuit has the opposite effect, because an open circuit has infinitely high resistance with practically zero current. Furthermore, in series-parallel circuits, an open or short circuit in one path changes the circuit for the other resistances. For example, in Fig. 18-1, the series-parallel circuit becomes a series circuit with only R_1 when there is a short circuit between points A and B.

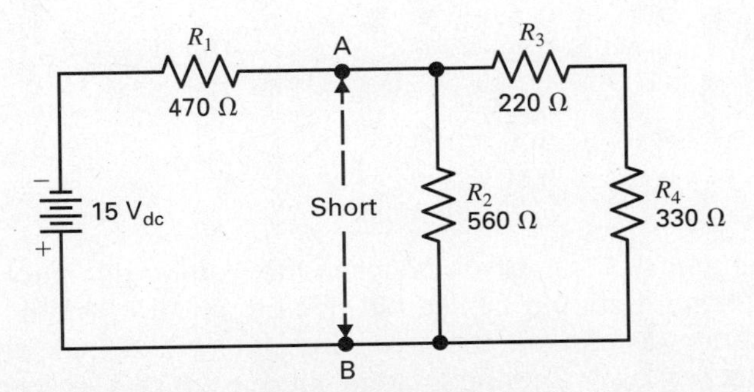

Fig. 18-1. Analysis of the short circuit.

Studying the Circuit without a Short: If the circuit shown in Fig. 18-1 does not have a short, R_T can be calculated so that R_3 and R_4 are in series and have an equivalent resistance of 550 Ω. This 550-Ω equivalent resistance is in parallel with 560-Ω R_2 values and creates an equivalent resistance of 277.48 Ω. This value is now in series with the 470-Ω value of R_1 and provides an overall total equivalent resistance of 747.48 Ω.

Since R_T is known, the main-line current can be determined from Ohm's law as follows:

$$I_T = V_T/R_T$$
$$= 15\ V_{dc}/747.48\ \Omega$$
$$= 0.0201\ A = 20.1\ mA$$

The total power of the circuit can be calculated as follows:

$$P_T = I_T \times V_T$$
$$= 0.0201\ A \times 15\ V$$
$$= 0.3010\ W = 301\ mW$$

Since the total main-line current I_T is known, the associated voltage drops across each of the resistors can be determined. For example:

$$V_{R_1} = I_T \times R_1$$
$$= 0.0201\ A \times 470\ \Omega$$
$$= 9.45\ V$$

Since the applied voltage is 15 V and 9.45 V was dropped across R_1, V_{R_2} can be determined to be 5.55 V, as follows:

$$V_{R_2} = V_T - V_{R_1}$$
$$= 15\ V - 9.45\ V$$
$$= 5.55\ V$$

Since 5.55 V is dropped across R_2, the current through R_2 can be determined as follows:

$$I_{R_2} = V_{R_2}/R_2$$
$$= 5.55\ V/560\ \Omega$$
$$= 0.0099\ A = 9.9\ mA$$

As you know, currents divide in parallel branches. The main-line current of 20.1 mA divides between the R_2 branch and the $R_3 + R_4$ branch. If 9.9 mA passes through R_2, and the total current I_T is 20.1 mA, the difference of 10.2 mA will pass through the series combination of the $R_3 + R_4$ branch. Since R_3 and R_4 are in series, this 10.2 mA of current will pass through both series resistors, as follows:

$$I_{R_3} = I_{R_4} = I_T - I_{R_2}$$
$$= 0.02010 \text{ A} - 0.0099 \text{ A}$$
$$= 0.0102 \text{ A} = 10.2 \text{ mA}$$

If the current through R_3 and R_4 is known to be 10.2 mA, the voltage drop across each can be determined:

$$V_{R_3} = I_{R_3} \times R_3$$
$$= 0.0102 \text{ A} \times 220\ \Omega$$
$$= 2.24 \text{ V}$$

and

$$V_{R_4} = I_{R_4} \times R_4$$
$$= 0.0102 \text{ A} \times 330\ \Omega$$
$$= 3.36 \text{ V}$$

Note that the sum of V_{R_3} and V_{R_4} is equivalent to V_{R_2}. This is to be anticipated, since these resistances are in a parallel branch arrangement, and voltage drops are found to be equivalent in parallel branches.

$$V_{R_3} + V_{R_4} = V_{R_2}$$
$$2.24 \text{ V} + 3.36 \text{ V} = 5.60 \text{ V}$$
(approximately equal to 5.55 V)

Power in the circuit can be determined as follows:

$$P_{R_1} = I_{R_1} \times V_{R_1}$$
$$= 0.0201 \text{ A} \times 9.45 \text{ V}$$
$$= 0.1899 \text{ W} = 189.9 \text{ mW}$$

$$P_{R_2} = I_{R_2} \times V_{R_2}$$
$$= 0.0099 \text{ A} \times 5.55 \text{ V}$$
$$= 0.0549 \text{ W} = 54.9 \text{ mW}$$

$$P_{R_3} = I_{R_3} \times V_{R_3}$$
$$= 0.0102 \text{ A} \times 2.24 \text{ V}$$
$$= 0.0228 \text{ W} = 22.8 \text{ mW}$$

$$P_{R_4} = I_{R_4} \times V_{R_4}$$
$$= 0.0102 \text{ A} \times 3.36 \text{ V}$$
$$= 0.0343 \text{ W} = 34.3 \text{ mW}$$

Studying the Same Circuit with a Short: If the circuit shown in Fig. 18-1 now possesses a short between points A and B, R_T can be calculated so that R_3 and R_4 are *still* in series and have an equivalent resistance of 550 Ω. This 550-Ω equivalent resistance is *still* in parallel with the 560-Ω R_2 value and creates an equivalent resistance of 277.48 Ω. However, this equivalent resistance is seen to be in parallel with a short, which displays practically no resistance (0 Ω). In this case, the equivalent resistance of the parallel branches is now 0 Ω. This ohmic value is in series with the 470-Ω value of R_1 and provides an overall total equivalent resistance of 470 Ω.

Since R_T is known, the main-line current can be determined from Ohm's law as follows:

$$I_T = V_T / R_T$$
$$= 15 \text{ V}_{dc} / 470\ \Omega$$
$$= 0.0319 \text{ A} = 31.9 \text{ mA}$$

The total power of the circuit can be calculated as follows:

$$P_T = I_T \times V_T$$
$$= 0.0319 \text{ A} \times 15 \text{ V}$$
$$= 0.4787 \text{ W} = 478.7 \text{ mW}$$

Since the total main-line current I_T is known, the associated voltage drops across each of the resistors can be determined. For example:

$$V_{R_1} = I_T \times R_1$$
$$= 0.0319 \text{ A} \times 470\ \Omega$$
$$= 14.99 \text{ V (which in practical terms is 15 V)}$$

Since the applied voltage is 15 V and 15 V was dropped across R_1, V_{R_2} can be determined to be 0 V, as follows:

$$V_{R_2} = V_T - V_{R_1}$$
$$= 15 \text{ V} - 15 \text{ V}$$
$$= 0 \text{ V}$$

Since 0 V is dropped across R_2, the current through R_2 can be determined as follows:

$$I_{R_2} = V_{R_2} / R_2$$
$$= 0 \text{ V} / 560\ \Omega$$
$$= 0 \text{ A} = 0 \text{ mA}$$

$$I_{R_3} = 0 \text{ A} = 0 \text{ mA}$$

$$I_{R_4} = 0 \text{ A} = 0 \text{ mA}$$

$$V_{R_3} = I_{R_3} \times R_3$$
$$= 0 \text{ A} \times 220\ \Omega$$
$$= 0 \text{ V}$$

$$V_{R_4} = I_{R_4} \times R_4$$
$$= 0 \text{ A} \times 330\ \Omega$$
$$= 0 \text{ V}$$

$$P_{R_1} = I_{R_1} \times V_{R_1}$$
$$= 0.0319 \text{ A} \times 15 \text{ V}$$
$$= 0.4787 \text{ W} = 478.7 \text{ mW}$$

$$P_{R_2} = I_{R_2} \times V_{R_2}$$
$$= 0 \text{ A} \times 0 \text{ V}$$
$$= 0 \text{ W}$$

$$P_{R_3} = I_{R_3} \times V_{R_3}$$
$$= 0 \text{ A} \times 0 \text{ V}$$
$$= 0 \text{ W}$$

$$P_{R_4} = I_{R_4} \times V_{R_4}$$
$$= 0 \text{ A} \times 0 \text{ V}$$
$$= 0 \text{ W}$$

Summary Comparison between the Normal and Short Circuit: It should be seen in this circuit that, when a short was created, the overall resistance of the circuit decreased, main-line current increased, and overall power dissipation increased markedly.

	Normal Operation	Short Circuit
R_T	747.48 Ω	470 Ω
I_T	20.1 mA	31.9 mA
P_T	301 mW	478.7 mW
V_{R_1}	9.45 V	15 V
V_{R_2}	5.55 V	0 V
I_{R_2}	9.9 mA	0 mA
I_{R_3}	10.2 mA	0 mA
I_{R_4}	10.2 mA	0 mA
V_{R_3}	2.24 V	0 V
V_{R_4}	3.36 V	0 V
P_{R_1}	189.9 mW	478.7 mW
P_{R_2}	54.9 mW	0 mW
P_{R_3}	22.8 mW	0 mW
P_{R_4}	34.3 mW	0 mW

The Open Circuit: As an example of an open circuit, the series-parallel circuit in Fig. 18-2 becomes a series circuit with just R_1 and R_2 when there is an open circuit between terminals C and D. Since the component values and supply voltages are the same as in the circuit shown in Fig. 18-1, we will develop the characteristics of the open in this circuit by concentrating on the component calculated values.

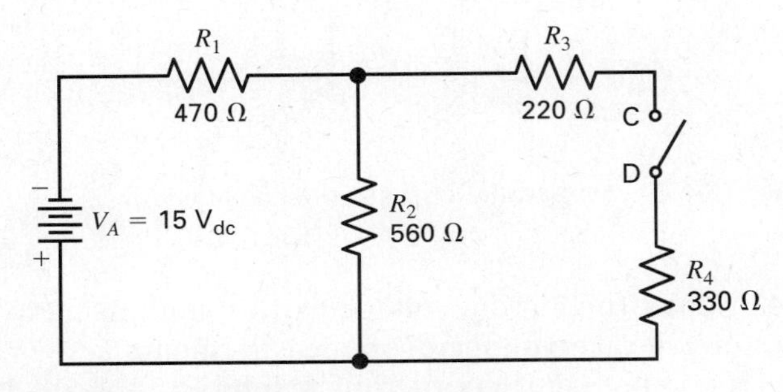

Fig. 18-2. Analysis of the open circuit.

When analyzing the effects of this open circuit problem, remember that, in the normal closed circuit, $R_T = 747.48\ \Omega$, $I_T = 20.1$ mA, $P_T = 301$ mW, $V_{R_1} = 9.45$ V, $V_{R_2} = 5.55$ V, $I_{R_2} = 9.9$ mA, $I_{R_3} = 10.2$ mA, $I_{R_4} = 10.2$ mA, $V_{R_3} = 2.24$ V, $V_{R_4} = 3.36$ V, $P_{R_1} = 189.9$ mW, $P_{R_2} = 54.9$ mW, $P_{R_3} = 22.8$ mW, and $P_{R_4} = 34.3$ mW.

Studying the Effect of an Open Circuit: If the circuit shown in Fig. 18-2 is open from points C to D, R_T can be calculated so that the series resistances R_3 and R_4 are open and maintain an infinite resistance. This infinite resistance is in parallel with R_2, and the parallel equivalent resistance can be considered to be equivalent to R_2, or 560 Ω. This value is now in series with the 470-Ω value of R_1 and provides an overall total equivalent resistance of 1030 Ω.

Since R_T is known, the main-line current can be determined from Ohm's law as follows:

$$I_T = V_T/R_T = 15\ \text{V}_{\text{dc}}/1030\ \Omega = 0.0146\ \text{A} \approx 14.6\ \text{mA}$$

The total power of the circuit can be calculated as follows:

$$P_T = I_T \times V_T = 0.0146\ \text{A} \times 15\ \text{V} = 0.219\ \text{W} = 219\ \text{mW}$$

Since the total main-line current I_T is known, the associated voltage drops across each of the resistors can be determined, for example:

$$V_{R_1} = I_T \times R_1 = 0.0146\ \text{A} \times 470\ \Omega = 6.8620\ \text{V}$$

Since the applied voltage is 15 V and 6.8620 V was dropped across R_1, V_{R_2} can be determined to be 8.1380 V, as follows:

$$V_{R_2} = V_T - V_{R_1} = 15\ \text{V} - 6.8620\ \text{V} = 8.1380\ \text{V}$$

Since 8.1380 V is dropped across R_2, the current through R_2 can be determined to be:

$$I_{R_2} = V_{R_2}/R_2 = 8.1380\ \text{V}/560\ \Omega = 0.0145\ \text{A} = 14.5\ \text{mA}$$

As you know, currents divide in parallel branches. However, the main-line current of 14.6 mA does not divide between the R_2 branch and the $R_3 + R_4$ branch, since the $R_3 + R_4$ branch is open. It would follow therefore that:

$$I_{R_3} = I_{R_4} = 0\ \text{A}$$

If the current is known to be 0 A through R_3 and R_4, the voltage drop across each can be determined, as follows:

$$V_{R_3} = I_{R_3} \times R_3 = 0\ \text{A} \times 220\ \Omega = 0\ \text{V}$$

and

$$V_{R_4} = I_{R_4} \times R_4 = 0\ \text{A} \times 330\ \Omega = 0\ \text{V}$$

Power in the circuit can be determined as follows:

$$P_{R_1} = I_{R_1} \times V_{R_1} = 0.0146\ \text{A} \times 6.8620\ \text{V} = 0.1002\ \text{W} = 100.2\ \text{mW}$$

$$P_{R_2} = I_{R_2} \times V_{R_2} = 0.0146\ \text{A} \times 8.1380\ \text{V} = 0.1188\ \text{W} = 118.8\ \text{mW}$$

$$P_{R_3} = I_{R_3} \times V_{R_3}$$
$$= 0\ \text{A} \times 0\ \text{V}$$
$$= 0\ \text{W}$$
$$P_{R_4} = I_{R_4} \times V_{R_4}$$
$$= 0\ \text{A} \times 0\ \text{V}$$
$$= 0\ \text{W}$$

Summary Comparison between the Normal and Short Circuit: It should be seen in this circuit that, when an open was created, the overall resistance of the circuit increased, main-line current decreased, and overall power dissipation changed markedly.

	Normal Operation	Open Circuit
R_T	747.48 Ω	1030 Ω
I_T	20.1 mA	14.6 mA
P_T	301 mW	218.4 mW
V_{R_1}	9.45 V	6.8620 V
V_{R_2}	5.55 V	8.1380 V
I_{R_2}	9.9 mA	14.5 mA
I_{R_3}	10.2 mA	0 mA
I_{R_4}	10.2 mA	0 mA
V_{R_3}	2.24 V	0 V
V_{R_4}	3.36 V	0 V
P_{R_1}	189.9 mW	100.2 mW
P_{R_2}	54.9 mW	118.8 mW
P_{R_3}	22.8 mW	0 mW
P_{R_4}	34.3 mW	0 mW

EQUIPMENT

Breadboard
DC power supply
VOM/DMM
  Voltmeter
  Ammeter
  Ohmmeter

COMPONENTS

All resistors are 0.25 W unless indicated otherwise:

(1) 100 Ω (1) 560 Ω
(1) 120 Ω (1) 680 Ω
(1) 470 Ω (1) 820 Ω

PROCEDURE

1. Measure and record each resistor value for the resistors required in this experiment. Record the results in Table 18-1.

2. Connect the circuit shown in Fig. 18-3. First calculate and then measure the total resistance from point A to point B. Record this information in Table 18-2. In addition, record the percentage of error between these values, where:

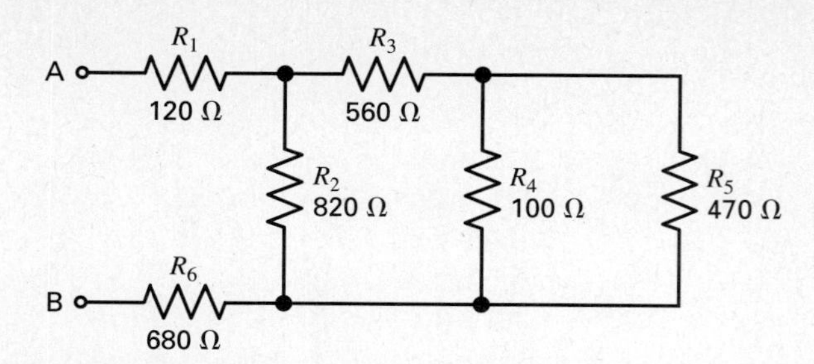

Fig. 18-3. Finding the total resistance of a series-parallel circuit.

$$\%\ \text{error} = \left| \frac{\text{difference between meas. and calc. values}}{\text{calc. values}} \right| \times 100$$

If the error is greater than 10 percent, repeat the calculations and measurements.

3. Connect the circuit shown in Fig. 18-4. Calculate all voltage drops and component currents, and record them in Table 18-3.

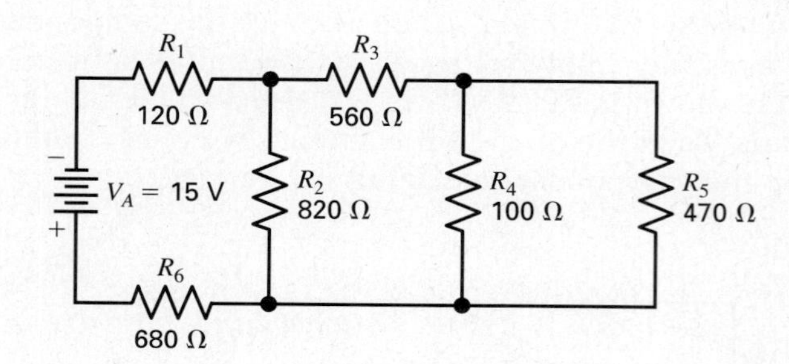

Fig. 18-4. Series-parallel circuit under analysis.

4. Adjust the supply voltage to 15 V and, using a voltmeter, take voltage drop measurements across each component. Record your results in Table 18-3.

Voltage Measurements—Short Circuits

5. Maintaining a supply voltage of 15 V, use a clip lead to short R_1. Take voltage drop measurements V_{R_1}, V_{R_2}, V_{R_3}, V_{R_4}, V_{R_5}, and V_{R_6}. Record the results in Table 18-3.

6. Remove the clip-lead short across R_1.

7. Maintaining a supply voltage of 15 V, use a clip lead to short R_2. Take voltage drop measurements V_{R_1}, V_{R_2}, V_{R_3}, V_{R_4}, V_{R_5}, and V_{R_6}. Record the results in Table 18-3.

8. Remove the clip-lead short across R_2.

9. Maintaining a supply voltage of 15 V, use a clip lead to short R_3. Take voltage drop measurements V_{R_1}, V_{R_2}, V_{R_3}, V_{R_4}, V_{R_5}, and V_{R_6}. Record the results in Table 18-3.

10. Remove the clip-lead short across R_3.

11. Maintaining a supply voltage of 15 V, use a clip lead to short R_4. Take voltage drop measurements

V_{R_1}, V_{R_2}, V_{R_3}, V_{R_4}, V_{R_5}, and V_{R_6}. Record the results in Table 18-3.

12. Remove the clip-lead short across R_4.

13. Maintaining a supply voltage of 15 V, use a clip lead to short R_5. Take voltage drop measurements V_{R_1}, V_{R_2}, V_{R_3}, V_{R_4}, V_{R_5}, and V_{R_6}. Record the results in Table 18-3.

14. Remove the clip-lead short across R_5.

15. Maintaining a supply voltage of 15 V, use a clip lead to short R_6. Take voltage drop measurements V_{R_1}, V_{R_2}, V_{R_3}, V_{R_4}, V_{R_5}, and V_{R_6}. Record the results in Table 18-3.

16. Remove the clip-lead short across R_6.

Current Measurements—Short Circuits

17. Maintaining a supply voltage of 15 V, use a clip lead to short R_1 from your circuit. With an ammeter, take current measurements of I_{R_2}, I_{R_3}, I_{R_4}, I_{R_5}, and I_{R_6}. Do not take the current measurement through R_1. Record this information in Table 18-3.

18. Remove the clip-lead circuit short across R_1.

19. Maintaining a supply voltage of 15 V, use a clip lead to short R_2 from your circuit. With an ammeter, take current measurements of I_{R_1}, I_{R_3}, I_{R_4}, I_{R_5}, and I_{R_6}. Do not take the current measurement through R_2. Record this information in Table 18-3.

20. Remove the clip-lead circuit short across R_2.

21. Maintaining a supply voltage of 15 V, use a clip lead to short R_3 from your circuit. With an ammeter, take current measurements of I_{R_1}, I_{R_2}, I_{R_4}, I_{R_5}, and I_{R_6}. Do not take the current measurement through R_3. Record this information in Table 18-3.

22. Remove the clip-lead circuit short across R_3.

23. Maintaining a supply voltage of 15 V, use a clip lead to short R_4 from your circuit. With an ammeter, take current measurements of I_{R_1}, I_{R_2}, I_{R_3}, I_{R_5}, and I_{R_6}. Do not take the current measurement through R_4. Record this information in Table 18-3.

24. Remove the clip-lead circuit short across R_4.

25. Maintaining a supply voltage of 15 V, use a clip lead to short R_5 from your circuit. With an ammeter, take current measurements of I_{R_1}, I_{R_2}, I_{R_3}, I_{R_4}, and I_{R_6}. Do not take the current measurement through R_5. Record this information in Table 18-3.

26. Remove the clip-lead circuit short across R_5.

27. Maintaining a supply voltage of 15 V, use a clip lead to short R_6 from your circuit. With an ammeter, take current measurements of I_{R_1}, I_{R_2}, I_{R_3}, I_{R_4}, and I_{R_5}. Do not take the current measurement through R_6. Record this information in Table 18-3.

28. Remove the clip-lead circuit short across R_6.

Voltage Measurements—Open Circuits

29. Maintaining a supply voltage of 15 V, open R_1 by removing it from the circuit. Take voltage drop measurements V_{R_2}, V_{R_3}, V_{R_4}, V_{R_5}, and V_{R_6}. Do not take the voltage drop measurement across R_1. Record these measurements in Table 18-4.

30. Remove the open by replacing R_1 into the circuit.

31. Maintaining a supply voltage of 15 V, open R_2 by removing it from the circuit. Take voltage drop measurements V_{R_1}, V_{R_3}, V_{R_4}, V_{R_5}, and V_{R_6}. Do not take the voltage drop measurement across R_2. Record these measurements in Table 18-4.

32. Remove the open by replacing R_2 into the circuit.

33. Maintaining a supply voltage of 15 V, open R_3 by removing it from the circuit. Take voltage drop measurements V_{R_1}, V_{R_2}, V_{R_4}, V_{R_5}, and V_{R_6}. Do not take the voltage drop measurement across R_3. Record these measurements in Table 18-4.

34. Remove the open by replacing R_3 into the circuit.

35. Maintaining a supply voltage of 15 V, open R_4 by removing it from the circuit. Take voltage drop measurements V_{R_1}, V_{R_2}, V_{R_3}, V_{R_5}, and V_{R_6}. Do not take the voltage drop measurement across R_4. Record these measurements in Table 18-4.

36. Remove the open by replacing R_4 into the circuit.

37. Maintaining a supply voltage of 15 V, open R_5 by removing it from the circuit. Take voltage drop measurements V_{R_1}, V_{R_2}, V_{R_3}, V_{R_4}, and V_{R_6}. Do not take the voltage drop measurement across R_5. Record these measurements in Table 18-4.

38. Remove the open by replacing R_5 into the circuit.

39. Maintaining a supply voltage of 15 V, open R_6 by removing it from the circuit. Take voltage drop measurements V_{R_1}, V_{R_2}, V_{R_3}, V_{R_4}, and V_{R_5}. Do not take the voltage drop measurement across R_6. Record these measurements in Table 18-4.

40. Remove the open by replacing R_6 into the circuit.

Current Measurements—Open Circuits

41. Maintaining a supply voltage of 15 V, open R_1 by removing it from the circuit. Take current measurements I_{R_2}, I_{R_3}, I_{R_4}, I_{R_5}, and I_{R_6}. Do not take the current measurement through R_1. Record these measurements in Table 18-4.

42. Remove the open by replacing R_1 into the circuit.

43. Maintaining a supply voltage of 15 V, open R_2 by removing it from the circuit. Take current measurements I_{R_1}, I_{R_3}, I_{R_4}, I_{R_5}, and I_{R_6}. Do not take the current measurement through R_2. Record these measurements in Table 18-4.

44. Remove the open by replacing R_2 into the circuit.

45. Maintaining a supply voltage of 15 V, open R_3 by removing it from the circuit. Take current measurements I_{R_1}, I_{R_2}, I_{R_4}, I_{R_5}, and I_{R_6}. Do not take the current measurement through R_3. Record these measurements in Table 18-4.

46. Remove the open by replacing R_3 into the circuit.

47. Maintaining a supply voltage of 15 V, open R_4 by removing it from the circuit. Take current measurements I_{R_1}, I_{R_2}, I_{R_3}, I_{R_5}, and I_{R_6}. Do not take the current measurement through R_4. Record these measurements in Table 18-4.

48. Remove the open by replacing R_4 into the circuit.

49. Maintaining a supply voltage of 15 V, open R_5 by removing it from the circuit. Take current measurements I_{R_1}, I_{R_2}, I_{R_3}, I_{R_4}, and I_{R_6}. Do not take the current measurement through R_5. Record these measurements in Table 18-4.

50. Remove the open by replacing R_5 into the circuit.

51. Maintaining a supply voltage of 15 V, open R_6 by removing it from the circuit. Take current measurements I_{R_1}, I_{R_2}, I_{R_3}, I_{R_4}, and I_{R_5}. Do not take the current measurement through R_6. Record these measurements in Table 18-4.

52. Remove the open by replacing R_6 into the circuit.

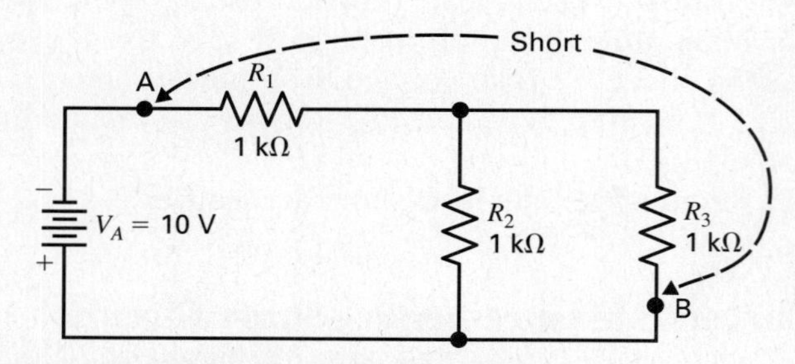

Fig. 18-5. Shorted circuit for Question 2.

NAME ______________________________ DATE ______________

RESULTS FOR EXPERIMENT 18

QUESTIONS

1. What effect would a short across a resistor located in series with a parallel resistive branch have on the level of main-line current flow? Explain.

There would be as much current as there should

2. What effect would a short from point A to point B within the circuit shown in Fig. 18-5 on page 98 have on individual branch circuit levels? Explain.

To short out point A.

3. If in Fig. 18-1, R_2 was shorted, what would happen to the current flow and voltage drop of R_3? What would happen to the voltage and current of R_2? Explain.

The voltage drop would go down, the current would go up.
The voltage and would stay + current would go down

4. Calculate the needed level of power dissipation for each resistor shown in Fig. 18-4. How does power dissipation change for a shorted component? How would it change across an open component? Explain.

Using the proper voltage is allowing power to dissipate equally.

5. According to Grob, *Basic Electronics,* Eighth Edition, what is the potential difference across an open? Explain.

Across an open shorts deal with possible to leave to equal 0 or infinity.

CRITICAL THINKING QUESTIONS

Note: The following questions are designed to help you analyze the previous laboratory experiment in a complete and in-depth fashion. To answer these questions, you should review the related material in Grob, *Basic Electronics,* Eighth Edition.

1. Create a table that compares the calculated values for the normal circuit, short circuit, and open circuit in Figs. 18-1 and 18-2. Describe the similarities and differences in this table.

2. For the short circuit current analysis in step 17, the following statement is made: "Maintaining a supply voltage of 15 V, use a clip lead to short R_1 from your circuit. With an ammeter, take current measurements of I_{R_2}, I_{R_3}, I_{R_4}, I_{R_5}, and I_{R_6}. Do not take the current measurement through R_1. Record this information in Table 18-3." Why was the current measurement I_{R_1} excluded from the original measurements? What is the anticipated value for I_{R_1}?

3. For the open circuit voltage analysis in step 29, the following statement is made: "Maintaining a supply voltage of 15 V, open R_1 by removing it from the circuit. Take voltage drop measurements V_{R_2}, V_{R_3}, V_{R_4}, V_{R_5}, and V_{R_6}. Do not take the voltage drop measurement across R_1. Record these measurements in Table 18-4." Why was the voltage measurement V_{R_1} excluded from the original measurements? What is the anticipated value for V_{R_1}?

4. For the open circuit current analysis in step 41, the following statement is made: "Maintaining a supply voltage of 15 V, open R_1 by removing it from the circuit. Take current measurements I_{R_2}, I_{R_3}, I_{R_4}, I_{R_5}, and I_{R_6}. Do not take the current measurement through R_1. Record these measurements in Table 18-4." Why was the current measurement I_{R_1} excluded from the original measurements? What is the anticipated value for I_{R_1}?

5. From your results and tables, describe the significance of opens and shorts in analyzing circuit behavior.

REPORT

Turn in a complete report.

TABLE 18–1. Individual Resistor Values

Resistor	Nominal Value, Ω	Resistive Measurement
R_1	120	120
R_2	820	820
R_3	560	550
R_4	100	100
R_5	470	470
R_6	680	680

TABLE 18–2. Total Resistance R_T and Percentage of Error

	Calculated	Measurement	% Error
R_T	1160.22	1201	3.5%

TABLE 18–3. Short Circuit Calculations and Measurements

	Normal Circuit Calculations	Normal Circuit Measurements	Measurements (with Each Resistor *Shorted* One at a Time) R_1	R_2	R_3	R_4	R_5	R_6
V_{R_1}	1.5	15v	0	2.3	2.1	1.6	1.6	3.7
V_{R_2}	6.6	11.5	4	0	1.3	4.4	4.5	10.6
V_{R_3}	4.6	12.5	4	13.2	1.3	4.4	4.5	10
V_{R_4}	4.6	4.5v	0	0.7	1.3	0	0	1.6
V_{R_5}	4.6	1.5	6.6	0.7	10.7	0	0	15
V_{R_6}	8.7	15v	8.9	13.2	19	7.6	7	0
I_{R_1}	12.9	13 [illegible]		24	0.7	18	19	43
I_{R_2}	5.6	6.4	13		18	67	0	130
I_{R_3}	7.2	7.4	6	24		18	18	79
I_{R_4}	10.9	6.5	7.8	20	18.3		0	34
I_{R_5}	23.2	3	1	10	0	0		34
I_{R_6}	12.9	13	42	130	100	100	100	

TABLE 18–4. Open Circuit Calculations and Measurements

	Measurements (with Each Resistor *Opened* One at a Time) R_1	R_2	R_3	R_4	R_5	R_6
V_{R_1}		0	0	0	0	0
V_{R_2}	1.22		3.9	.9	2.6	7.2
V_{R_3}	1.1	7.8		0	9	6.4
V_{R_4}	1.4	5.6	3		0	7.9
V_{R_5}	1.6	4.8	4.1	.9		9
V_{R_6}	0	0	0	0	7.6	
I_{R_1}		.0	0	0	0	0
I_{R_2}	11		17	11	0	11
I_{R_3}	10	19		0	11	16
I_{R_4}	13	19	9		8	26
I_{R_5}	14	19	15	8		31
I_{R_6}	0	0	0	0	0	

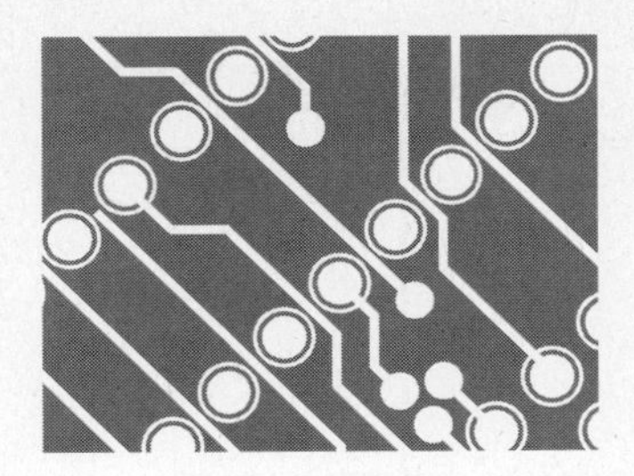

EXPERIMENT 19

ADDITIONAL SERIES-PARALLEL CIRCUITS

OBJECTIVES

At the completion of this experiment, you will be able to:

- Redraw and simplify a series-parallel circuit.
- Write an equation for the total resistance.
- Determine which resistances have the greatest effect on R_T.

SUGGESTED READING

Chapter 6, *Basic Electronics,* B. Grob, Eighth Edition

INTRODUCTION

This experiment is similar to Experiment 15 on series-parallel circuits. The same concepts discussed in that experiment apply here. The following points summarize the concepts of a series-parallel circuit:

- The R_T of two parallel branches equals the product divided by the sum.

$$R_T = \frac{R_1 \times R_2}{R_1 + R_2}$$

- Adding resistance in series increases the total resistance and decreases the total current.
- Adding resistance in parallel increases the total current and decreases the total resistance.
- The equivalent resistance R_{eq} of a series-parallel network must be determined before the total resistance R_T can be found.

Consider the circuit shown in Fig. 19-1. This resistive network has a total resistance of

$$R_T = R_1 \parallel R_{eq}$$

The two vertical lines in the equation are used as a symbol to indicate resistances in parallel. Thus, $R_T = R_1 \parallel R_{eq}$ can be literally taken to mean

$$R_T = R_1 \text{ in parallel with } R_{eq}$$

To determine R_T, the circuit must be reduced or redrawn so that all the resistors, except R_1, can be combined into one equivalent resistance R_{eq}. This is because R_1 is in parallel with the equivalent total resistance of R_2 through R_5.

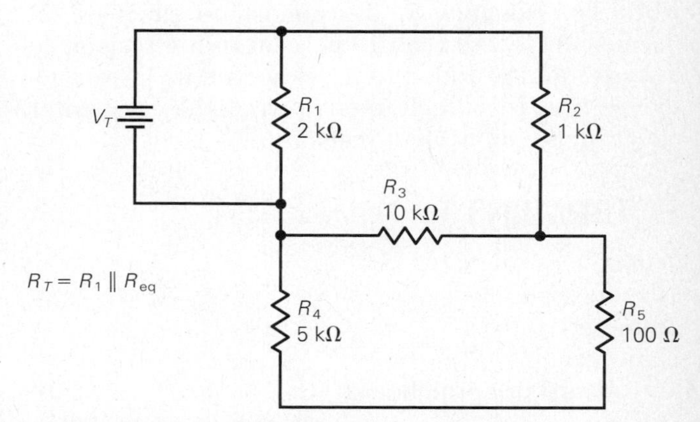

Fig. 19-1. Resistive network.

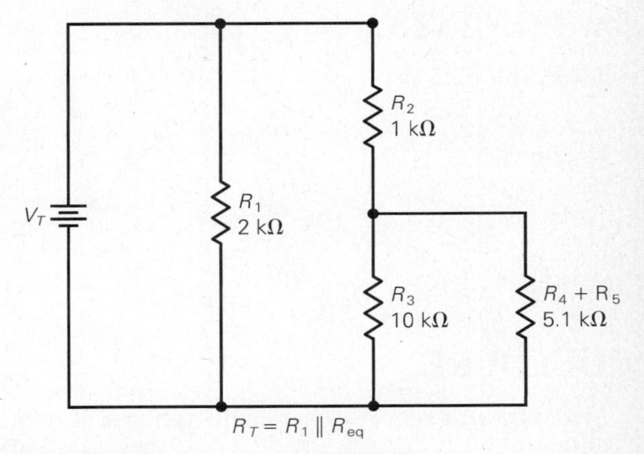

Fig. 19-2. Redrawn resistive network.

Although the circuit can be redrawn in more than one way, there is a method that can be used easily: Look for the resistors farthest from the power source, and combine them, working backward toward the source. The result of this method is

$$R_{eq} = [(R_4 + R_5) \parallel R_3] + R_2$$

The network can be redrawn as shown in Fig. 19-2. Notice that the redrawn figure makes it easier to write the equation. In this case, you can begin with the sum of $R_5 + R_4$ in parallel with R_3. This would be

$$R_4 + R_5 = 5.1 \text{ k}\Omega$$

Then, by using the product-over-the-sum method

$$\frac{R_3 \times 5.1 \text{ k}\Omega}{R_3 + 5.1 \text{ k}\Omega} = \frac{10 \text{ k}\Omega \times 5.1 \text{ k}\Omega}{10 \text{ k}\Omega + 5.1 \text{ k}\Omega} = \frac{51.0 \text{ k}\Omega}{15.1 \text{ k}\Omega} = 3.38 \text{ k}\Omega$$

Next, add 3.38 kΩ to 1 kΩ R_2 so that $R_{eq} = 4.38$ kΩ. Finally,

$$R_T = R_1 \parallel R_{eq} = \frac{2\text{ k}\Omega \times 4.38\text{ k}\Omega}{2\text{ k}\Omega + 4.38\text{ k}\Omega} = \frac{8.76\text{ k}\Omega}{6.38\text{ k}\Omega} = 1.37\text{ k}\Omega$$

Not only can you write an equation for R_T by redrawing the circuit, but also you can see how certain resistances have a greater or lesser effect on the network. For example, R_5 has almost no effect on R_T because R_5 is less than 10 percent of the resistance in series and is added to R_4. However, if R_4 were removed from the circuit, then R_5 would have a greater effect on the equivalent resistance.

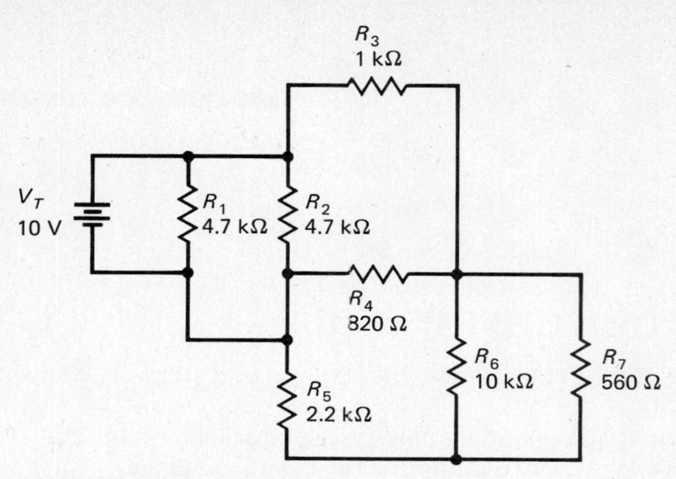

Fig. 19-3. Resistive network.

EQUIPMENT

Ohmmeter
DC power supply
Ammeter
Voltmeter
Protoboard or springboard
Leads

COMPONENTS

Resistors (all 0.25 W):

(2) 4.7 kΩ
(1) 560 Ω
(1) 820 Ω
(2) 10 kΩ
(1) 2.2 kΩ
(1) 1 kΩ

PROCEDURE

1. Measure and record the resistor values shown in Table 19-1.
2. Connect the circuit shown in Fig. 19-3.
3. Measure and record the voltages around the circuit as shown in Table 19-1.
4. Disconnect the power supply V_T, and measure the total circuit resistance. Record the results in Table 19-1.
5. Disconnect R_1 and V_T, and measure and record the resistance R_{eq}.
6. Calculate the current through each resistor, using Ohm's law and the measured voltage drops. Record the results in Table 19-1 and include I_T, the total circuit current.
7. Remove R_6 from the circuit and measure the total circuit resistance. Record the results in Table 19-1.
8. Replace R_2 with a 10-kΩ resistor, and measure the total circuit resistance. Record the results in Table 19-1. (R_6 is still removed.)
9. On a separate sheet of 8 × 11 in. paper, redraw the circuit so that only four resistances represent the simplified circuit. Label all resistances so that the combined resistances are easy to identify. For example, one resistance might be $(R_3 + R_4) \parallel R_2$, etc.
10. Write an equation for the total resistance, and show how to calculate R_T by using R_{eq} and the product-over-the-sum method. Use the same sheet of paper as in step 9 above.

NAME DATE

RESULTS FOR EXPERIMENT 19

QUESTIONS

1. Which resistor in the circuit of Fig. 19-2 has the least effect on R_T and why?

It is resistor is 560 Ω.

2. What would happen to the circuit of Fig. 19-2 if R_1 were decreased to 10 Ω?

The current would be increased.

3. What would happen to the circuit of Fig. 19-2 if R_1 were increased to 10 MΩ?

The greater the resistor the less current passes through.

4. Which resistor in the circuit of Fig. 19-2 has the least effect on I_T?

It is $R_t = 560$ Ω

5. Which resistor in the circuit of Fig. 19-2 has the greatest effect on I_T?

It is $R_t = 10{,}000$

REPORT

Turn in all data and the equations. No formal report is required for this experiment.

TABLE 19–1

Resistance Values Nominal or Calculated	Ω Measured	*V* Measured	*I* Calculated
$R_1 = 4.7\ k\Omega$	4.7	10	2.1
$R_2 = 4.7\ k\Omega$	4.7	10	2.1
$R_3 = 1\ k\Omega$	1K	6.6	6
$R_4 = 820\ \Omega$	820	3.9	4.7
$R_5 = 2.2\ k\Omega$	2.2K	3.9	1.7
$R_6 = 10\ k\Omega$	10K	.6	10 10
$R_7 = 560\ \Omega$	560	.6	
R_T = 962.6	950		I_T =
R_{eq} = 12K			
R_T with R_6 removed			
R_T with $R_2 = 10\ k\Omega$			

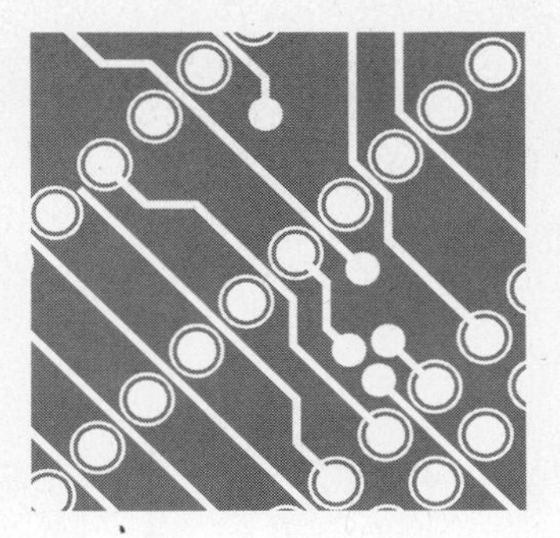

EXPERIMENT 20

OPENS AND SHORTS IN SERIES-PARALLEL CIRCUITS

OBJECTIVES

At the completion of this experiment, you will be able to:

- Determine the changes in circuit current and voltage drops resulting from a short circuit.
- Determine the changes in circuit current and voltage drops resulting from an open circuit.

SUGGESTED READING

Chapter 6, *Basic Electronics,* B. Grob, Eighth Edition

INTRODUCTION

A short circuit has practically zero resistance. Its effect, therefore, is to allow excessive current to flow in a circuit, although this is not usually intentional. An open circuit has the opposite effect because an open circuit has infinitely high resistance with practically zero current.

Therefore, if one path in a circuit changes (becomes open or short), the circuit's voltage, resistance, and current in the other paths change as well. For example, the series-parallel circuit shown in Fig. 20-1 becomes a series circuit when there is a short across circuit points A and B.

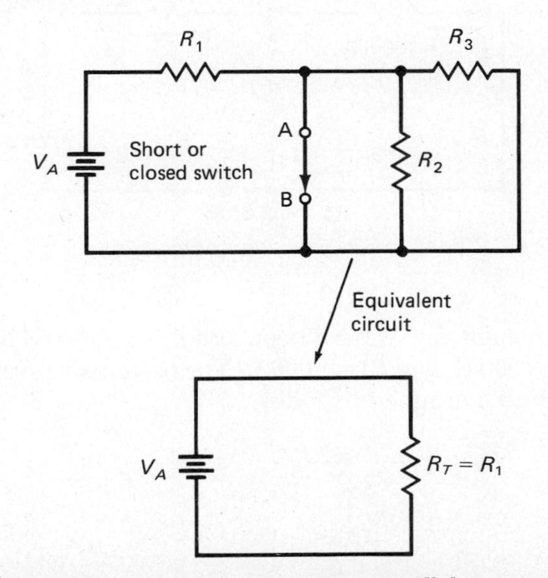

Fig. 20-1. Effect of a short in a series-parallel circuit.

As an example of an open circuit, the series-parallel circuit in Fig. 20-2 becomes a series circuit with just R_1 and R_2 when there is an open between points A and B.

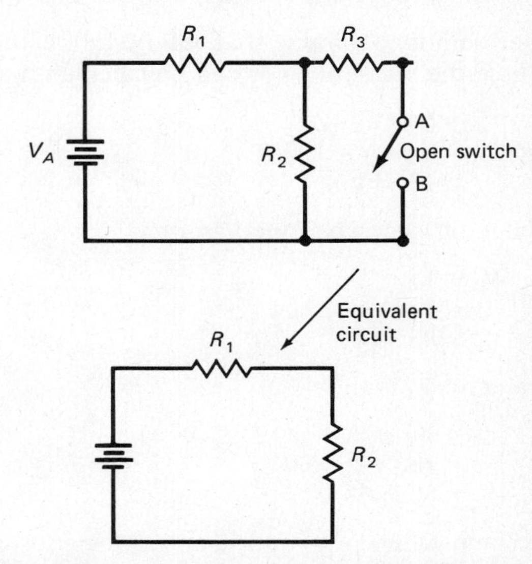

Fig. 20-2. Effects of an open in a series-parallel circuit.

The Short Circuit

You can determine the effect of a short in a series-parallel circuit. For example, in the circuit of Fig. 20-1, a switch is shown between points A and B. This switch represents a possible flaw in construction or operation of an actual circuit.

Refer to Fig. 20-3 where the circuit does not have a short. Specific component values have been assigned to the same circuit as in Fig. 20-1. As shown in Fig. 20-3,

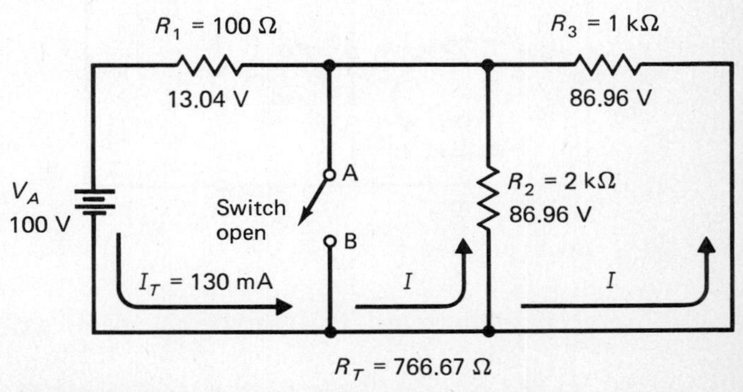

Fig. 20-3. Circuit values where no short exists.

$R_1 = 100\ \Omega$, $R_2 = 1000\ \Omega$, and $R_3 = 2000\ \Omega$. The total resistance R_T can be determined as follows:

$$R_T = R_1 + \frac{R_2 \times R_3}{R_2 + R_3}$$
$$= 766.67\ \Omega$$

Knowing the total resistance is essential in determining the total circuit current. If the applied voltage V_A is 100 V, then

$$I_T = \frac{V_A}{R_T}$$
$$= \frac{100\ \text{V}}{766.67\ \Omega}$$
$$= 0.13\ \text{A} \quad (\text{or } 130\ \text{mA})$$

Another component value that will be interesting to identify is the value of V_1. It can be calculated as

$$V_1 = I_T \times R_1$$
$$= 0.13\ \text{A} \times 100\ \Omega$$
$$= 13.04\ \text{V}$$

The value of V_2 can be found as well:

$$V_2 = V_A - V_1$$
$$= 100\ \text{V} - 13.04\ \text{V}$$
$$= 86.96\ \text{V}$$

The value of V_3 is then

$$V_3 = V_A - V_1$$
$$= 100\ \text{V} - 13.04\ \text{V}$$
$$= 86.96\ \text{V}$$

The voltage values of V_2 and V_3 should be equivalent since R_2 and R_3 form a parallel circuit.

Figure 20-3 shows the calculated effect of a short with a series-parallel circuit. If the circuit is shorted from point A to B, then the effects on resistors R_2 and R_3 are eliminated. The elimination of R_2 and R_3 creates predictable changes in circuit current and the voltage drop of R_1. The circuit of Fig. 20-4 shows the electrical effects. Since R_2 and R_3 are eliminated, the only effective resistance left in the circuit is R_1.

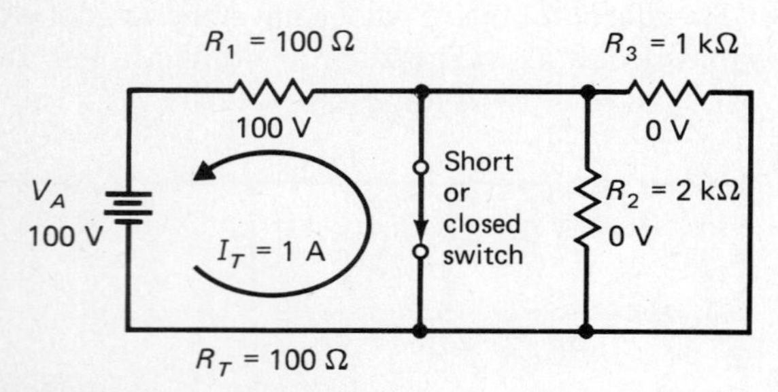

Fig. 20-4. Effects of a short.

The total circuit current I_T can then be calculated as

$$I_T = \frac{V_A}{R_1}$$
$$= \frac{100\ \text{V}}{100\ \Omega}$$
$$= 1\ \text{A}$$

The voltage drop across R_1 is then

$$V_1 = I_T \times R_1$$
$$= 1\ \text{A} \times 100\ \Omega$$
$$= 100\ \text{V}$$

The voltage drop across R_2 is thus

$$V_2 = V_A - V_1$$
$$= 100\ \text{V} - 100\ \text{V}$$
$$= 0\ \text{V}$$

The voltage drop across R_3 is

$$V_3 = V_A - V_1$$
$$= 100\ \text{V} - 100\ \text{V}$$
$$= 0\ \text{V}$$

The voltage drops across R_2 and R_3 should equal 0 V since their resistance values are reduced to 0 Ω because of the short.

In summary, these circuit changes occur in two ways. First, the circuit currents increase significantly. Second, the voltage drop from the increase in current flow also increases.

The Open Circuit

An open circuit provides practically infinite resistance to the applied voltage V_A. Its overall effect on the circuit would be zero or minimal current flow. You can determine the effect of an open path in a series-parallel circuit. For example, in the circuit of Fig. 20-5,

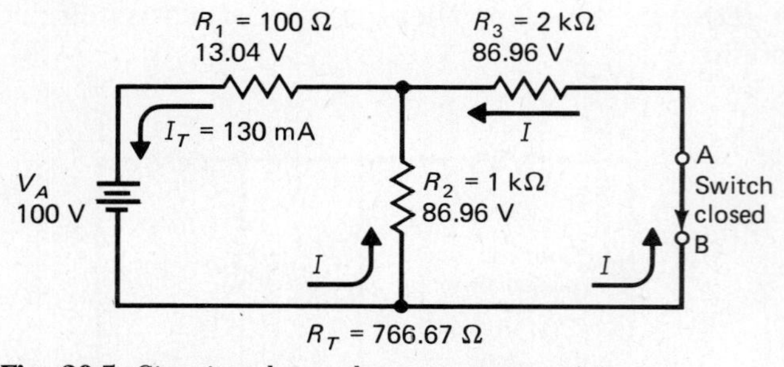

Fig. 20-5. Circuit values where no open exists.

component values have been assigned as $R_1 = 100\ \Omega$, $R_2 = 1000\ \Omega$, and $R_3 = 2000\ \Omega$. The total resistance R_T can be determined as follows:

$$R_T = R_1 + \frac{R_2 \times R_3}{R_2 + R_3}$$
$$= 766.67\ \Omega$$

Knowing the total resistance is essential in determining the total circuit current. If the applied voltage

V_A is 100 V, then

$$I_T = \frac{V_A}{R_T} = \frac{100\text{ V}}{766.67\ \Omega} = 0.13\text{ A} \quad \text{(or 130 mA)}$$

Another component value that will be important to identify is the voltage value of V_1. It can be calculated as

$$V_1 = I_T \times R_1 = 0.13\text{ A} \times 100\ \Omega = 13.04\text{ V}$$

The voltage of V_2 is

$$V_2 = V_A - V_1 = 100\text{ V} - 13.04\text{ V} = 86.96\text{ V}$$

The voltage of V_3 is

$$V_3 = V_A - V_1 = 100\text{ V} - 13.04\text{ V} = 86.96\text{ V}$$

The values are shown in Fig. 20-5.

If the circuit is open between points A and B, then R_3 is no longer part of the circuit. The removal of R_3 creates a predictable change in the circuit current and voltage drops of R_1 and R_2.

The circuit of Fig. 20-6 shows the overall electrical effects when the switch is opened between points A and B. The circuit current I_T can be calculated after the total resistance R_T is found:

$$R_T = R_1 + R_2 = 100\ \Omega + 1000\ \Omega = 1100\ \Omega$$

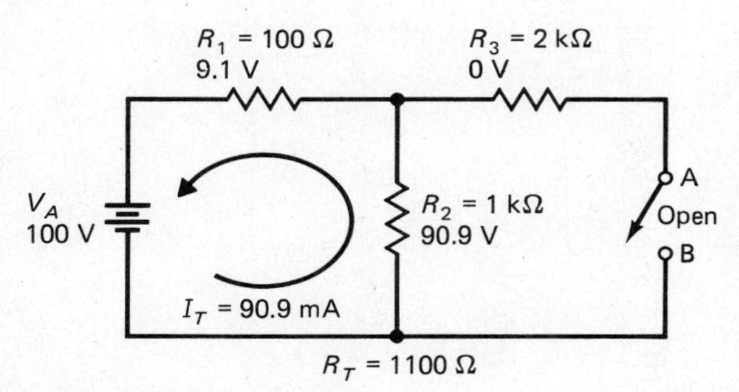

Fig. 20-6. Effects of an open.

Then I_T can be calculated as

$$I_T = \frac{V_A}{R_1} = \frac{100\text{ V}}{1100\ \Omega} = 0.0909\text{ A} \quad \text{(or 90.9 mA)}$$

The voltage drop across R_1 is then

$$V_1 = I_T \times R_1 = 0.0909\text{ A} \times 100\ \Omega = 9.09 \text{ or } 9.1\text{ V}$$

The voltage drop across R_2 is then

$$V_2 = I_T \times R_2 = 0.0909\text{ A} \times 1000\ \Omega = 90.9\text{ V}$$

The voltage value of R_3 is 0 V, due to the open circuit.

EQUIPMENT

Voltmeter
Power supply
Protoboard

COMPONENTS

(1) 150-Ω 1-W resistor
(2) 150-Ω 0.25 W resistors
(1) SPST switch

PROCEDURE

1. Measure and record in Table 20-1 the values of the three resistors used in this experiment.

2. Construct the circuit of Fig. 20-7, and adjust the voltage of the power supply to 20 V.

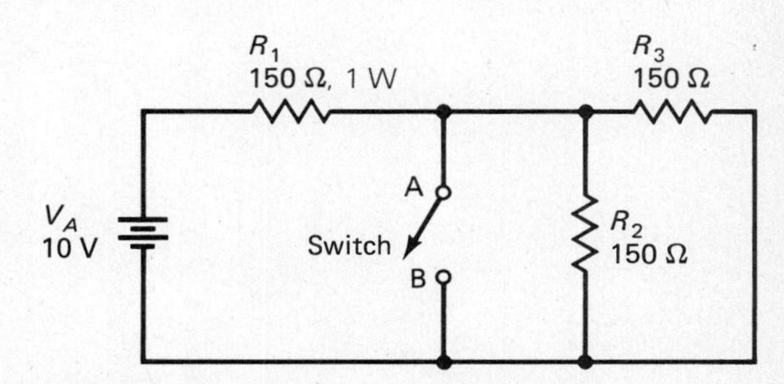

Fig. 20-7. Series-parallel circuit.

3. Calculate and record in Table 20-1, for the circuit of Fig. 20-7, the values of the total resistance R_T; the currents I_{R_1}, I_{R_2}, and I_{R_3}; and the voltages V_{R_1}, V_{R_2}, and V_{R_3}.

4. Measure and record in Table 20-1 the measured values of I_{R_1}, I_{R_2}, I_{R_3}, V_{R_1}, V_{R_2}, and V_{R_3}.

5. Connect points A and B.

6. Calculate and record in Table 20-1 the values of R_T, I_{R_1}, I_{R_2}, I_{R_3}, V_{R_1}, V_{R_2}, and V_{R_3}.

7. Measure and record in Table 20-1 the values of I_{R_1}, I_{R_2}, I_{R_3}, V_{R_1}, V_{R_2}, and V_{R_3}.

8. Turn off the power supply, and disconnect the circuit.

9. Measure and record in Table 20-2 the values of the three resistors used in this experiment.

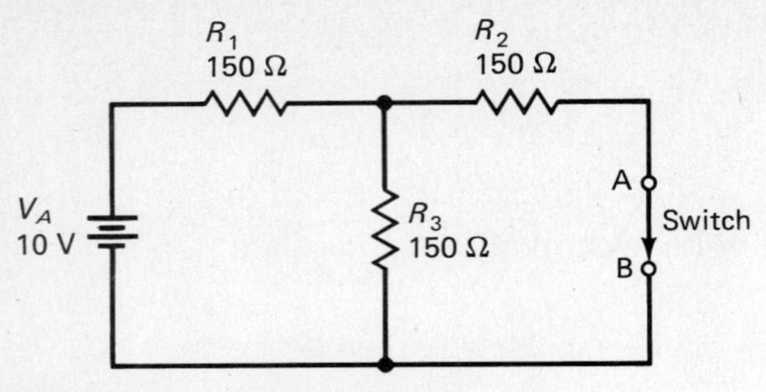

Fig. 20-8. Series-parallel circuit.

10. Construct the circuit of Fig. 20-8, and adjust the voltage of the power supply to 10 V.

11. Calculate and record in Table 20-2, for the circuit of Fig. 20-8, the values of the total resistance R_T; currents I_{R_1}, I_{R_2}, and I_{R_3}; and voltages V_{R_1}, V_{R_2}, and V_{R_3}.

12. Measure and record in Table 20-2 the measured values of I_{R_1}, I_{R_2}, I_{R_3}, V_{R_1}, V_{R_2}, and V_{R_3}.

13. Disconnect or open points A and B.

14. Calculate and record in Table 20-2 the values of R_T, I_{R_1}, I_{R_2}, I_{R_3}, V_{R_1}, V_{R_2}, and V_{R_3}.

15. Measure and record in Table 20-2 the values of I_{R_1}, I_{R_2}, I_{R_3}, V_{R_1}, V_{R_2}, and V_{R_3}.

16. Turn off the power supply and disconnect the circuit.

NAME ______________________ DATE __________

RESULTS FOR EXPERIMENT 20

QUESTIONS

1. What are the characteristics of a shorted circuit?

It doesn't allow anything to bypass.

2. What are the characteristics of an open circuit?

The circuit with out [illegible] because there's nothing to pass.

3. Compare Tables 20-1 and 20-2. What are the differences and similarities?

The difference is that one is different in a series parallel circuit. and they're all different.

REPORT

Write a complete report. Discuss the measured and calculated results. Discuss the three most significant aspects of the experiment and write a conclusion.

TABLE 20–1 (V_A = 10 V)

Unshorted Circuit, Fig. 20–7		
Component	Measured	Calculated
R_1	150	
R_2	150	
R_3	150	
R_T		225Ω
I_{R_1}	64	646
I_{R_2}	67	66.6
I_{R_3}	62	666
V_{R_1}	9.7	9.6v
V_{R_2}	10	6.6.
V_{R_3}	10	6.6

Shorted Circuit, Fig. 20–7		
R_T		0
I_{R_1}	0	0
I_{R_2}	0	0
I_{R_3}	0	0
V_{R_1}	0	0
V_{R_2}	0	0
V_{R_3}	0	0

TABLE 20–2 (V_A = 10 V) I·R

Shorted Circuit, Fig. 20–8		
Component	Measured	Calculated
R_1	150	
R_2	150	
R_3	150	
R_T	42	R=V/I 188
I_{R_1}	mA	I=V/R .064mA
I_{R_2}	22mA	.044mA
I_{R_3}	22	.044
V_{R_1}	6.6v	V=IR=
V_{R_2}	32.8	
V_{R_3}	32.8	

Opened Circuit, Fig. 20–8		
R_T	0	0
I_{R_1}	0	0
I_{R_2}	0	0
I_{R_3}	0	0
V_{R_1}	10v	10v
V_{R_2}	10v	10v
V_{R_3}	10v	10v

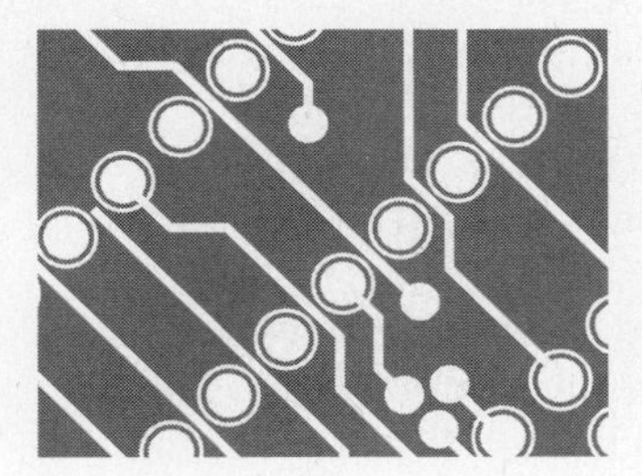

EXPERIMENT 21

KIRCHHOFF'S LAWS

OBJECTIVES

At the completion of this experiment, you will be able to:

- Validate Kirchhoff's current and voltage laws.
- Gain proficiency with lab equipment and technique.

SUGGESTED READING

Chapter 9, *Basic Electronics*, B. Grob, Eighth Edition

INTRODUCTION

In 1847, Gustav R. Kirchhoff formulated two laws that have become fundamental to the studies of basic electronics. They are as follows:

1. The algebraic sum of the currents into and out of any point must be equal to zero.
2. The algebraic sum of the applied source voltages and the *IR* voltage drops on any closed path must be equal to zero.

At first, Kirchhoff's laws seem obvious. That is, it seems obvious to state that whatever goes into a circuit must also equal what comes out of it. However, Kirchhoff's laws are used to analyze circuits that are not simple series or parallel or series-parallel circuits. For example, circuits that contain more than one voltage source and circuits called *unbalanced bridges* often cannot be understood without using Kirchhoff's laws to analyze those circuits. In its simplest form, Kirchhoff's law could be used to analyze the circuit in Fig. 21-1.

Simplified version:

$I_1 = I_2 + I_6$ $\quad I_2 = I_3 + I_4$ $\quad I_5 = I_2$
$I_6 = I_1 - I_2$ $\quad I_3 = I_2 - I_4$ $\quad I_7 = I_6 + I_5$
$I_2 = I_1 - I_6$ $\quad I_4 = I_5 - I_3$ $\quad I_7 = I_1$

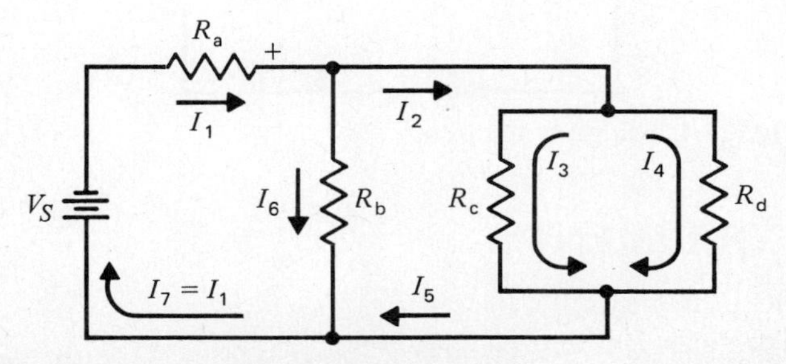

Fig. 21-1. Series-parallel circuit.

Algebraic version:

$+I_1 - I_6 - I_2 = 0$ $\quad +I_5 + I_6 - I_7 = 0$
$+I_2 - I_3 - I_4 = 0$ $\quad I_T = I_1 = I_7$

Note: For the circuit of Fig. 21-1, if $V_S = 20$ V, the sum of the *IR* voltage drops across the series-parallel combination of R_a, R_b, R_c, and R_d will also equal 20 V.

Be sure that you understand the algebraic version of the circuit. It has become standard practice to assign positive and negative values to the currents as follows: The current into any point is positive (+), and the current out of any point is negative (−). Also, this would be true if there were more than one path for the current to enter or leave. Do not confuse this with electron flow.

Although the circuit of Fig. 21-1 is a series-parallel circuit, it was used to demonstrate how Kirchhoff's laws operate. Now consider the circuit of Fig. 21-2. This circuit could not be solved for its currents and *IR* voltage drops without using Kirchhoff's laws because of the two source voltages.

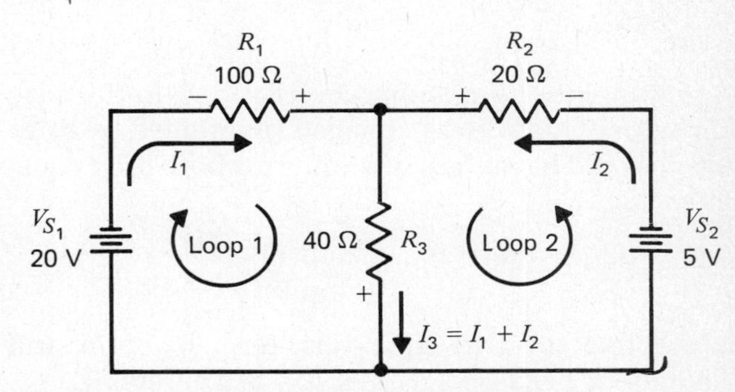

Fig. 21-2. Circuit with two voltage sources.

By using the loop method, Kirchhoff's laws can be used to determine the currents and *IR* voltages in the circuit by calculation. For example,

$$V_{S_1} = 20\text{ V} - V_{R_1} - V_{R_3} = 0 \qquad \text{(loop 1)}$$
$$V_{S_2} = 5\text{ V} - V_{R_2} - V_{R_3} = 0 \qquad \text{(loop 2)}$$

By following the loop around its path, Kirchhoff's law provides a method. Take the source as positive, and take the individual path resistance as negative. The sum is equal to zero. This means that circuits will be divided into separate loops as if the other voltage source and its corresponding path did not exist. The *IR* voltage drops would be calculated as follows.

$$V_{R_1} = I_1R_1 = I_1 \times 100\ \Omega$$
$$V_{R_2} = I_2R_2 = I_2 \times 20\ \Omega$$
$$V_{R_3} = I_3R_3 = (I_1 + I_2)R_3 = (I_1 + I_2) \times 40\ \Omega$$

Refer to the equations for loops 1 and 2. The *IR* voltages would now be replaced in the formulas as follows:

For loop 1,

$$20\text{ V} - 100(I_1) - 40(I_1 + I_2) = 0$$
$$-140I_1 - 40I_2 = -20\text{ V}$$

and for loop 2,

$$5\text{ V} - 20(I_2) - 40(I_1 + I_2) = 0$$
$$-60I_2 - 40I_1 = -5\text{ V}$$

Note that the final equations are transposed versions that can be simplified further by division:

$$\frac{-140I_1 - 40I_2}{-20\text{ V}} = \frac{-20\text{ V}}{-20\text{ V}} \text{ or } 7I_1 + 2I_2 = 1 \qquad \text{(loop 1)}$$
$$\frac{-60I_2 - 40I_1}{-5\text{ V}} = \frac{-5\text{ V}}{-5\text{ V}} \text{ or } 12I_2 + 8I_1 = 1 \qquad \text{(loop 2)}$$

To solve for the currents, isolate the I_2 currents by making them the same value. Multiply the loop 1 equation by 6:

$$42I_1 + 12I_2 = 6 \qquad \text{(loop 1)}$$

Note:

$$6 = \frac{12I_2}{2I_2}$$

Note that either loop could be changed. In the case above, only loop 1 was changed (multiplied by 6) so that I_2 would have the same value for both loop equations:

$$42I_1 + 12I_2 = 6 \qquad \text{(loop 1)}$$
$$8I_1 + 12I_2 = 1 \qquad \text{(loop 2)}$$

Subtracting the two equations, term by term, will eliminate I_2 because $12I_2 - 12I_2 = 0$. Therefore,

$$34I_1 = 5$$
$$I_1 = 147\text{ mA}$$

By using the loop equation method, Kirchhoff's law, the current through the resistance of R_1 is determined. Also, the direction of current flow is correct as assumed because the answer was a positive value.

To calculate I_2, substitute 147 mA for I_1 in either loop equation. Substituting in loop 2,

$$8(147\text{ mA}) + 12I_2 = 1$$
$$1.18\text{ A} + 12I_2 = 1$$
$$12I_2 = 1 - 1.18\text{ A} = -0.18\text{ A}$$
$$I_2 = -0.015\text{ A} = -15\text{ mA}$$

Because the negative sign appears in the solution for the current I_2, it follows that the current through I_2 is opposite in direction from the polarity shown in the circuit of Fig. 21-2, the assumed direction using the loop method.

Now that Kirchhoff's law has been used to determine the currents through the circuit of Fig. 21-2, the circuit can be redrawn to reflect the correct values, as shown in Fig. 21-3.

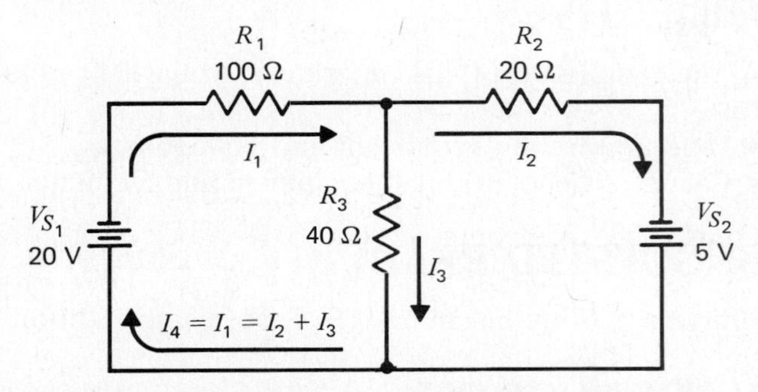

Fig. 21-3. Redrawn version of the circuit in Fig. 21-2.

In the case of the circuit in Fig. 21-3, the 20-V dc source actually overrides the 5-V dc source. This series opposition results in approximately 15 V dc.

Because R_1 is 100 Ω, it is easy to verify the Kirchhoff's law loop equation solution as follows:

$$\frac{15\text{ V}}{100\ \Omega + (20\ \Omega \parallel 40\ \Omega)} = \frac{15\text{ V}}{113.3\ \Omega} = 132\text{ mA}$$

$$\text{Loop 1 } I_T = 147\text{ mA}$$
$$\text{Loop 2 } I_T = -15\text{ mA} \qquad \text{(Subtract negative value)}$$

$$\text{Total } I_T = 132\text{ mA}$$

Finally, note that the circuit in Fig. 21-4 is a bridge type of circuit. Kirchhoff's law could be used to calculate the unknown values in this circuit as well as circuits that contain many voltage sources and many current paths.

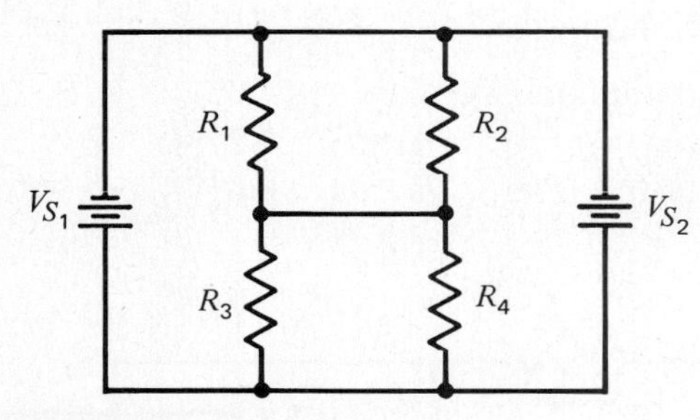

Fig. 21-4. Bridge-type circuit.

EQUIPMENT

DC power supply, 0–10 V
Ammeter (milliamp capability)
Voltmeter or VTVM

Springboard or protoboard
Connecting leads

COMPONENTS

Resistors (all 0.25 W):

(1) 100 Ω (1) 390 Ω
(1) 220 Ω (1) 470 Ω
(1) 330 Ω

(2) Dry cells (flashlight batteries, 1.5 V)

PROCEDURE

1. Measure and record the values of voltage for each dry cell you are using. It may be necessary to solder connecting wires onto the ends of the batteries. Record the results in Table 21-1. Together, series-aiding, the two batteries should be approximately 3.0 V.

2. For each of the three circuits in Figs. 21-5 to 21-7, use batteries for voltages of 1.5 V and use the power supply for the other source voltage. If 3.0 V and 1.5 V are both used, connect the two 1.5-V batteries in series for 3.0 V. Measure and record the values of current in Table 21-2. Also, measure and record the value of the *IR* voltage drop across each resistance. Finally, use arrows to indicate the direction of current flow.

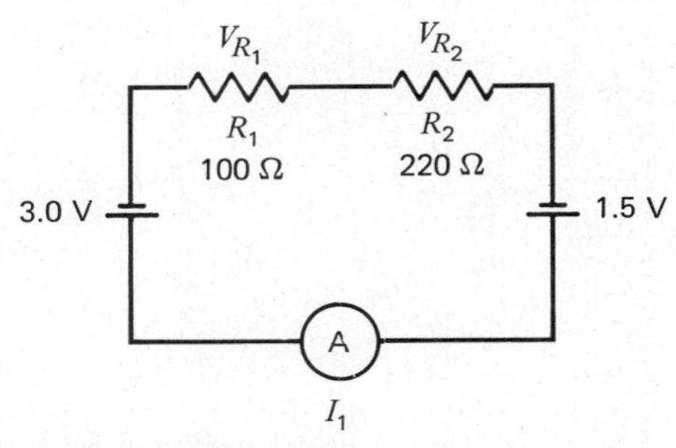

Fig. 21-5. Series-opposing voltage circuit.

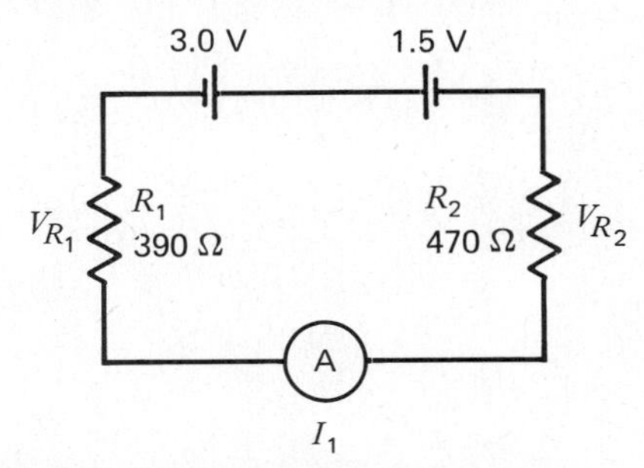

Fig. 21-6. Series-opposing voltage circuit.

3. For the circuit of Fig. 21-8, refer to the procedure outlined in the introduction to this experiment. Preferably, use the loop method of Kirchhoff's law to determine the values and polarities of both current and voltage for the circuit. Then use the lab to verify the values (within 10 to 15 percent). Record all the calculated values, and then measure and record in Table 21-3 all the values determined in the lab for the circuit. Be sure to include arrows alongside or directly above the meters marked A. Include Fig. 21-8 in your report. Note that Fig. 21-8 will be used to verify Kirchhoff's law. That is, you will compare your calculations to your measurements. Do not forget to include the values of *IR* drops across each resistance.

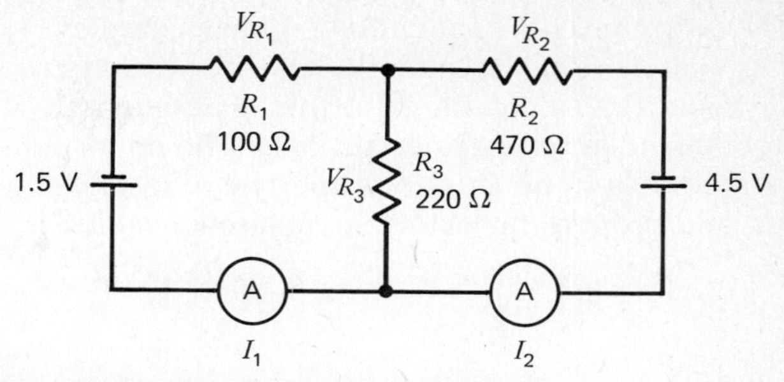

Fig. 21-7. Kirchhoff's circuit for analysis.

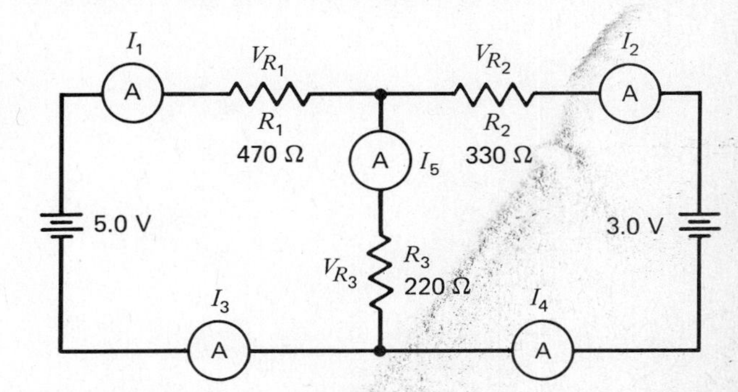

Fig. 21-8. Kirchhoff's circuit. Use loop method to determine the values and polarities of current and voltage.

4. Connect the circuit of Fig. 21-9. Measure and record in Table 21-4 all the values of *IR* voltage drops

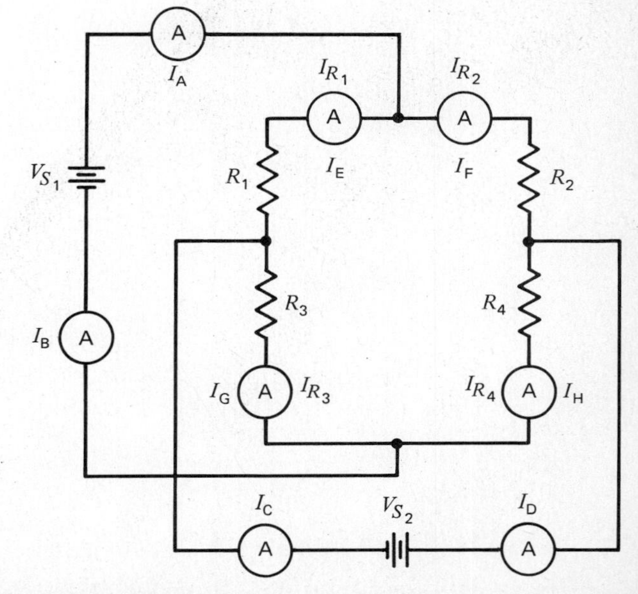

Fig. 21-9. Kirchhoff's law circuit (values to be given by instructor).

and currents. This final circuit is more complex than the previous circuits. Check with your instructor about the calculations for this experiment. It is recommended for extra credit only. The important thing here is to be able to properly connect the circuit and properly measure the unknown values.

Note: Your instructor will assign values for V_{S_1}, V_{S_2}, R_1, R_2, R_3, and R_4. This ensures that the experiment cannot be precalculated.

NAME ______________________ DATE ______________

RESULTS FOR EXPERIMENT 21

QUESTIONS

1. State Kirchhoff's current law.

2. State Kirchhoff's voltage law.

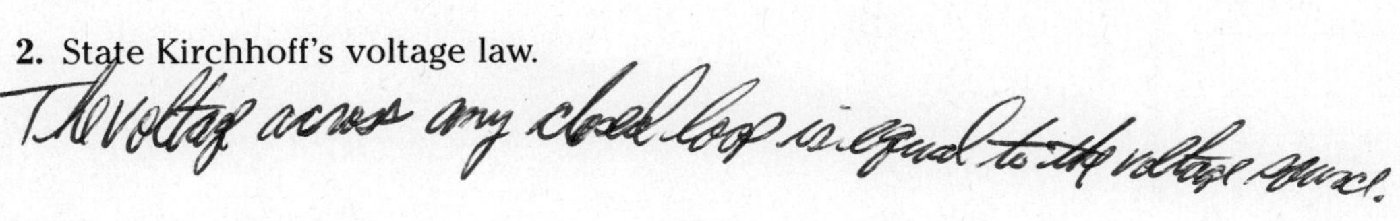

REPORT

Write a complete report. Discuss the measured and calculated results. Discuss the three most significant aspects of the experiment and write a conclusion.

TABLE 21–1. Dry Cell Voltages

Battery	Measured Voltage
1	1.4
2	1.4

TABLE 21–2

Circuit	V_{R_1}	V_{R_2}	V_{R_3}	I_1	I_2
Fig. 21-5	1.7	1.7		17	
Fig. 21-6	2	2.1		5	
Fig. 21-7	1.9	1.9	1.9	22	7

TABLE 21–3

	Calculated	Measured
I_1		
I_2		
I_3		
I_4		
I_5		
V_{R_1}		
V_{R_2}		
V_{R_3}		

TABLE 21–4

	Current	Voltage
R_1		
R_2		
R_3		
R_4		
I_A		
I_B		
I_C		
I_D		
I_E		
I_F		
I_G		
I_H		

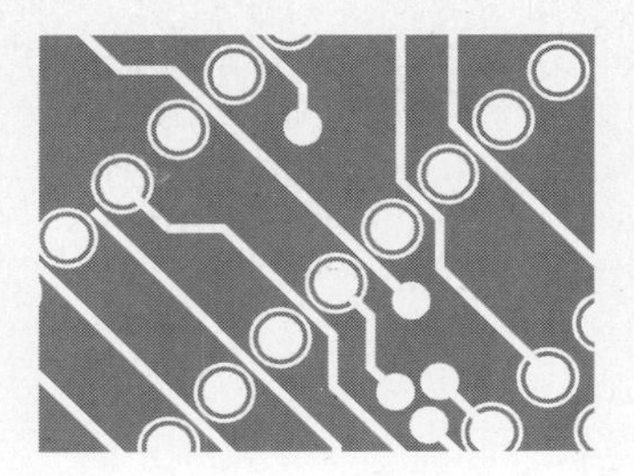

EXPERIMENT 22

THE WHEATSTONE BRIDGE

OBJECTIVES

At the completion of this experiment, you will:

- Be able to measure current and voltage in a Wheatstone bridge.
- Know how to use a galvanometer.
- Understand how a Wheatstone bridge can be balanced.

SUGGESTED READING

Chapters 5, 6, and 10, *Basic Electronics,* B. Grob, Eighth Edition

INTRODUCTION

Many types of bridge circuits are used in electronics. The bridge circuit in this experiment can become a functional ohmmeter as well as a balanced circuit. Here, the Wheatstone bridge has two input terminals, where the battery (or power supply) terminals are connected to the ratio arms. The ratio arms are the key to understanding how the Wheatstone bridge is balanced. The bridge is balanced when there is an equal division of voltages across the bridge output. This output is a current path across the ratio arms, like a bridge between two series-parallel paths. It does not matter what the ratios are for the bridge to be in a balanced state, because resistances in parallel (two series resistors in this case) have the same voltage across both branches. However, some ratios may create a more sensitive balance than others, depending upon the total current and total resistance of the ratio arms.

If there is an imbalance in the bridge, current will flow through the output path from one ratio arm to the other. In this experiment, a galvanometer is used. It is a dual directional microammeter with the needle zeroed at top dead center.

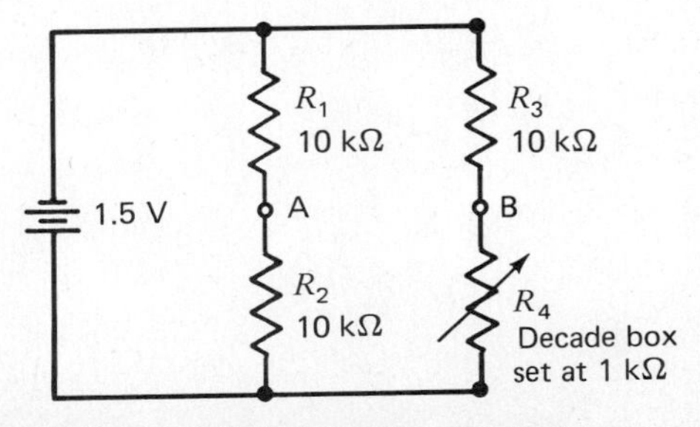

Fig. 22-1. Series-parallel circuit for analysis.

It is possible to use a VOM. However, extreme caution will be needed to prevent damage to the meter.

EQUIPMENT

DC power supply, 0–10 V
Decade box
Galvanometer
Test leads
VTVM or DVM

COMPONENTS

(3) 10-kΩ 0.25 W resistors
Plus other desired resistors (all 0.25 W):

(1) 5.6 kΩ   (1) 2.7 kΩ
(1) 1 kΩ   (1) 560 Ω
(1) 2.2 kΩ

PROCEDURE

1. Connect the circuit of Fig. 22-1.

2. Usually, a galvanometer is placed across the output terminals (A and B) to complete the bridge. However, it is better to study the series-parallel aspects of the Wheatstone bridge first to gain a better understanding of how it works. Thus, measure the voltage across points A and B and record the results in Table 22-1. Put the ground side of the voltmeter on point B. Also, determine the direction of current flow.

3. Increase the value of R_4 to 5 kΩ and measure the voltage across points A and B and determine current direction. Record the results in Table 22-1.

4. Increase the value of R_4 in 1-kΩ steps from 5 to 15 kΩ. Measure the voltage across points A and B at each step, determine current direction, and record the results in Table 22-1. This should lead to an understanding of how the value of the ratio arms determines the voltage across the AB output. When finished, turn the power off.

CAUTION: It will be necessary to reverse the voltmeter leads at some point.

5. Insert a galvanometer across points A and B as shown in Fig. 22-2. Be sure R_4 is 10 kΩ. The circuit is now a Wheatstone bridge, because there is a true current path across points A and B.

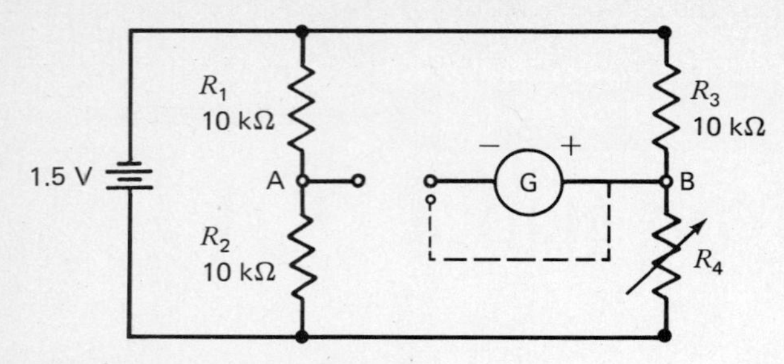

Fig. 22-2. Galvanometer circuit.

Note: Many galvanometers have a switch (button or toggle switch on the front of the meter). Until the switch is closed, current flows through a wire (or short circuit) to protect the meter movement. When the switch is closed, current flows through the meter movement. Be careful not to peg the meter.

6. With equal nominal values of R_1 and R_4, turn the power on and finely adjust R_4 so that no current flows across points A and B. This is the same as 0 V across points A and B. Thus, R_4 (decade box) will be finely adjusted and may be 10.5 kΩ or 11.1 kΩ, etc., unless, of course, you are using precision resistors (1 percent tolerance). The important thing is that both voltage and current at points A and B = 0. If so, the bridge is now balanced. Record the exact value of R_4 (decade box) in Table 22-2.

7. Now adjust R_4 so that the needle deflects to the right, approximately halfway to full scale, as shown in Fig. 22-3. Measure and record in Table 22-2 the voltage across R_4 and R_2. Repeat this procedure by adjusting R_4 with the needle deflecting to the left. Record the value of R_4 and the voltage across R_4 and R_2. Keep in mind the following: the bridge was balanced. Then, the bridge was unbalanced on both ratio arms (left and right). This procedure can be analyzed later to determine how the direction of current flow across the bridge indicates the condition of the bridge. Also record the adjusted value of R_4.

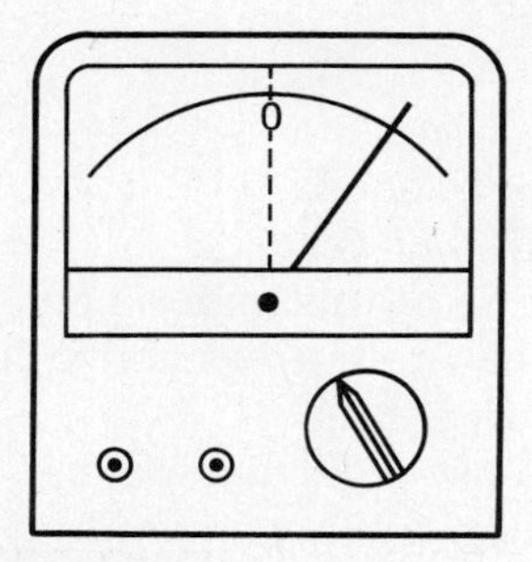

Fig. 22-3. Galvanometer.

8. Bring the bridge back to a balanced condition by readjusting R_4 and monitoring the galvanometer. The needle should be dead center—zero current.

9. Turn the power off. Replace R_2 with an unknown resistor with a value between 2 and 8 kΩ. Simply put electrical tape over a resistor. Or, if this is not possible, use a 5.6-kΩ resistor, and pretend you do not know the value.

10. Turn power on. Adjust R_4 until the bridge is balanced. The value of R_4 (decade box) should be the true value of R_2. Repeat steps 9 and 10 with several resistors (1 kΩ, 2.2 kΩ, 2.7 kΩ, and 560 Ω, for example). R_4 should be equal to R_2 (unknown resistor) each time. Every time you adjust R_4, notice the amount of needle deflection. Record the results in a separate table. Be sure to label all values.

NAME DATE

RESULTS FOR EXPERIMENT 22

QUESTIONS

1. In procedure steps 9 and 10, the Wheatstone bridge was balanced by matching a decade box to the unknown resistor. Thus, the Wheatstone bridge was used as what kind of meter?

2. Explain the difference between a galvanometer and an ohmmeter.

3. In procedure step 5, suppose the schematic of Fig. 22-2 showed R_4 as 50 kΩ, and R_1 to R_3 remained at 10 kΩ. With power on, would the needle deflect to the right or the left?

4. Which circuit in Fig. 22-4 would be more sensitive (greater needle deflection) when attempting to balance the bridge? Why?

5. Explain any differences and/or similarities between the two circuits in Fig. 22-5.

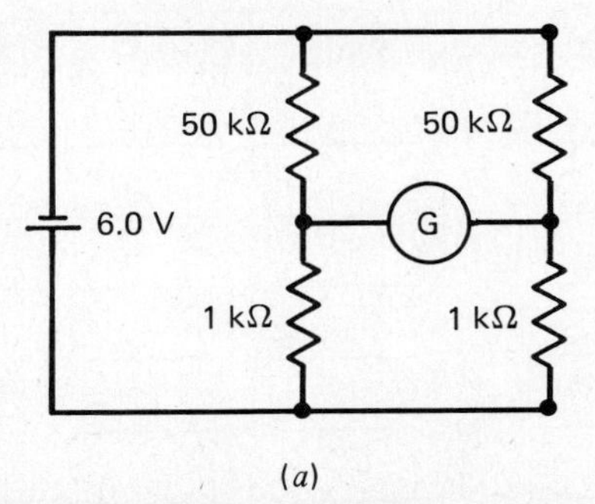

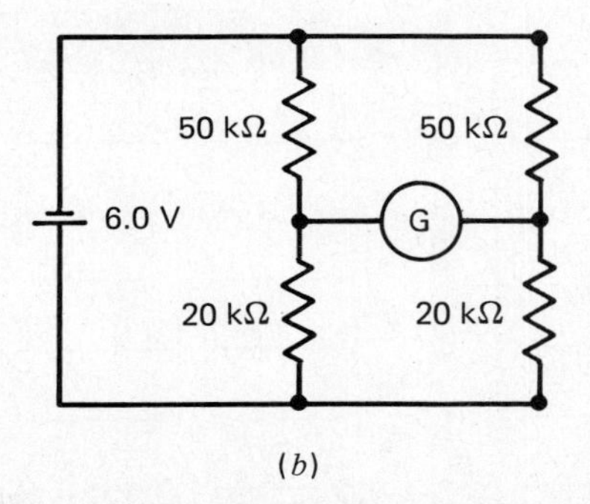

Fig. 22-4. Circuits for question 4.

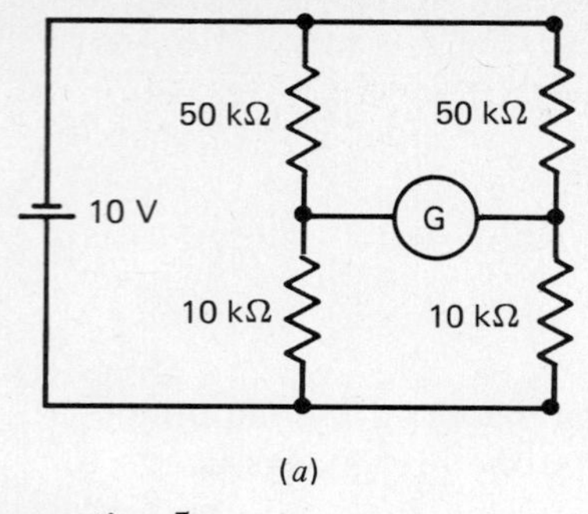

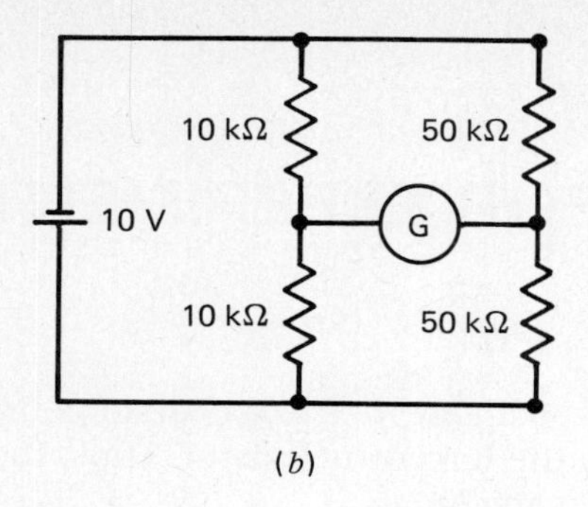

Fig. 22-5. Circuits for question 5.

REPORT

Write a report that describes how the bridge operates, based upon your data.

TABLE 22–1. Data from Fig. 22-1

R_4, kΩ	Voltage AB	Current Direction
1		
5		
6		
7		
8		
9		
10		
11		
12		
13		
14		
15		

TABLE 22–2. R_1 and R_3 = 10 kΩ, R_4 = Decade Box

	Voltage and Current at A and B = 0	Needle Deflection to Right			Needle Deflection to Left		
	R_4, Ω	R_4, Ω	V_{R_4}	V_{R_2}	R_4, Ω	V_{R_4}	V_{R_2}
R_2 = 10 kΩ							
R_2 = 5.6 kΩ							
R_2 = 1 kΩ							
R_2 = 2.2 kΩ							
R_2 = 2.7 kΩ							
R_2 = 560 Ω							

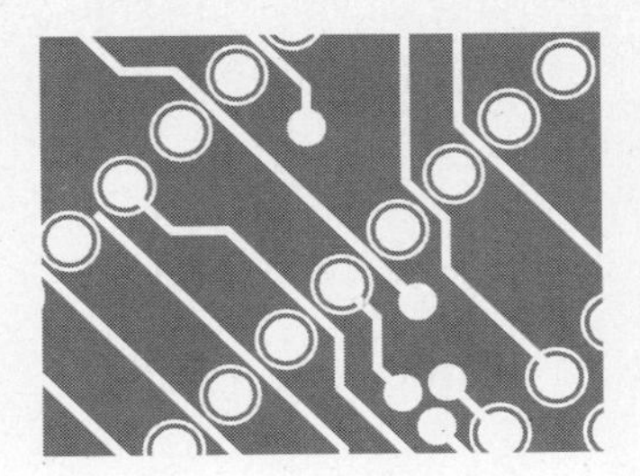

VOLTAGE DIVIDERS WITH LOADS

OBJECTIVES

At the completion of this experiment, you will be able to:

- Identify a voltage divider circuit.
- Define the purpose for voltage divider circuits.
- Describe voltage divider loading effects.

SUGGESTED READING

Chapter 7, *Basic Electronics,* B. Grob, Eighth Edition

INTRODUCTION

A series circuit is also a voltage divider. That is, the total voltage applied to a series circuit is divided among the series resistors. Because the current is the same value in all parts of a series circuit, voltage is divided among the series resistances in direct proportion to the value of resistance.

For example, imagine four resistors in series. Each resistor is equal in value. Therefore, any one resistor will receive one-fourth the total applied voltage. In other words, the total voltage is divided by 4 across each resistor.

Another way to determine the voltage across any resistor in series, without using a meter, is to add the total resistance, divide that value into any single resistor in series, and multiply by the total voltage. This is the proportional method. For example, see Fig. 23-1. There,

$$V_{R_2} = \frac{R_2}{R_T} \times V_T = \frac{2\ \text{k}\Omega}{6\ \text{k}\Omega} \times 6\ \text{V} = 2\ \text{V}$$

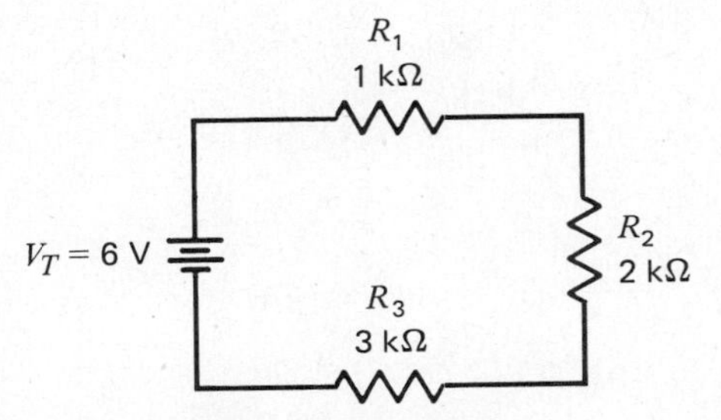

Fig. 23-1. Proportional method circuit.

Although these simple voltage dividers are limited in their use, when a load is placed across any series resistance, the voltage divider is then extremely useful as a voltage tap. For example, the circuit in Fig. 23-2 shows a parallel load current through R_{load}.

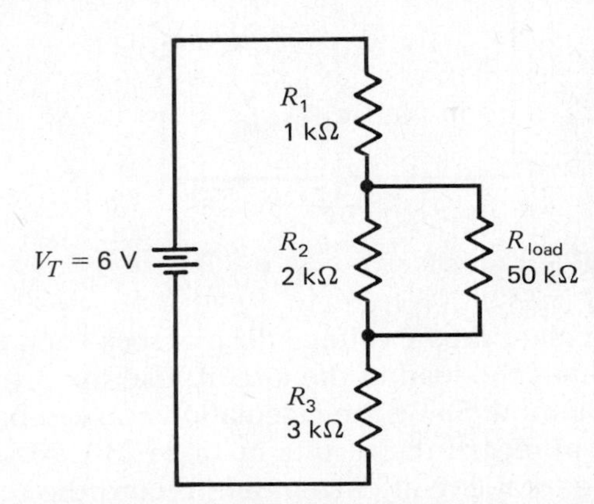

Fig. 23-2. Simple voltage divider with parallel load.

This parallel load, if its resistance was more than 10 times the value of R_2, would actually be sharing the *IR* voltage drops across R_2 without changing the division of voltage considerably. For example, if $R_{\text{load}} = 50\ \text{k}\Omega$,

$$\frac{R_2 \times R_{\text{load}}}{R_2 + R_{\text{load}}} = \frac{100 \times 10^6}{52 \times 10^3} = 2\ \text{k}\Omega\ \text{(approx.)}$$

Thus, R_{load} could share the same approximate voltage as R_2, but it would have its own current.

While voltage dividers are mainly used to tap off part of a total voltage, it is necessary to remember that the addition of a load will always have some effect upon the circuit current and, many times, the proportional *IR* voltage drops.

EQUIPMENT

DC power supply, 0–10 V
Voltmeter (VTVM, VOM)
Test leads

COMPONENTS

Resistors (all 0.25 W):

(3) 1 kΩ	(1) 47 kΩ
(3) 10 kΩ	(1) 4.7 kΩ
(1) 470 Ω	(1) 100 kΩ

PROCEDURE

1. Connect the circuit of Fig. 23-3. Do not connect R_{load}.

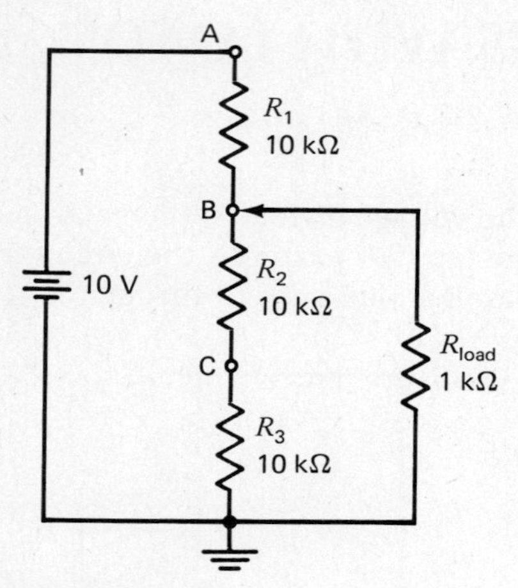

Fig. 23-3. Voltage divider.

2. Calculate the *IR* voltage drop across each resistor without the load in the circuit. Use the proportional method. Show the calculations on a separate sheet and record the results in Table 23-1. Also, measure total circuit current and record the results in Table 23-1.

3. With the load connected to point B, measure the total circuit current, load current, and bleeder current. The bleeder current is the steady drain on the source, the current through R_3. Record the values in Table 23-2.

4. Measure the voltages across R_1, R_2, R_3, and R_{load}. Record these values in Table 23-2.

5. Connect R_{load} to point A. Repeat steps 3 and 4. Record the results.

6. Connect R_{load} to point C. Repeat steps 3 and 4. Record the results.

7. Change the value of R_{load} to 100 kΩ and repeat steps 3 to 6.

8. Connect the circuit of Fig. 23-4. This is a voltage divider with loads.

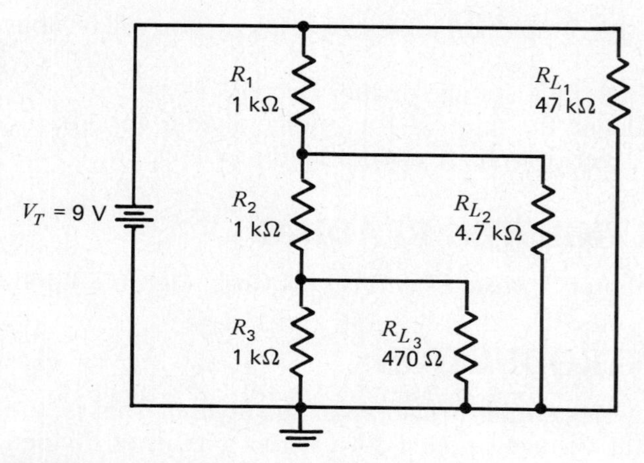

Fig. 23-4. Complex voltage divider.

9. Measure and record the *IR* voltage drops across R_1, R_2, R_3, R_{L_1}, R_{L_2}, and R_{L_3}.

10. Calculate the current through each resistor and the total circuit current. Record the results in Table 23-3.

NAME ____________________ DATE ____________

RESULTS FOR EXPERIMENT 23

QUESTIONS

1. Explain what is meant by the term *voltage divider.*

2. Refer to the circuit of Fig. 23-4 (loaded voltage divider). Explain what would happen to the total circuit current, voltage, and resistance if R_{L_2} and R_{L_3} were removed.

3. If Fig. 23-4 were used to tap the total voltage of 9 V into three equal parts (without the loads), explain why V_{R_1}, V_{R_2}, and V_{R_3} would no longer be 3 V each. Does the value of any one load greatly affect the original unloaded divider?

4. Redraw Fig. 23-4 and show the path of current flow by drawing arrows where necessary.

5. What effect would reversing the battery polarity have on the circuit of Fig. 23-4?

REPORTS

Write a complete report. Discuss the measured and calculated results. Discuss the three most significant aspects of the experiment and write a conclusion.

TABLE 23–1. No Load Values for Fig. 23-3

	Calculated *IR* Drop	Calculated Current
R_1	________	
R_2	________	
R_3	________	
I_T		________

TABLE 23–2. Measured Values for Fig. 23-3, Circuit under Load

R_L = 1 kΩ	Load at Point A *IR* Drops	Load at Point A Current	Load at Point B *IR* Drops	Load at Point B Current	Load at Point C *IR* Drops	Load at Point C Current
R_1	______		______		______	
R_2	______		______		______	
R_3	______		______		______	
R_{load}	______	______	______	______	______	______
I_T		______		______		______
I_B		______		______		______
R_L = 100 kΩ						
R_1	______		______		______	
R_2	______		______		______	
R_3	______		______		______	
R_{load}	______	______	______	______	______	______
I_T		______		______		______
I_B		______		______		______

TABLE 23–3. Circuit Values for Fig. 23-4

	IR Drop, Measured	Current, Calculated*
R_1	______	______
R_2	______	______
R_3	______	______
R_{L_1}	______	______
R_{L_2}	______	______
R_{L_3}	______	______
R_T	______	______

*V (*IR* drop measured)/R nominal = calculated current.

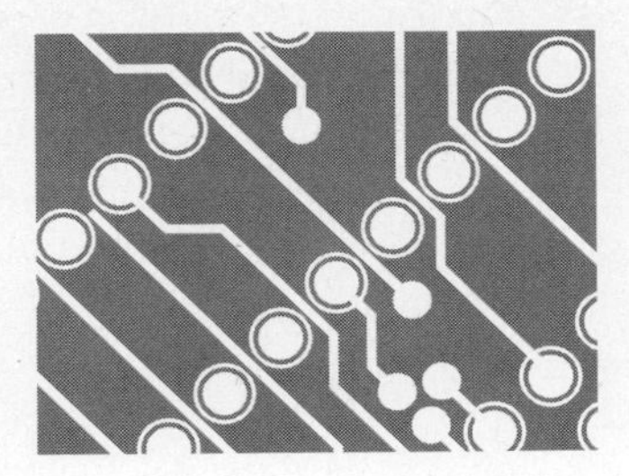

EXPERIMENT 24

CURRENT DIVIDERS

OBJECTIVES

At the completion of this experiment, you will be able to:

- Understand how parallel circuits act as current dividers.
- Be familiar with the proportional method for solving branch currents.
- Be familiar with the parallel conductance method for solving branch currents.

SUGGESTED READING

Chapter 7, *Basic Electronics*, B. Grob, Eighth Edition

INTRODUCTION

In the same way that series circuits are also voltage dividers, parallel circuits are also current dividers. That is, the total current is divided among the parallel branches in inverse proportion to the resistance in any branch. Therefore, main-line current increases as branches are added.

To find the branch currents without knowing the total voltage across the bank, a formula can be used. This formula is a proportional method for solving unknown branch currents. For example, the branch currents for Fig. 24-1 can be found by using this proportional method. It is based on the fact that currents divide in inverse proportion to their resistances.

Notice two things in Fig. 24-1. First, the numerator for each branch resistance is the value of the opposite branch. Second, it is only necessary to calculate one branch current and subtract it from the total current. The remainder will be the other branch current.

Another method for determining branch current division is the parallel conductance method. Remember that conductance $G = 1/R$. Note that conductance and current are directly proportional. This is true because the greater the resistance, the less will be the current. With any number of parallel branches, each branch current can be calculated without knowing the voltage across the bank. The formula is

$$I_x = \frac{G_x}{G_T} \times I_T$$

For example, the branch current I_{R_1} in Fig. 24-2 can be found as follows:

$$I_{R_1} = \frac{G_1}{G_T} \times I_T$$

$$G_1 = \frac{1}{R_1} = \frac{1}{10\ \Omega} = 0.1\ \text{S}$$

Note: Siemens (S) is the reciprocal of ohms.

$$R_T = \frac{1}{1/R_1 + 1/R_2 + 1/R_3} = 6.25\ \Omega$$

$$G_T = \frac{1}{R_T} = \frac{1}{6.25\ \Omega} = 0.16\ \text{S}$$

$$I_{R_1} = \frac{0.1}{0.16} \times 40\ \text{mA} = 25\ \text{mA}$$

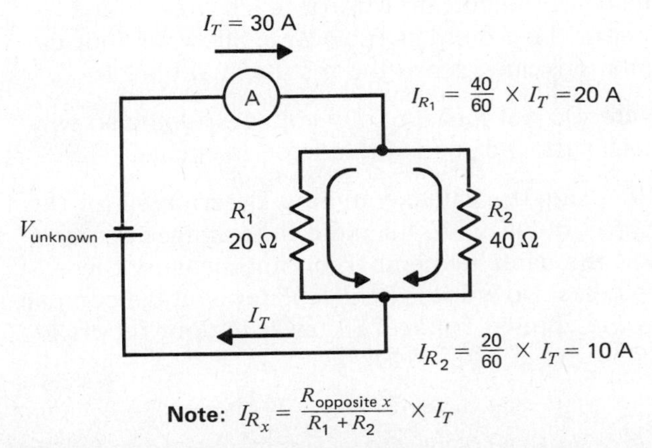

Fig. 24-1. Two-branch current divider.

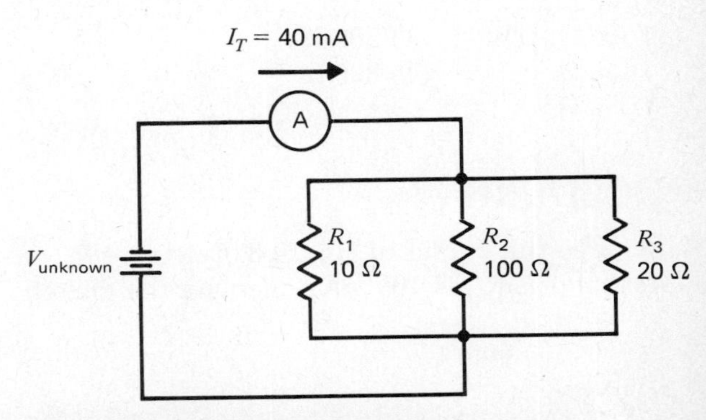

Fig. 24-2. Three-branch current divider.

Because $I_{R_1} = 25$ mA, it is easy to see that the remaining currents will be

$$I_{R_2} + I_{R_3} = +40 \text{ mA} - 25 \text{ mA} = 15 \text{ mA}$$

Thus, the previous formula (proportional method) can be used to solve for the remaining two branch currents.

Another method is to find the total conductance and use the following formula to solve for each branch current in Fig. 24-2:

$$G_1 = \frac{1}{R_1} = \frac{1}{10\ \Omega} = 0.10\text{ S}$$
$$G_2 = \frac{1}{R_2} = \frac{1}{100\ \Omega} = 0.01\text{ S}$$
$$G_3 = \frac{1}{R_3} = \frac{1}{20\ \Omega} = 0.05\text{ S}$$

Therefore, the total conductance is

$$G_1 + G_2 + G_3 = 0.1 + 0.01 + 0.05 = 0.16\text{ S}$$

To calculate branch currents, use the following formula:

$$I_{R_x} = \frac{G_{R_x}}{G_T} \times I_T$$

In the case of Fig. 24-2,

$$I_{R_1} = {}^{10}\!/_{16} \times 40\text{ mA} = +25.0\text{ mA}$$
$$I_{R_2} = {}^{1}\!/_{16} \times 40\text{ mA} = +\ 2.5\text{ mA}$$
$$I_{R_3} = {}^{5}\!/_{16} \times 40\text{ mA} = +12.5\text{ mA}$$
$$I_T = +40.0\text{ mA}$$

EQUIPMENT

DC power supply
Protoboard or springboard
Ammeter
VTVM/VOM
Leads

COMPONENTS

Resistors (all 0.25 W unless indicated otherwise):

(1) 100 Ω, 1 W
(1) 150 Ω
(1) 390 Ω
(1) 560 Ω
(1) 820 Ω

PROCEDURE

1. Refer to the circuit of Fig. 24-3. Calculate R_T.

2. Assume that $I_T = 100$ mA. Calculate the current through R_1 and R_2 by using the proportional method for two branches in parallel. Show your calculations and record the results in Table 24-1.

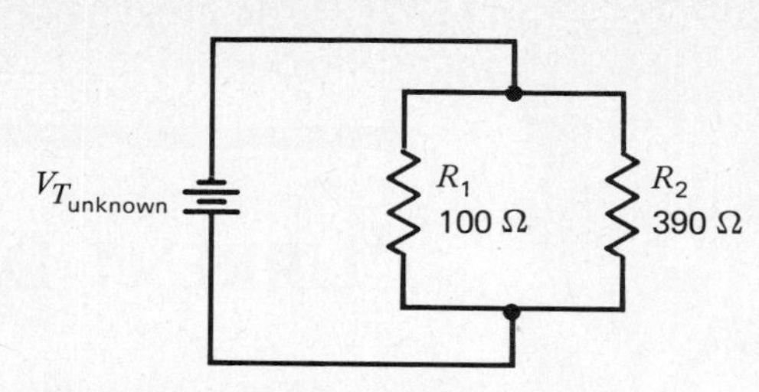

Fig. 24-3. Two-branch current divider.

3. Using the values you calculated for I_{R_1} and I_{R_2}, calculate the total voltage across the bank (use Ohm's law). Show your calculations on a separate sheet, and record the value of V_T in Table 24-1.

4. Connect the circuit of Fig. 24-3. Calculate R_T.

5. Add another resistor, $R_3 = 820\ \Omega$, to the bank and apply the total voltage you calculated in step 3 to the circuit.

6. Measure the total current and the current through each branch. Record the results in Table 24-2.

7. Connect the circuit of Fig. 24-4.

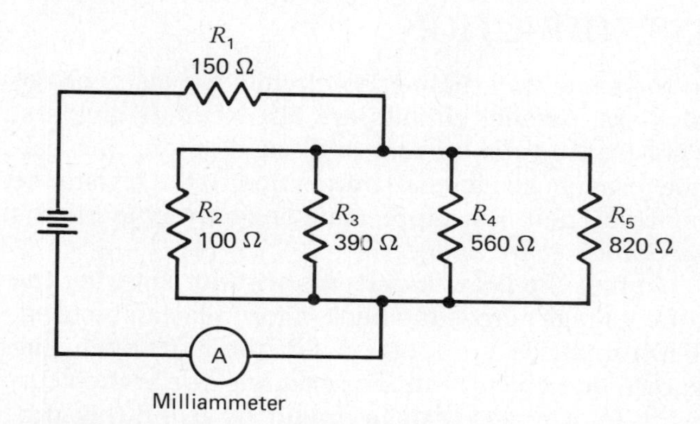

Fig. 24-4. Four-branch current divider.

8. Adjust the voltage so that total current = 30 mA.

9. Use the parallel conductance formula to determine the branch conductances G_{R_2} to G_{R_5}. Also, measure the current through each branch and record the results in Table 24-3. Show all your calculations and record the results in Table 24-3.

Note: Do not measure *any* voltages. Doing so will defeat the purpose of this experiment.

10. Using the values you have determined for the circuit of Fig. 24-4, calculate the voltages across R_1 and the bank. Remember, do not measure these voltages. How does the calculated voltage compare to the applied voltage? (Answer in your report.)

NAME ______________________ DATE ______________

RESULTS FOR EXPERIMENT 24

QUESTIONS

Answer TRUE (T) or FALSE (F) to the following:

_____ **1.** Series circuits divide current, and parallel circuits divide voltages.

_____ **2.** Conductance G is the reciprocal of branch current.

_____ **3.** Refer to Fig. 24-4. If another resistor, $R_6 = 100\ \Omega$, were added in parallel to the bank, the voltage across the bank would increase.

_____ **4.** Refer to Fig. 24-4. If the series resistor R_1 were short-circuited, the total current would decrease.

_____ **5.** Refer to Fig. 24-4. If R_3 and R_4 were opened, the voltage across the series resistor R_1 would decrease.

_____ **6.** Refer to Fig. 24-4. If the total voltage were halved and the total circuit resistance doubled, there would be no effect upon total current.

_____ **7.** Refer to Fig. 24-4. If R_1 were opened, the total circuit current would increase.

_____ **8.** The voltage across any parallel bank is increased as the total conductance of the bank is increased.

_____ **9.** The total current in a parallel bank is inversely proportional to its conductance.

_____ **10.** The total current in a parallel bank is directly proportional to its total resistance.

REPORT

Write a complete report.

TABLE 24-1

	Nominal R, Ω	Calculated I, mA	Total Calculated V, V
R_1	100		
R_2	390		
R_T			

TABLE 24-2

	Nominal R, Ω	Measured I, mA	From Table 24-1 V, V
R_1	100		
R_2	390		
R_2	820		
R_T			

TABLE 24-3

	Nominal R, Ω	Calculated G, S	Calculated I, mA	Calculated V, V*	Measured I, mA
R_1	150		30.0		30.0
R_2	100				
R_3	390				
R_4	560				
R_5	820				
R_T			30.0		3.0

Note: Calculate R_T.

*$V_x = I$ calculated $\times R$ nominal

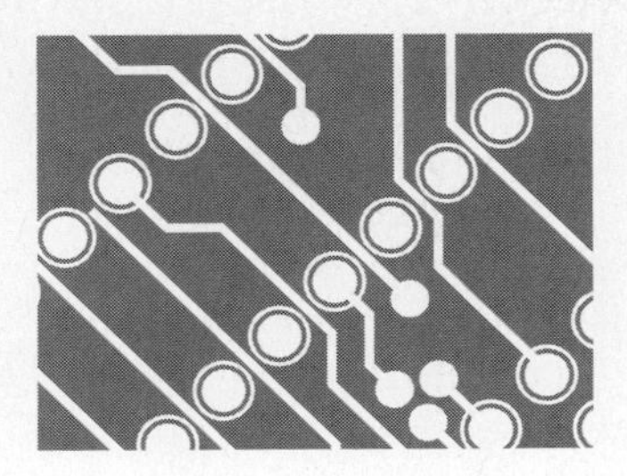

EXPERIMENT 25

VOLTAGE DIVIDER DESIGN

OBJECTIVES

At the completion of this experiment, you will be able to:

- Design a voltage divider for given load requirements.
- Understand the concept of negative voltage.
- Understand the concepts of common ground and bleeder current.

SUGGESTED READING

Chapter 7, *Basic Electronics,* B. Grob, Eighth Edition

INTRODUCTION

This experiment requires that you design and test a loaded voltage divider circuit. You can imagine that you are actually designing this divider for the output of a power supply in any piece of electronic equipment. Often, designing a circuit teaches you more than simply measuring and analyzing data.

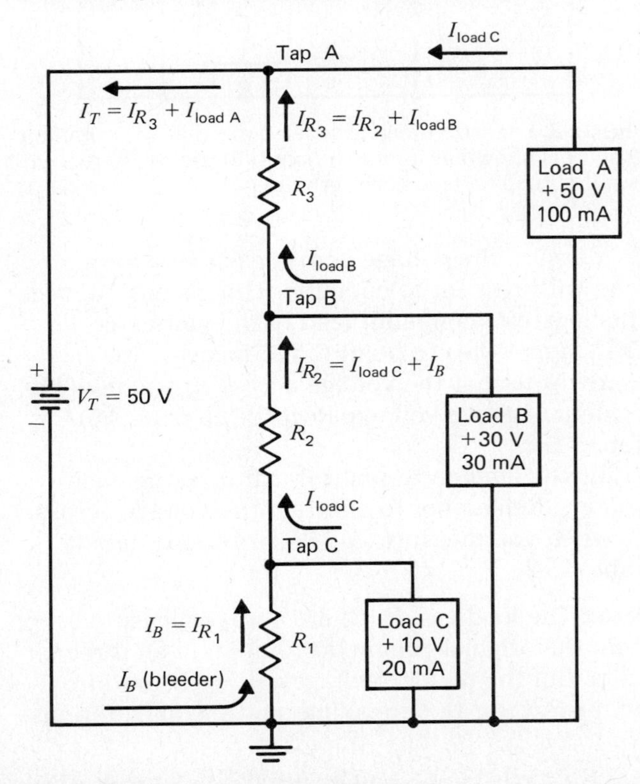

Fig. 25-1. Loaded voltage divider.

In previous experiments, you became familiar with the concepts of voltage and current dividers. You may recall that the loads on a voltage divider are also current dividers because they are parallel circuits.

To review, consider the circuit of Fig. 25-1.

1. *Loads*: The loads are resistances that require specific voltages and, often, specific currents. Here, imagine each load is a separate circuit board that requires certain voltages and currents in order to properly perform a function such as amplification.
2. I_B: This is known as *bleeder current.* It is a steady drain on the source and has no load currents passing through it. Typically, bleeder currents are calculated to be 10 percent of the total current.
3. V_T: Total voltage is fixed. It is like a budget that the designer is allowed to work with.
4. *Taps*: These are the places where the loads are connected in order to tap off their specified voltages.
5. R_1, R_2, R_3: These are the voltage divider resistances that you, the designer, will be determining by your calculations. In this case, Fig. 25-1 has a given budget of 50 V (total). Your calculations will divide this voltage into the necessary values to supply the loads.
6. *Ground*: This symbol shows a common or earth ground that is connected to one side of the power supply. Remember, ground is a reference point, like zero.

How to Calculate the Voltage Divider

Use a table, as shown in Table 25-1, in order to keep your values organized. Find the current in each R.

$$I_{R_1} = I_B = \text{approx 10 percent of } I_T \text{ loads}$$

Thus

$$I_B = 150 \text{ mA} \times 0.1 = 15 \text{ mA}$$

$$\begin{aligned} I_{load\ A} &= 100 \text{ mA} \\ I_{load\ B} &= 30 \text{ mA} \\ I_{load\ C} &= \underline{20 \text{ mA}} \\ I_T &= 150 \text{ mA} \end{aligned}$$

Knowing the value of $I_B = I_{R_1}$, I_{R_2} and I_{R_3} are calculated as follows (compare to Fig. 25-1):

$$I_{R_2} = I_B + I_{load\ C} = 15 \text{ mA} + 20 \text{ mA} = 35 \text{ mA}$$
$$I_{R_3} = I_{R_2} + I_{load\ B} = 35 \text{ mA} + 30 \text{ mA} = 65 \text{ mA}$$

How to Calculate the Voltage Across Each Resistor

The voltages at the taps are also the voltages across the loads with respect to ground. However, the voltages across R_2 and R_3 are not in parallel only with these loads. Therefore, only the voltage across R_1 is the same as $V_{\text{load C}} = 10$ V. V_{R_2} and V_{R_3} are calculated as follows (compare to Fig. 25-1):

$$V_{R_1} = V_{\text{tap C}} = 10 \text{ V}$$
$$V_{R_2} = V_{\text{tap B}} - V_{\text{tap C}} = 30 \text{ V} - 10 \text{ V} = 20 \text{ V}$$
$$V_{R_3} = V_{\text{tap A}} - V_{\text{tap B}} = 50 \text{ V} - 30 \text{ V} = 20 \text{ V}$$

How to Calculate Each Resistor

Now that the voltages and currents for each resistor have been determined, it is easy to use Ohm's law to calculate the value of each resistor:

$$R_1 = \frac{V_{R_1}}{I_{R_1}} = \frac{10 \text{ V}}{15 \text{ mA}} = 666.7\ \Omega$$
$$R_2 = \frac{V_{R_2}}{I_{R_2}} = \frac{20 \text{ V}}{35 \text{ mA}} = 571.4\ \Omega$$
$$R_3 = \frac{V_{R_3}}{I_{R_3}} = \frac{20 \text{ V}}{65 \text{ mA}} = 307.7\ \Omega$$

These values of voltage divider resistance should provide the specified load requirements.

EQUIPMENT

DC power supply
Ohmmeter
Ammeter (VOM) optional
Voltmeter (VOM/VTVM)
Protoboard or springboard
Leads

COMPONENTS

Resistors (all 0.25 W):

(1) 150 Ω (3) 470 Ω

PROCEDURE

1. Design a voltage divider, similar to Fig. 25-1, with the following specifications:

$V_T = 20$ V
Load A = 20 V, 40 mA
Load B = 15 V, 25 mA
Load C = 5 V, 10 mA

2. On a separate sheet, draw the circuit similar to Fig. 25-1 and fill in Table 25-1 (columns 1, 2, and 4).

3. Verify that your circuit works, by connecting the circuit and measuring the voltages across R_1, R_2, R_3, and each load. Use resistors within 10 percent of the load values. Record the voltages (measured) in Table 25-1 (column 3). If any value of voltage falls outside plus or minus 20 percent of your calculated values, redesign the circuit.

4. With your circuit connected, remove earth ground (if attached).

5. Using the circuit of Fig. 25-2 as an example, you will move the ground point (common: without an earth ground connection) to point C. Although no actual connection is yet made, point C now becomes the zero reference point.

Note: $V_{R_3} = V_{\text{point A}} - V_{R_2}$.

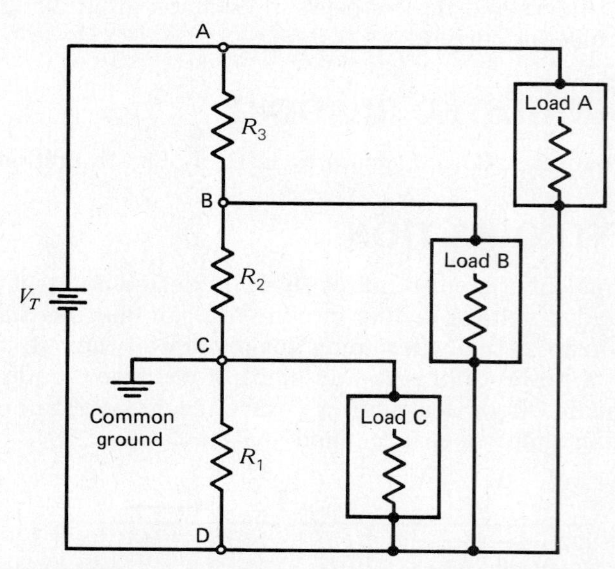

Fig. 25-2. Loaded voltage divider. Note that the common ground is shown as an earth (symbol) ground here, but it is not actually a true earth ground.

6. Measure the voltage across each resistor and load with respect to common. This means connect the negative (common) lead of the voltmeter (VTVM or VOM) to point C and measure from there. Note that the voltage across R_1 will now become a negative voltage. Record the results in Table 25-2.

7. Move common to point B and measure each voltage. Remember to subtract the voltage across R_2 when you measure V_{R_1}. Record the results in Table 25-2.

Note: The loads (A, B, C) are always measured from the original common (point D) in all three circuits. But the divider voltages are measured from points B, C, or D, depending on the configurations.

NAME

DATE

RESULTS FOR EXPERIMENT 25

QUESTIONS

1. Explain the difference between earth ground and a common reference point ground.

2. Explain how a negative voltage can be obtained from a voltage divider. Explain the effects upon *I, V,* and *R,* if any.

3. Explain, in your own words, what is meant by *bleeder current.*

4. Explain the difference, if any, between a loaded voltage divider and a series-parallel circuit.

5. Explain how the circuit of Fig. 25-1 would be affected if:
   A. R_2 were short-circuited **B.** R_2 were opened

REPORT

Write a complete report. Discuss how load changes affect the design and the current values.

TABLE 25–1

Divider	(1) Calculated R, Ω	(2) Actual R Value, Ω	(3) Measured V, V	(4) Calculated I, mA
Load A				
Load B				
Load C				
R_1				
R_2				
R_3				

TABLE 25–2

Divider	Measured V, V Common = Point C	Measured V, V Common = Point B
Load A		
Load B		
Load C		
R_1		
R_2		
R_3		

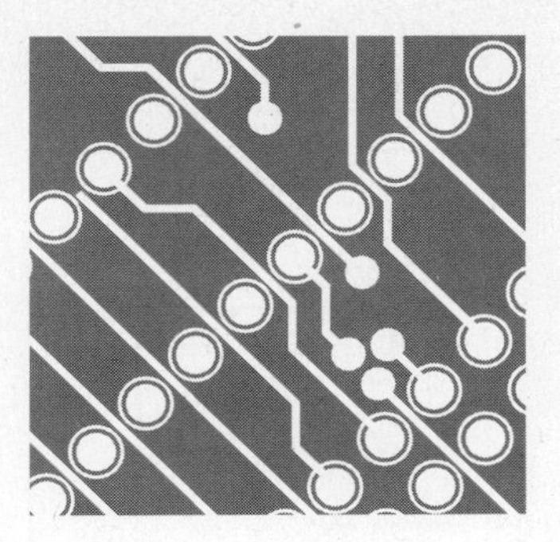

EXPERIMENT 26

POSITIVE AND NEGATIVE VOLTAGES TO GROUND

OBJECTIVES

At the completion of this experiment, you will be able to:

- Calculate circuit current and voltage drops found in a voltage-divider circuit.
- Determine the polarity of voltages found in a voltage divider circuit with a common ground.

SUGGESTED READING

Chapters 6 and 7, *Basic Electronics,* B. Grob, Eighth Edition

INTRODUCTION

In the wiring of practical circuits, one side of the voltage source is usually grounded. In electronic equipment the ground often indicates a metal chassis, which is used as a common return for connections to the voltage source. Where printed-circuit boards are used, usually a common ground path is run around the outside perimeter of the circuit board. In other cases the entire back side of a two-sided board may be used as a common-return path. Note that the chassis ground may or may not be connected to earth ground.

When a circuit has a chassis as a common return, measure the voltages with respect to chassis ground. Consider the voltage divider in Fig. 26-1. In Fig. 26-1, the circuit shows no ground system. It is instead a closed series circuit. This circuit has an applied power supply voltage V_A of 20 V. To determine the total circuit current, the total circuit resistance R_T must be determined. And R_T can be calculated as

Fig. 26-1. Voltage divider circuit without a common ground.

$$
\begin{aligned}
R_T &= R_1 + R_2 + R_3 \\
&= 4.7\ \text{k}\Omega + 4.7\ \text{k}\Omega + 10\ \text{k}\Omega \\
&= 19.4\ \text{k}\Omega
\end{aligned}
$$

The circuit current can now be calculated from the Ohm's law relationship:

$$
\begin{aligned}
I_T &= \frac{V_A}{R_T} \\
&= \frac{20\ \text{V}}{19.4\ \text{k}\Omega} \\
&= 1.03\ \text{mA}
\end{aligned}
$$

After the current has been calculated, the individual voltage drops V_1, V_2, and V_3 of the voltage divider can be found from the Ohm's law relationship of

$$V = I \times R$$

For V_1:

$$
\begin{aligned}
V_1 &= I_T \times R_1 \\
&= 1.03\ \text{mA} \times 4.7\ \text{k}\Omega \\
&= 4.84\ \text{V} \quad (\text{or } +4.84\ \text{V})
\end{aligned}
$$

For V_2:

$$
\begin{aligned}
V_2 &= I_T \times R_2 \\
&= 1.03\ \text{mA} \times 4.7\ \text{k}\Omega \\
&= 4.84\ \text{V} \quad (\text{or } +4.84\ \text{V})
\end{aligned}
$$

For V_3:

$$
\begin{aligned}
V_3 &= I_T \times R_3 \\
&= 1.03\ \text{mA} \times 10\ \text{k}\Omega \\
&= 10.31\ \text{V} \quad (\text{or } +10.31\ \text{V})
\end{aligned}
$$

Also the sum of the voltage drops will equal the applied voltage:

$$
\begin{aligned}
V_A &= V_1 + V_2 + V_3 \\
&= 4.84\ \text{V} + 4.84\ \text{V} + 10.31\ \text{V} \\
&= 19.99\ \text{V (round to 20 V)}
\end{aligned}
$$

Refer to Fig. 26-1 and note that the polarities are included on this schematic. The polarity is determined by how the circuit current and the individual voltmeters are connected. The polarity of the resistors,

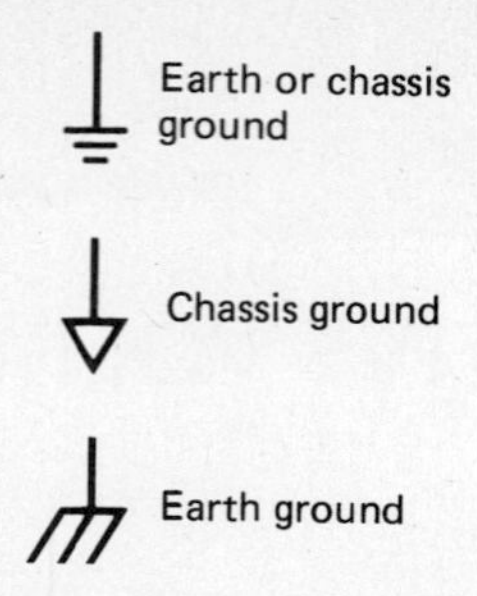

Fig. 26-2. Schematic symbols for ground.

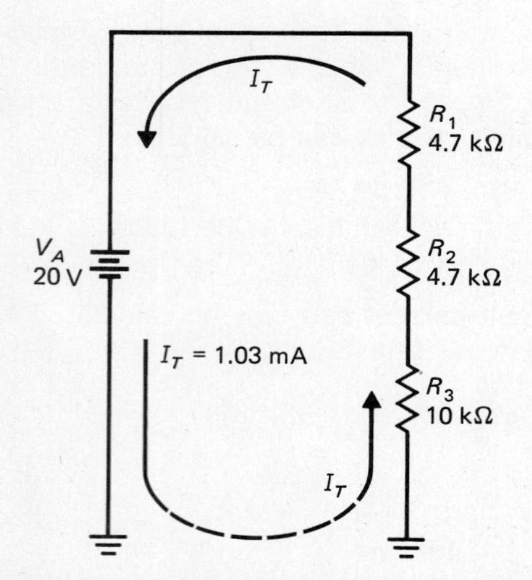

Fig. 26-3. Voltage divider circuit using a ground return.

which indicates the direction of current flow, and the color of the test leads are also indicated in Fig. 26-1.

Figure 26-2 shows the schematic symbols for ground. The ground symbol is used in Fig. 26-3. Here the same circuit with the same component values and applied voltage is shown. The only addition is the "ground return." Also note that the voltage drops of this circuit are equivalent to those shown in Fig. 26-1. The 1.03 mA generated by the battery is pushed out into ground point A and returns to ground point B. This, in effect, means that the ground symbols are connected, perhaps through a cable, foil pattern, or metal chassis.

The circuit shown in Fig. 26-4 details the same circuit of Figs. 26-3 and 26-1. The difference here is that all voltages are taken "with respect to ground." In this case, the voltage from point C to D is +10.31 V. The voltage from point B to D is +15.15 V (where $V_{BD} = VR_2 + VR_3$). The voltage from point A to D is +19.99 V (or 20 V), where $V_{AD} = VR_1 + VR_2 + VR_3$).

The circuit in Fig. 26-5 is similar to the one in Fig. 26-4. The main difference is that the ground has been moved to point C. This then indicates that all measurements should be taken "with reference" to this point. In this case V_{AC} = +9.68 V (where $V_{AC} = VR_1 + VR_2$). The voltage V_{BC} = +4.84 V (where $V_{BC} = VR_2$). The voltage V_{DC} = −10.31 V (where $V_{DC} = VR_3$). The

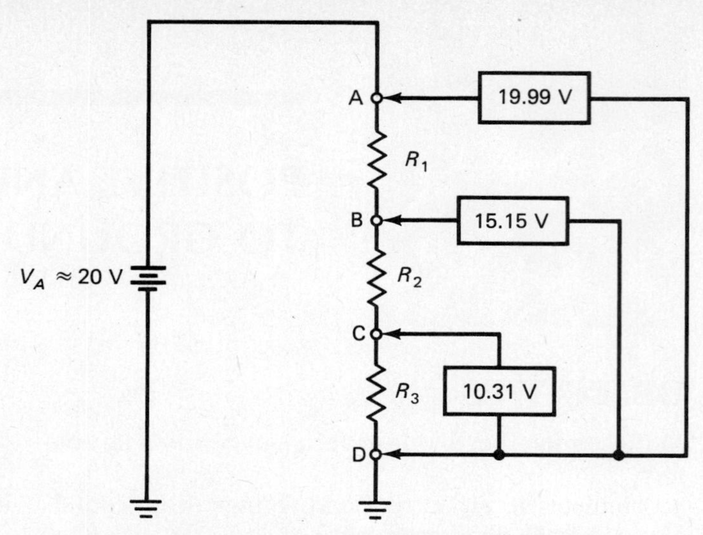

Fig. 26-4. Voltage divider circuit where voltages are measured to common ground.

voltage measured from point D to C results in a negative voltage. This circuit is known as a positive and negative voltage divider.

In summary, these dc circuits operate in the same way with or without the ground symbol shown in the schematic. The only factor that changes is the reference point for measuring the voltage.

While this experiment focuses on the use of ground as a reference point, keep in mind that there are several different symbols for ground, as shown in Fig. 26-2. The earth ground symbol usually indicates that one side of the power supply is connected to the earth, usually by a metal pipe in the ground (this is the third prong on the ac wall plug). The other two ground symbols are chassis grounds and may or may not be connected to earth (an automobile or an airplane is a good example).

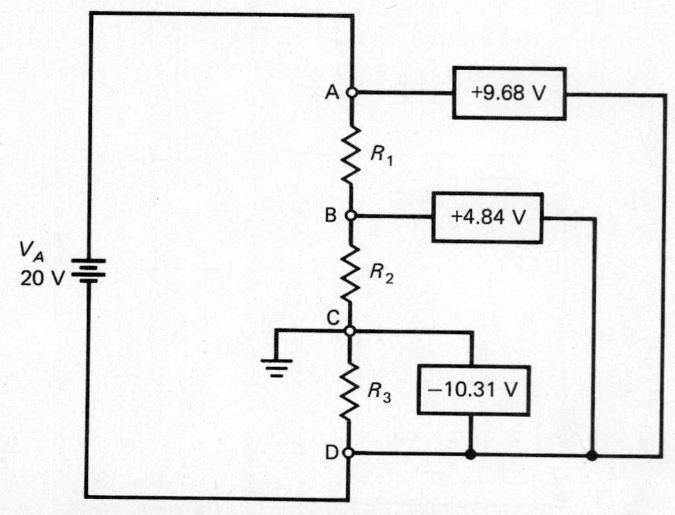

Fig. 26-5. Voltage divider displaying both positive and negative voltages to ground.

EQUIPMENT

DC power supply, 0 to 20 V
Leads
Breadboard
Voltmeter

COMPONENTS

Resistors (all 0.25 W):

(2) 4.7 kΩ
(1) 10 kΩ

PROCEDURE

1. Connect the circuit of Fig. 26-6 to the dc power supply as shown.

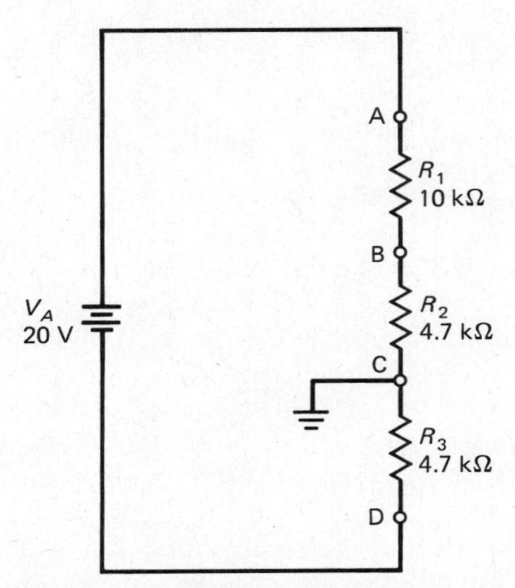

Fig. 26-6. Positive and negative voltage divider circuit with ground.

2. With the power supply turned off and disconnected, measure and record in Table 26-1 the resistance values of R_1, R_2, and R_3.
3. With the power supply turned off and disconnected, measure and record in Table 26-1 the resistive value of R_T.
4. Reconnect the power supply to the circuit shown in Fig. 26-6.
5. Calculate and record in Table 26-1 the values of R_T, I_T, V_{R_1}, V_{R_2}, and V_{R_3} referenced to ground.
6. Turn on the power supply and adjust its voltage value to 20 V dc.
7. Measure and record in Table 26-1: I_T, V_A, V_{R_1}, V_{R_2}, and V_{R_3}. Also note the polarities of V_{R_1}, V_{R_2}, and V_{R_3} in Table 26-1.
8. Turn off the power supply, and reverse its polarity.
9. Reconnect the circuit with $V_A = -20$ V, repeat steps 2–7, and record the results in Table 26-2.

NAME ______________________ DATE ____________

RESULTS FOR EXPERIMENT 26

QUESTIONS

1. Explain the circuit function of a voltage divider.

2. What is the purpose of a circuit ground?

3. Draw an example of a circuit where a voltage is negative with respect to ground.

REPORT

Write a complete report. Discuss the measured and calculated results. Discuss the three most significant aspects of the experiment, and write a conclusion.

TABLE 26–1 (Steps 2–7)

	Measured	Calculated	Polarity
R_1	______		
R_2	______		
R_3	______		
R_T	______	______	
I_T	______	______	
V_{R_1}	______	______	______
V_{R_2}	______	______	______
V_{R_3}	______	______	______
V_A	______		

*Note: Polarity with respect to common ground.

TABLE 26–2 (Steps 8 and 9)

	Measured	Calculated	Polarity
R_1	______		
R_2	______		
R_3	______		
R_T	______	______	
I_T	______	______	
V_{R_1}	______	______	______
V_{R_2}	______	______	______
V_{R_3}	______	______	______
V_A	______		

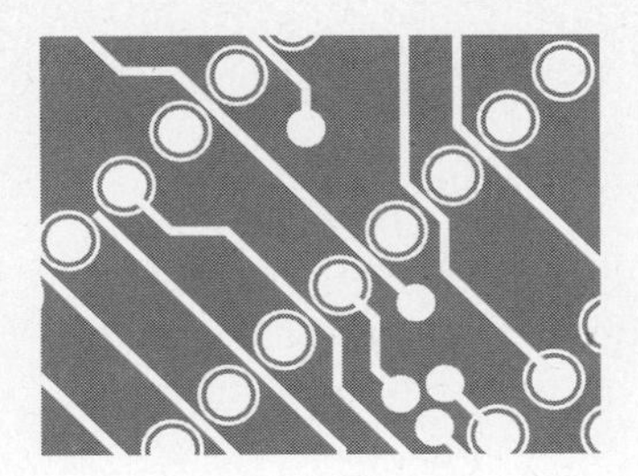

EXPERIMENT 27

AMMETER DESIGN

OBJECTIVES

At the completion of this experiment, you will be able to:

- Determine the internal resistance of a basic D'Arsonval meter movement.
- Design an ammeter circuit from this meter movement.
- Use this ammeter for actual ammeter measurements.

SUGGESTED READING

Chapter 8, *Basic Electronics*, B. Grob, Eighth Edition

INTRODUCTION

Range of an Ammeter

The small size of the wire with which an ammeter's movable coil is wound places severe limits on the current that may be passed through the coil. Consequently, the basic D'Arsonval movement may be used to indicate or measure only very small currents—for example, microamperes or milliamperes, depending on meter sensitivity.

To measure a larger current, a shunt must be used with the meter. A shunt is a heavy, low-resistance conductor connected across the meter terminals to carry most of the load current. This shunt has the correct amount of resistance to cause only a small part of the total circuit current to flow through the meter coil. The meter current is proportional to the load current. If the shunt is of such a value that the meter is calibrated in milliamperes, the instrument is called a *milliammeter.* If the shunt is of such a value that the meter is calibrated in amperes, it is called an *ammeter.*

A single type of standard meter movement is generally used in all ammeters, no matter what the range of a particular meter. For example, meters with working ranges of 0 to 10 A, 0 to 5 A, or 0 to 1 A all use the same galvanometer movement. The designer of the ammeter calculates the correct shunt resistance required to extend the range of the meter movement to measure any desired amount of current. This shunt is then connected across the meter terminals. Shunts may be located inside the meter case (internal shunt) or somewhere away from the meter (external shunt), with leads going to the meter.

Extending the Range by Use of Shunts

For limited current ranges (below 50 A), internal shunts are most often employed. In this manner, the range of the meter may be easily changed by selecting the correct internal shunt having the necessary current rating. Before the required resistance of the shunt for each range can be calculated, the resistance of the meter movement must be known.

For example, suppose it is desired to use a 100-μA D'Arsonval meter having a resistance of 100 Ω to measure line currents up to 1 A. The meter deflects full scale when the current through the 100-Ω coil is 100 μA. Therefore, the voltage drop across the meter coil is IR, or

$$0.0001 \times 100 = 0.01 \text{ V}$$

Because the shunt and coil are in parallel, the shunt must also have a voltage drop of 0.01 V. The current that flows through the shunt is the difference between the full-scale meter current and the line current. In this case, the meter current is 0.0001 A. This current is negligible compared with the line (shunt) current, so the shunt current is approximately 1 A. The resistance R_S of the shunt is therefore

$$R_S = \frac{V}{I} = \frac{0.01}{1} = 0.01\ \Omega \text{ (approx.)}$$

and the range of the 100-μA meter has been increased to 1 A by paralleling it with the 0.01-Ω shunt.

The 100-μA instrument may also be converted to a 10-A meter by the use of a proper shunt. For full-scale deflection of the meter, the voltage drop V across the shunt (and across the meter) is still 0.01 V. The meter current is again considered negligible, and the shunt current is now approximately 10 A. The resistance R_S of the shunt is therefore

$$R_S = \frac{V}{I} = \frac{0.01}{10} = 0.001\ \Omega$$

The same instrument may likewise be converted to a 50-A meter by the use of the proper type of shunt. The current I_S through the shunt is approximately 50 A, and the resistance R_S of the shunt is

$$R_S = \frac{V}{I_S} = \frac{0.01}{50} = 0.0002\ \Omega$$

EQUIPMENT

DC power supply
Protoboard or springboard
Leads
VTVM or DVM

COMPONENTS

(1) 0- to 1-mA meter movement

Resistors:

(1) 150-kΩ 0.25-W Other resistors as calculated.
(1) 470-Ω 0.25-W

Potentiometers:

(1) 5 kΩ (1) 100 kΩ

(1) SPST switch
(1) SPDT switch

PROCEDURE

1. Measure the internal resistance of the meter movement by connecting the circuit shown in Fig. 27-1.

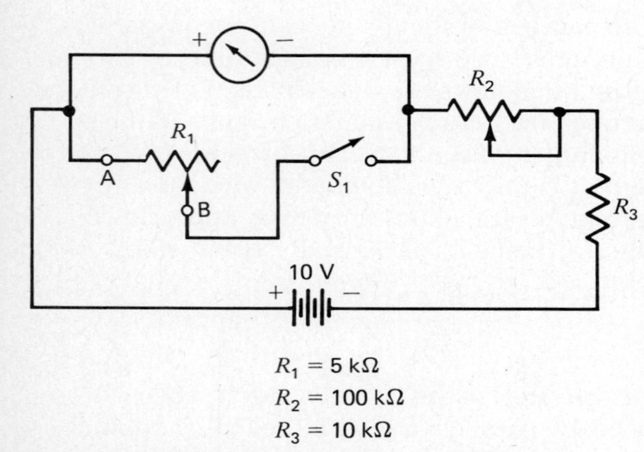

Fig. 27-1. Internal resistance measurement.

2. With S_1 open, turn on the power supply and adjust it for 10 V.

3. Adjust R_2 so that the scale upon the meter movement reads at full-scale deflection.

4. Close S_1 and adjust R_1 so that the scale upon the meter movement reads at half-scale deflection. The currents will evenly divide between R_1 and the internal resistance r_m of the meter movement when $R_1 = r_m$.

5. Measure and record in Table 27-1 the voltage dropped across V_m.

6. Measure and record r_m in Table 27-1 by turning the power supply off, disconnecting R_1 from the circuit, and measuring from point A to B. At this point, $r_m = R_1$.

7. Calculate and record I_m in Table 27-1, where

$$I_m = \frac{V_m}{r_m}$$

8. Record in Table 27-1 the value of I_m for full-scale deflection, the r_m (meter movement's internal resistance) for the meter movement, and the value V_m needed for full-scale deflection.

9. Construct the following dual-range ammeter in Fig. 27-2. Range 1 will measure 30 mA full-scale, and range 2 will measure 100 mA full-scale.

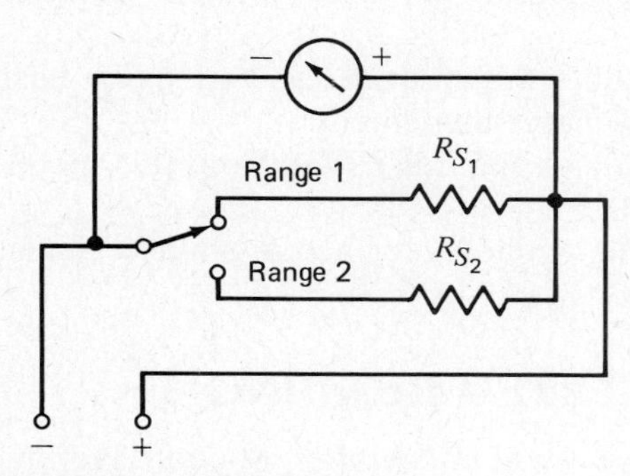

Fig. 27-2. Ammeter circuit.

10. Using the following formula determines the multiplier resistors R_{S_1} and R_{S_2}:

$$R_S = (I_m \times r_m)I_S$$

For a 30-mA full-scale deflection,

$$R_{S_1} = (I_m \times r_m)/30 \text{ mA}$$

Record this value in Table 27-2.

For a 100-mA full-scale deflection,

$$R_{S_2} = (I_m \times r_m)/100 \text{ mA}$$

Record this value in Table 27-2.

11. Connect your ammeter into the circuit configuration shown in Fig. 27-3, where I_2 is an ammeter of known accuracy and I_1 is your ammeter design. Complete Table 27-3 by turning on and adjusting the power supply in accordance with Table 27-3. Record the values of I_1 and I_2 for each power supply setting.

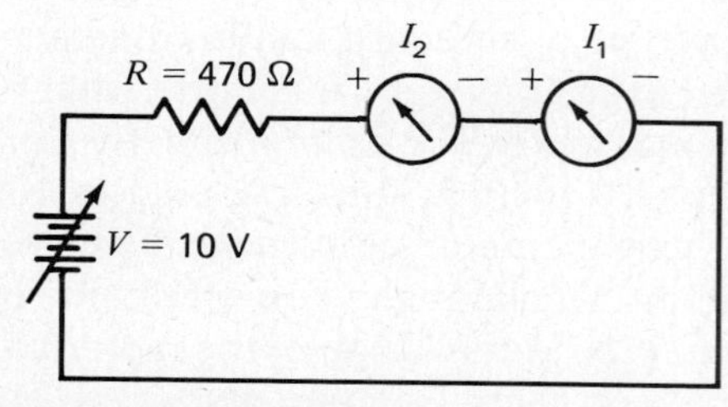

Fig. 27-3. Ammeter test setup.

12. Determine the percentage of accuracy for Table 27-3.

NAME ____________________ DATE ____________

RESULTS FOR EXPERIMENT 27

QUESTIONS

1. Describe how ammeters are connected in a circuit to measure current.

2. Design an ammeter circuit that will measure 1.5 A with a 0- to 100-mA full-scale deflection meter movement.

REPORT

Write a complete report. Discuss the measured and calculated results. Discuss the three most significant aspects of the experiment and write a conclusion.

TABLE 27–1

r_m	I_m	V_m

TABLE 27–2. Meter Movement

I_m, A	r_m, Ω	V_m, V
Shunt R_{S_1}	**Shunt R_{S_2}**	

TABLE 27–3

Range, mA	Voltage Setting	I_1	I_2	% Accuracy
0–30				
0–100				

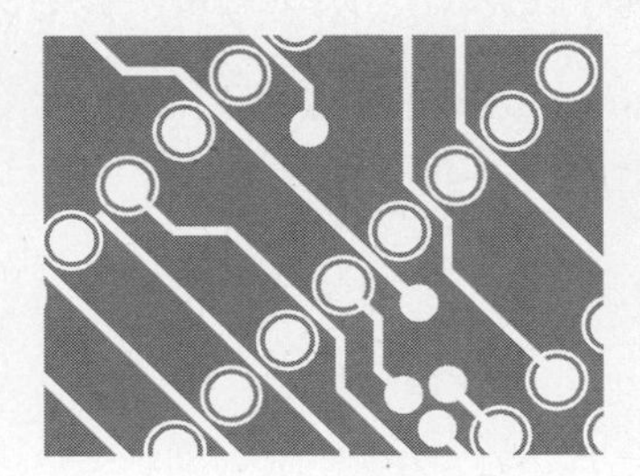

EXPERIMENT 28

VOLTMETER DESIGN

OBJECTIVES

At the completion of this experiment, you will be able to:

- Determine the internal resistance of a basic D'Arsonval movement.
- Design a voltmeter from this meter movement.
- Use this voltmeter for actual voltage measurements.

SUGGESTED READING

Chapter 8, *Basic Electronics*, B. Grob, Eighth Edition

INTRODUCTION

D'Arsonval Meter

The stationary permanent-magnet moving-coil meter is the basic movement used in most measuring instruments for servicing electric equipment. This type of movement is commonly called the D'Arsonval movement because it was first employed by the Frenchman D'Arsonval in making electrical measurements.

The basic D'Arsonval movement consists of a stationary permanent magnet and a movable coil. When current flows through the coil, the resulting magnetic field reacts with the magnetic field of the permanent magnet and causes the coil to rotate. The greater the amount of current flow through the coil, the stronger the magnetic field produced; the stronger this field, the greater the rotation of the coil. To determine the amount of current flow, a means must be provided to indicate the amount of coil rotation.

Voltmeter

The 100-μA D'Arsonval meter used as the basic meter for the ammeter may also be used to measure voltage if a high resistance is placed in series with the moving coil of the meter. When this is done, the unit containing the resistance is commonly called a *multiplier.* A simplified diagram of a voltmeter is shown in Fig. 28-1.

Extending the Range

The value of the necessary series resistance is determined by the current required for full-scale deflection of the meter and by the range of voltage to be measured. Because the current through the meter circuit is directly proportional to the applied voltage, the meter scale can be calibrated directly in volts for a fixed series resistance.

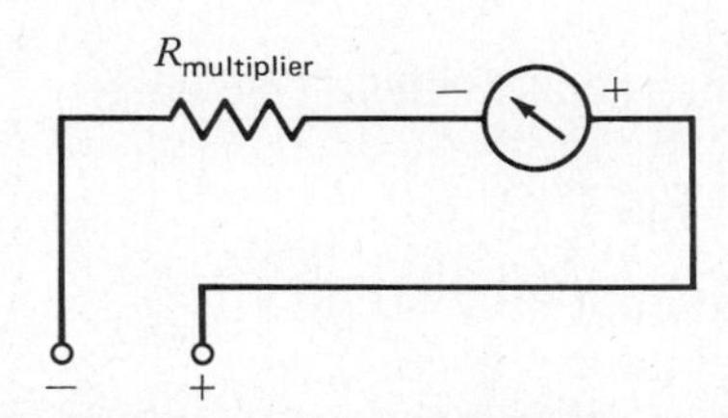

Fig. 28-1. Basic voltmeter circuit with $R_{multiplier}$.

For example, assume that the basic meter (microammeter) is to be made into a voltmeter with a full-scale reading of 1 V. The coil resistance of the basic meter is 100 Ω, and 0.0001 A causes a full-scale deflection. The total resistance R of the meter coil and the series resistance is

$$r_m = \frac{V_m}{I_m} = \frac{1}{100\ \mu\text{A}} = 10{,}000\ \Omega$$

and the series resistance alone is

$$R_1 = 10{,}000 - 100 = 9900\ \Omega$$

Multirange voltmeters utilize one meter movement with a convenient switching arrangement. A multirange voltmeter with three ranges is shown in Fig. 28-2. The total circuit resistance for each of the three ranges, beginning with the 1-V range, is

$$R_1 = \frac{V_m}{I_m} = \frac{1}{100} = 0.01\ \text{M}\Omega$$

$$R_2 = \frac{V_m}{I_m} = \frac{100}{100} = 1\ \text{M}\Omega$$

$$R_3 = \frac{V_m}{I_m} = \frac{1000}{100} = 10\ \text{M}\Omega$$

Voltage-measuring instruments are always connected across (in parallel with) a circuit. If the approximate value of the voltage to be measured is not known, it is best to start with the highest range of the voltmeter and progressively lower the range until a suitable middle third reading is obtained.

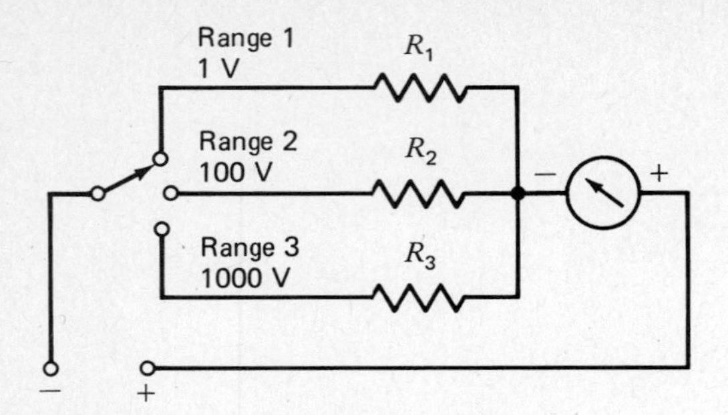

Fig. 28-2. Three-range voltmeter circuit.

EQUIPMENT

DC power supply, 10 V
Voltmeter of known accuracy
Protoboard or springboard
Test leads
VTVM or DVM

COMPONENTS

Resistors:

(1) 150-kΩ 0.25-W Other resistors as calculated.

Potentiometers (linear taper):

(1) 100 kΩ (1) 5 kΩ

(1) SPST switch
(1) SPDT switch
(1) 50-μA meter movement of unknown resistance

PROCEDURE

1. Measure the internal resistance of the meter movement by connecting the circuit shown in Fig. 28-3.

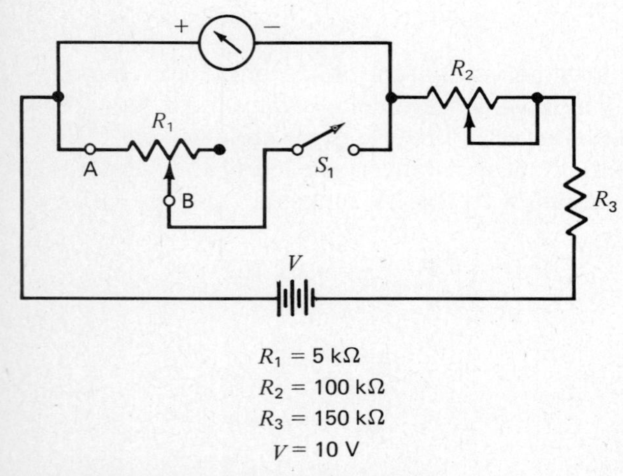

Fig. 28-3. Measuring internal resistance.

2. With S_1 open, turn on the power supply and adjust it for 10 V.

3. Adjust R_2 so that the scale upon the meter movement reads at full-scale deflection.

4. Close S_1 and adjust R_1 so that the scale upon the movement reads at half-scale deflection. The currents will evenly divide between R_1 and the internal resistance r_m of the meter movement when $R_1 = r_m$.

5. Measure and record in Table 28-1 the voltage dropped across V_m.

6. Measure and record r_m in Table 28-1 by turning the power supply off, disconnecting R_1 from the circuit, and measuring from points A to B. At this point, $r_m = R_1$.

7. Calculate and record I_m in Table 28-1, where

$$I_m = \frac{V_m}{r_m}$$

8. Record in Table 28-2 the I_m for full-scale deflection, the r_m (meter movement's internal resistance) for the meter movement, and the value of V_m for full-scale deflection.

9. Construct the dual-range voltmeter in Fig. 28-4 so that range 1 will measure 5 V full scale and range 2 will measure 10 V full scale. Use the following formula to determine the multiplier resistors R_1 and R_2:

$$R_{\text{multiplier}} = \frac{V_{\text{FS}}}{I_{\text{FS}}} - r_m = \frac{V_{\text{intended}}}{I_m} - r_m$$

Note: FS means "full scale."

For a 5-V full-scale deflection,

$$R_1 = \frac{5\text{ V}}{I_m} - r_m$$

For a 10-V full-scale deflection,

$$R_2 = \frac{10\text{ V}}{I_m} - r_m$$

Record these calculated values in Table 28-2.

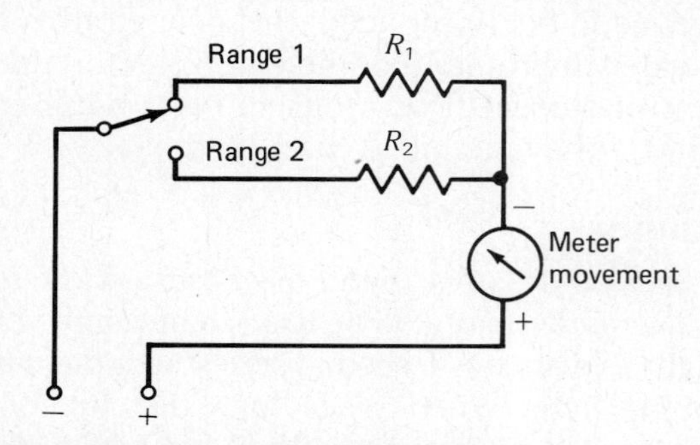

Fig. 28-4. Voltmeter dual-range circuit.

10. Connect your voltmeter into the circuit configuration of Fig. 28-5, where V_2 is a voltmeter of known accuracy and V_1 is your voltmeter design.

11. Complete Table 28-3 by turning on and adjusting the power supply in accordance with Table 28-3. Record the values of V_1 and V_2 for each power supply setting.

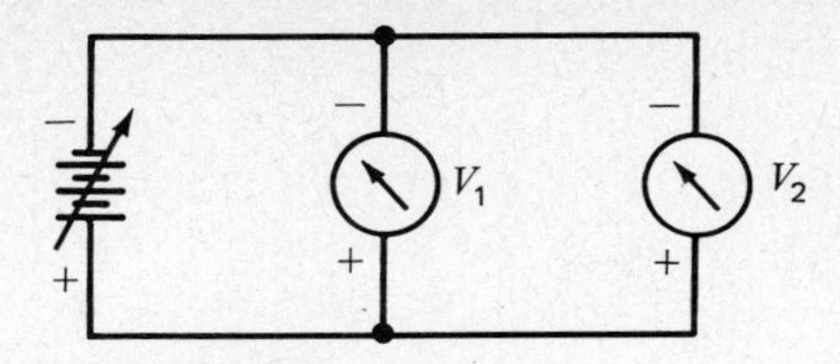

Fig. 28-5. Measuring voltages.

12. Determine the percentage of accuracy for Table 28-3.

NAME ______________________ DATE ____________

RESULTS FOR EXPERIMENT 28

QUESTION

1. Design a voltmeter that will measure 0 to 30 V dc by using a 100-mA meter movement.

REPORT

Write a complete report. Discuss the measured and calculated results. Discuss the three most significant aspects of this experiment and write a conclusion.

TABLE 28–1

0–50 μA
V_m = ________
r_m = ________
I_m = ________

TABLE 28–2. Meter Movement

I_m = ________
r_m = ________
V_m = ________
R_1 = ________
R_2 = ________

TABLE 28–3

Power Supply Voltages	V_1	V_2	% Accuracy
Range 1: 1–5 V			
1 V	______	______	______
2 V	______	______	______
3 V	______	______	______
4 V	______	______	______
5 V	______	______	______
Range 2: 1–10 V			
1 V	______	______	______
2 V	______	______	______
3 V	______	______	______
4 V	______	______	______
5 V	______	______	______
6 V	______	______	______
7 V	______	______	______
8 V	______	______	______
9 V	______	______	______
10 V	______	______	______

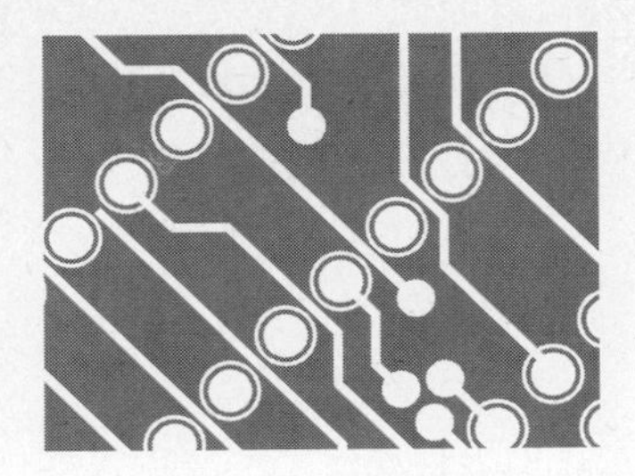

EXPERIMENT 29

OHMMETER DESIGN

OBJECTIVES

At the completion of this experiment, you will be able to:

- Determine the internal resistance of a basic D'Arsonval meter movement.
- Design an ohmmeter from this meter movement.
- Use this ohmmeter for actual ohm measurements.

SUGGESTED READING

Chapter 8, *Basic Electronics*, B. Grob, Eighth Edition

INTRODUCTION

The ohmmeter consists of a dc milliammeter, with a few added features. The added features are:

1. A dc source of potential
2. One or more resistors (one of which is variable)

A simple ohmmeter circuit is shown in Fig. 29-1.

The ohmmeter's pointer deflection is controlled by the amount of battery current passing through the moving coil. Before measuring the resistance of an unknown resistor or electric circuit, the test leads of the ohmmeter are first short-circuited together, as shown in Fig. 29-1. With the leads short-circuited, the meter is calibrated for proper operation on the selected range. (While the leads are short-circuited, meter current is maximum and the pointer deflects a maximum amount, somewhere near the zero position on the ohms scale.) When the variable resistor is adjusted properly, with the leads short-circuited, the meter pointer will come to rest exactly on the zero graduation. This indicates *zero resistance* between the test leads, which in fact are short-circuited together. The zero readings of series-type ohmmeters are sometimes on the right-hand side of the scale, whereas the zero reading for ammeters and voltmeters is generally to the left-hand side of the scale. When the test leads of an ohmmeter are separated, the meter pointer will return to the left side of the scale, due to the interruption of current and the spring tension acting on the movable-coil assembly.

After the ohmmeter is adjusted for zero reading, it is ready to be connected in a circuit to measure resistance. A typical circuit and ohmmeter arrangement is shown in Fig. 29-2.

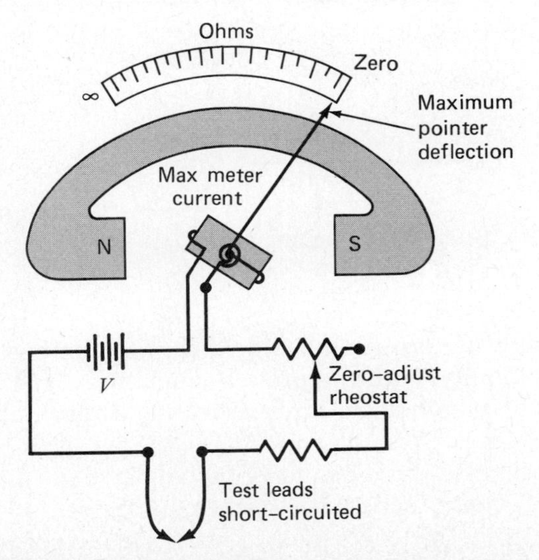

Fig. 29-1. Simple series ohmmeter.

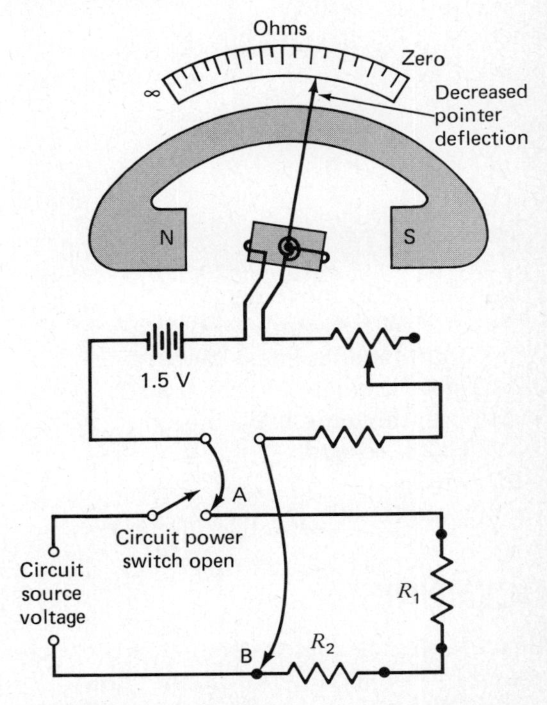

Fig. 29-2. Typical ohmmeter arrangement.

The power switch of the circuit to be measured should always be in the off position. This prevents the circuit's source voltage from being applied across the meter, which could cause damage to the meter movement.

The test leads of the ohmmeter are connected across (in parallel with) the circuit to be measured (see Fig. 29-2). This causes the current produced by the meter's internal battery to flow through the circuit being tested. Assume that the meter test leads are connected at points A and B of Fig. 29-2. The amount of current that flows through the meter coils will depend on the resistance of resistors R_1 and R_2, plus the resistance of the meter. Since the meter has been preadjusted (zeroed), the amount of coil movement now depends solely upon the resistance of R_1 and R_2. The inclusion of R_1 and R_2 raised the total series resistance, decreased the current, and thus decreased the pointer deflection. The pointer will now come to rest at a scale figure indicating the combined resistance of R_1 and R_2. If R_1 or R_2, or both, were replaced with a resistor(s) having a larger ohmic value, the current flow in the moving coil of the meter would be decreased still more. The deflection would also be further decreased, and the scale indication would read a still higher circuit resistance. Movement of the moving coil is proportional to the amount of current flow. The scale reading of the meter, in ohms, is inversely proportional to current flow in the moving coil.

EQUIPMENT

DC power supply, 0–10 V
Ohmmeter
Voltmeter
Ammeter
Test leads
VTVM or DVM

COMPONENTS

(1) 0- to 1-mA meter movement
(1) 150-kΩ 0.25-W resistor
(1) 5-kΩ potentiometer, linear taper
(1) 100-kΩ potentiometer, linear taper
(1) 1-MΩ potentiometer, linear taper
(1) 10-kΩ 0.25-W resistor
(1) SPST switch
(1) Decade box

PROCEDURE

1. Measure the internal resistance of the meter movement by connecting the circuit shown in Fig. 29-3, where $R_1 = 5\ \text{k}\Omega$, $R_2 = 100\ \text{k}\Omega$, and $R_3 = 10\ \text{k}\Omega$.

2. With S_1 open, turn on the power supply and adjust it for 10 V.

3. Adjust R_2 so that the scale upon the meter movement reads at full-scale deflection.

4. Close S_1 and adjust R_1 so that the scale upon the movement reads at half-scale deflection. The currents will evenly divide between R_1 and the internal r_m of the meter movement when $R_1 = r_m$.

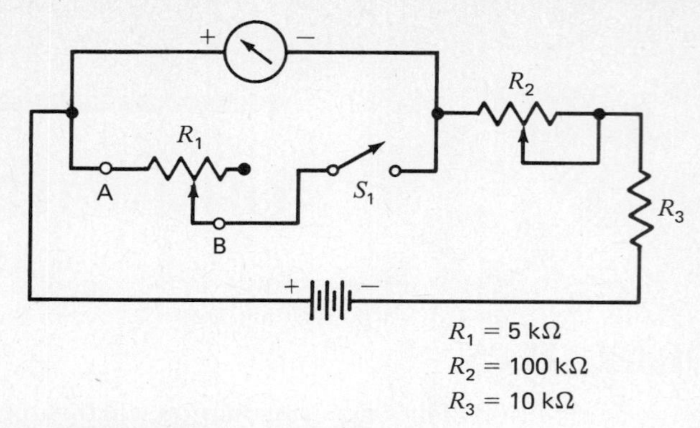

Fig. 29-3. Measuring internal resistance.

5. Measure and record in Table 29-1 the voltage dropped across V_m.

6. Measure and record r_m in Table 29-1 by turning the power supply off, disconnecting R_1 from the circuit, and measuring from points A to B. At this point, $r_m = R_1$.

7. Calculate and record I_m in Table 29-1, where

$$I_m = \frac{V_m}{r_m}$$

8. Record in Table 29-1 the r_m for full-scale deflection of a 0- to 1-mA meter movement.

9. Construct the series-type ohmmeter shown in Fig. 29-4, where $R_1 = 1.5\ \text{k}\Omega - r_m$. (The resistance value of R_1 may have to be created by using a resistance decade box.) R_2 will be used to set the ohmmeter to zero ohms.

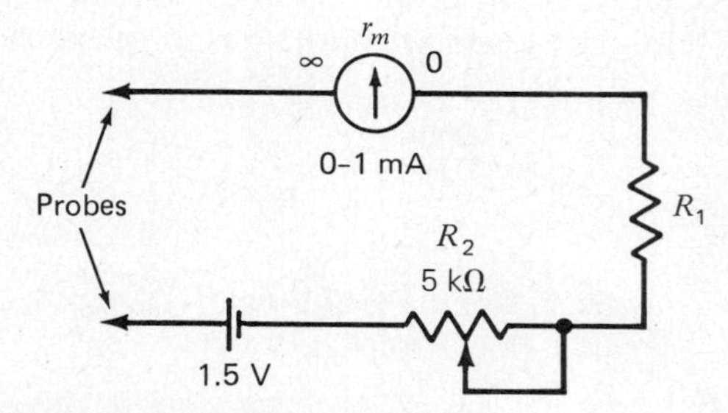

Fig. 29-4. Basic series ohmmeter.

10. With the probes not touching, the ohmmeter reads infinity. With the probes touching, adjust R_2 until the meter reads zero, indicating a zero ohms condition.

11. Calibrate this ohmmeter by connecting a 1-MΩ potentiometer across the probes, as shown in Fig. 29-5, using a grease pencil to mark the face of the ohmmeter. Complete Table 29-2.

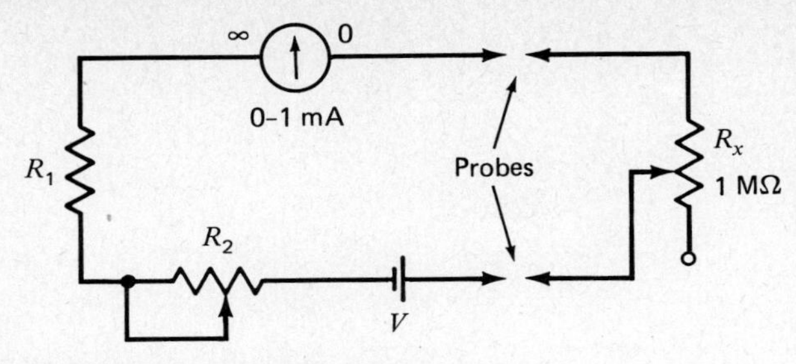

Fig. 29-5. Ohmmeter test circuit.

12. After calibrating the ohmmeter, measure the several resistances shown in Table 29-2 with an ohmmeter of known accuracy and your ohmmeter design. Complete Table 29-3, and determine the percentage of accuracy.

NAME ______________________ DATE ____________

RESULTS FOR EXPERIMENT 29

QUESTIONS

Answer TRUE (T) or FALSE (F) for each question.

_____ **1.** An ohmmeter is used to measure voltage and current.

_____ **2.** An ohmmeter has an internal battery.

_____ **3.** The infinity symbol (∞) on an ohmmeter indicates a short circuit.

_____ **4.** The ohmmeter's leads are placed across the resistance to be measured.

_____ **5.** When the ohmmeter leads are short-circuited, the needle will probably indicate zero.

_____ **6.** Ohmmeters do not require internal current-limiting resistances or shunt paths.

_____ **7.** The ohms or resistance scale that reads from left to right is called a *back-off scale.*

_____ **8.** The zero-ohms adjustment should not be used when changing ranges.

_____ **9.** For greater values of resistance, a less-sensitive meter is required to read lesser values of current.

_____ **10.** An ohmmeter can be destroyed or have its fuse blown if it is used to measure resistance in a circuit where power is applied.

REPORT

Write a complete report. Discuss the measured and calculated results. Discuss the three most significant aspects of the experiment and write a conclusion.

TABLE 29–1

Steps 5, 6, and 7
V_m = ____________
r_m = ____________
I_m = ____________
Step 8
r_m = ____________

TABLE 29–2

External R_x, Ω	Deflection	Scale Reading
0		
750		
1,500		
3,000		
150,000		
500,000		

TABLE 29–3

R	Known Meter	Design Meter	% Accuracy
100 Ω			
1 kΩ			
4.7 kΩ			
22 kΩ			
100 kΩ			
1 MΩ			

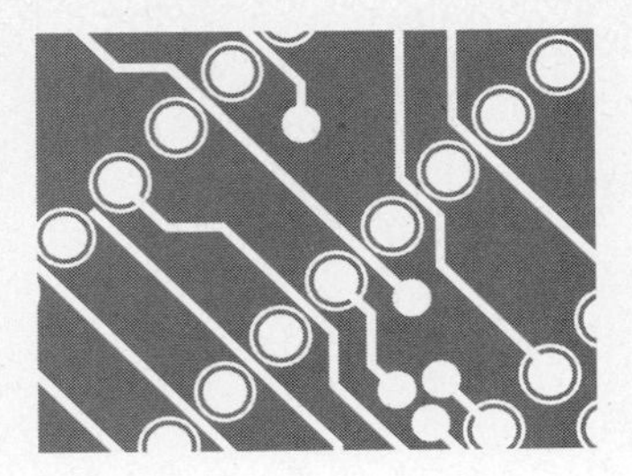

EXPERIMENT 30

NETWORK THEOREMS

OBJECTIVES

At the completion of this experiment, you will be able to:

- Thevenize a circuit.
- Nortonize a circuit.

SUGGESTED READING

Chapter 10, *Basic Electronics*, B. Grob, Eighth Edition

INTRODUCTION

The analysis of Ohm's law and Kirchhoff's laws have been of primary use in the solution of relatively simple solutions of dc circuits. In the analysis of relatively complex circuits, a more powerful method is required. In the case of simplifying complex circuits, Thevenin and Norton theorems are used. This technique involves reducing a complex network to a simple circuit, which acts like the original circuit. In general, any circuit with many voltage sources and components, with no regard made to interconnection, can be represented by an equivalent circuit with respect to a pair of terminals in the equivalent circuit.

Thevenin's theorem states that a circuit can be replaced by a single voltage source V_{Th} in series with a single resistance R_{Th} connected to two terminals. This is shown in Fig. 30-1.

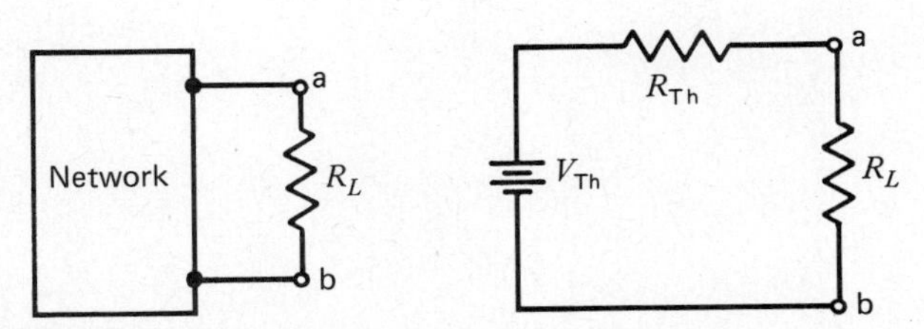

Fig. 30-1. Thevenin's circuit.

Norton's analysis is used to simplify a circuit in terms of currents rather than voltage, as is done in Thevenin circuits. Norton's circuit can be used to reduce a complex network into a simple parallel circuit that consists of a current source I_N and a parallel resistance to R_N. An example of this is shown in Fig. 30-2.

In the procedure that follows, the techniques of thevenizing and nortonizing simple voltage source–resistor networks will be developed as the procedure is completed.

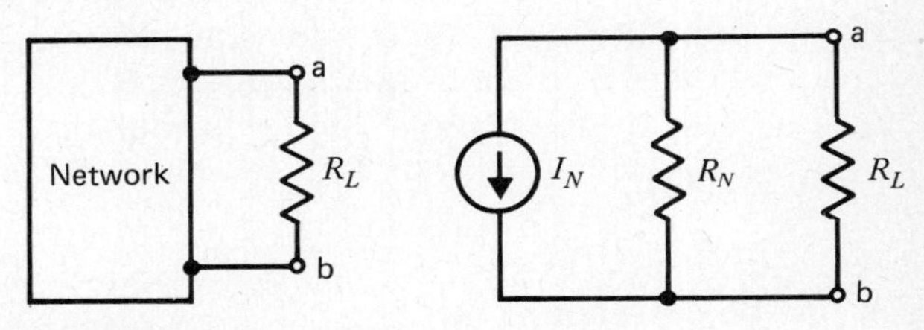

Fig. 30-2. Norton's circuit.

EQUIPMENT

DC power supply
Ammeter
Voltmeter
Protoboard or springboard
Test leads

COMPONENTS

Resistors:

(1) 100-Ω 1-W
(1) 220-Ω 0.25-W
(1) 270-Ω 0.25-W

PROCEDURE

Thevenizing

1. Construct the circuit shown in Fig. 30-3, where $R_1 = 100\ \Omega$, $R_2 = 270\ \Omega$, $R_L = 220\ \Omega$, and V is adjusted to 10 V.

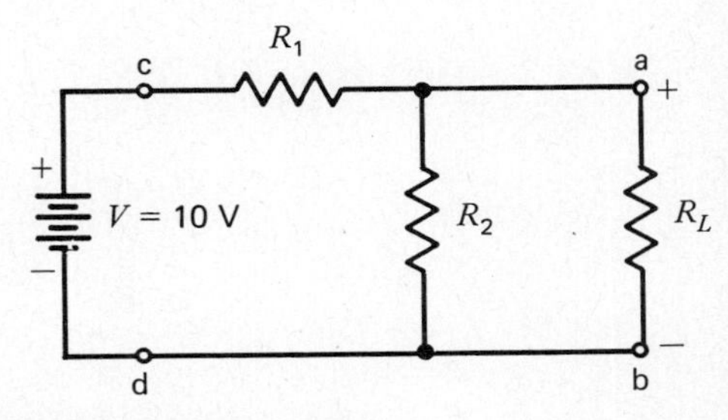

Fig. 30-3. Thevenizing a circuit.

2. Open the circuit at points a and b by disconnecting R_L from the circuit. The remainder of the circuit connected to a and b will be thevenized. Calculate, measure, and record in Table 30-1 the voltage across ab. Note that $V_{ab} = V_{Th}$.

3. Turn off the power supply and completely remove it from the circuit.
4. With the power supply removed, connect points c and d.
5. Calculate, measure, and record in Table 30-1 the value of R_{ab}. Note that $R_{ab} = R_{Th}$.

V_{Th} has now been determined and is found to be in series with R_{Th}. Since R_L was disconnected, this Thevenin equivalent can be applied to any value of R_L.

6. Reconnect the circuit shown in Fig. 30-3. Calculate (using the voltage divider formula), measure, and record V_L and I_L in Table 30-1 by reconnecting R_L. V_L is defined by the voltage divider formula as

$$V_L = \frac{R_L}{R_L + R_{Th}} \times V_{applied}$$

and I_L can be determined as

$$I_L = \frac{V_L}{R_L}$$

The same answers could be determined by using Ohm's law. The advantage of thevenizing the circuit is that the effect of R_L can be calculated easily for different values.

7. Complete Table 30-1 for the percentage of accuracy.

Nortonizing

8. Construct the circuit shown in Fig. 30-4, where $R_1 = 100\ \Omega$, $R_2 = 270\ \Omega$, $R_L = 220\ \Omega$, and V is adjusted to 10 V.

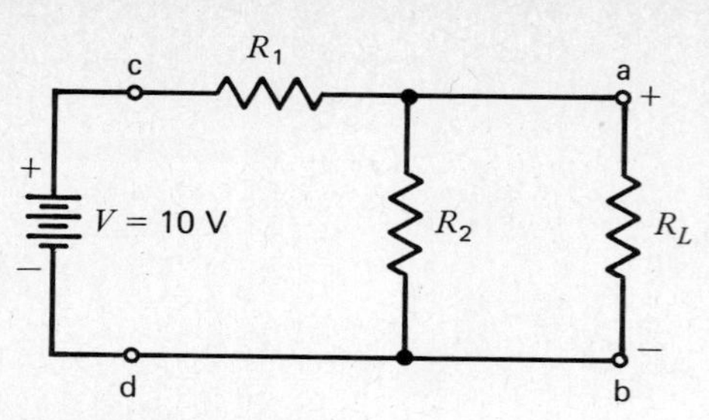

Fig. 30-4. Nortonizing a circuit.

9. Short-circuit points a and b together. This will also short-circuit R_2, and this will create a circuit condition in which resistor R_1 is in series with the power supply. Calculate, measure, and record in Table 30-2 the current flowing through R_1.

Note: $I_{R_1} = I_N$ (Norton)

10. Determine R_N by removing the short circuit, and remove R_L. This will leave points a and b unconnected to R_L.
11. Turn off the power supply and completely remove it from the circuit.
12. With the power supply removed, connect point c to d.
13. Calculate, measure, and record in Table 30-2 the value R_{ab}. Note that $R_{ab} = R_N$.
14. Reconnect the circuit shown in Fig. 30-4. Calculate, measure, and record I_L and V_L in Table 30-2 by reconnecting R_L.
15. Complete Table 30-2 for the percentage of accuracy.

NAME

DATE

RESULTS FOR EXPERIMENT 30

QUESTIONS

1. What are the primary use and importance of thevenizing a circuit?

2. What are the primary use and importance of nortonizing a circuit?

3. Draw a Thevenin equivalent of the circuit shown in Fig. 30-3.

4. Draw a Norton equivalent of Fig. 30-4.

5. Is the statement made at the end of procedure step 6, which reads, "the advantage of thevenizing the circuit is that the effect of R_L can be calculated easily for different values," valid? Explain and prove by example.

REPORT

Write a complete report. Discuss the measured and calculated results. Discuss the three most significant aspects of the experiment and write a conclusion.

TABLE 30–1

	Calculated	Measured	% Accuracy
V_{Th}			
R_{Th}			
V_L			
I_L			

TABLE 30–2

	Calculated	Measured	% Accuracy
I_N			
R_N			
I_L			
V_L			

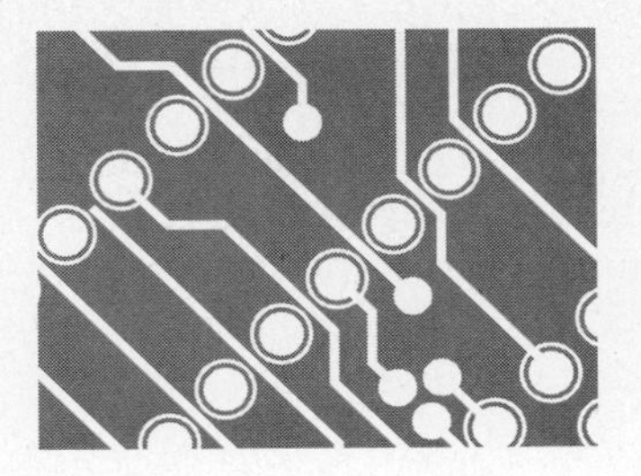

EXPERIMENT 31

POTENTIOMETERS AND RHEOSTATS

OBJECTIVES

At the completion of this experiment, you will be able to:

- Identify the circuit configuration of a potentiometer.
- Identify the circuit configuration of a rheostat.

SUGGESTED READING

Chapter 2, *Basic Electronics*, B. Grob, Eighth Edition

INTRODUCTION

Potentiometers and rheostats are variable resistances and are used to vary voltage and current in a circuit. A rheostat is a two-terminal device. The potentiometer is a three-terminal device, as shown in Fig. 31-1.

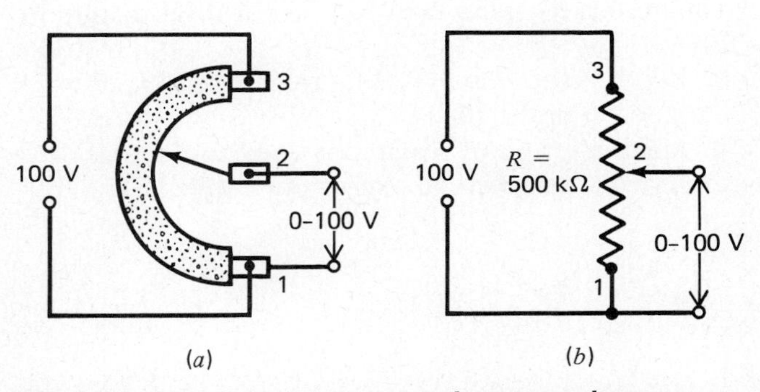

Fig. 31-1. Potentiometer connected across voltage source to function as a voltage divider. (*a*) Wiring diagram. (*b*) Schematic diagram.

The maximum resistance is seen between the two end terminals. The middle terminal mechanically adjusts and taps a proportion of this total resistance. A potentiometer can be used as a rheostat by connecting one end terminal to the other, as shown in Fig. 31-2.

The primary purpose of a potentiometer (pot) is to tap off a variable voltage from a voltage source, as shown in Fig. 31-3.

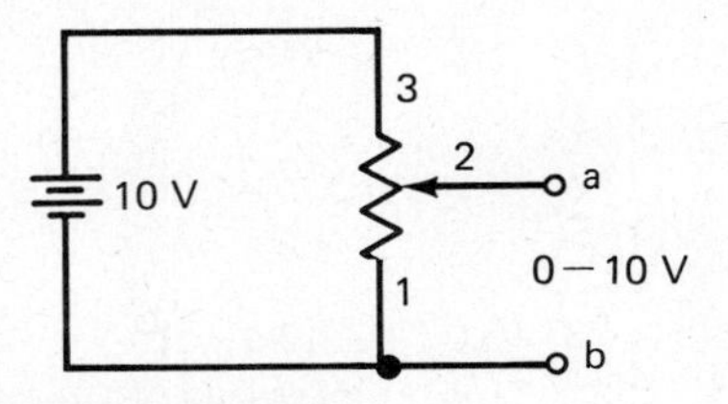

Fig. 31-3. Variable voltage source.

As pin 2 is rotated up toward pin 3, the voltage at ab increases until a 10-V level is achieved. If pin 2 is rotated downward toward pin 1, then the voltage present at ab decreases to zero, or approximately zero. The variance of voltages may appear to be presented in a linear or a nonlinear fashion, depending upon the manufacturer's type of potentiometer.

The primary purpose of a rheostat is to vary current though a load. This is accomplished by locating the rheostat in series with the load and source voltage. In this way, the total resistance R_T can be varied and indirectly vary the total current. This circuit configuration is shown in Fig. 31-4.

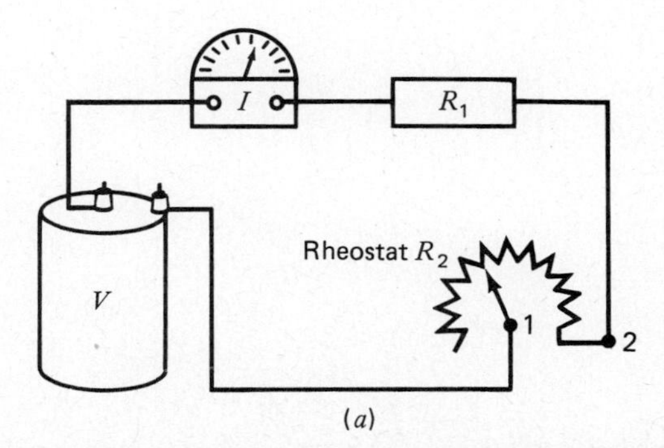

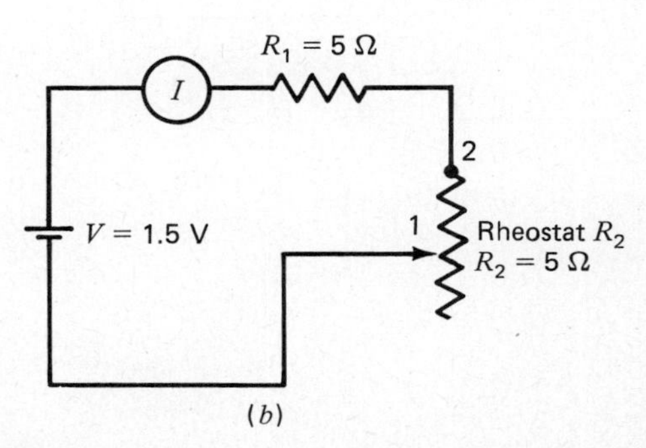

Fig. 31-2. Rheostat connected in series circuit to vary the current. (*a*) Wiring diagram with ammeter to measure *I*. (*b*) Schematic diagram.

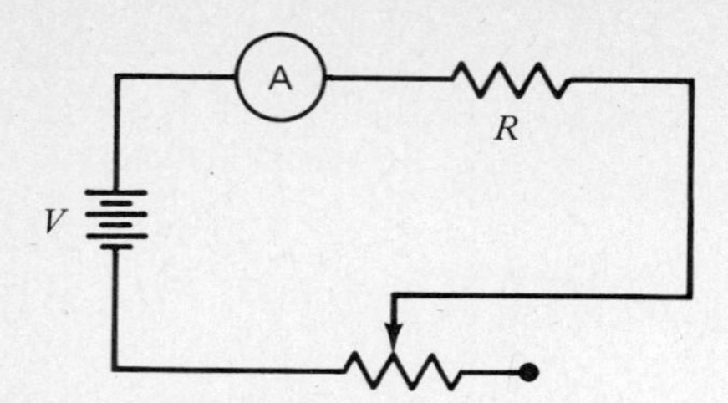

Fig. 31-4. Rheostat circuit to vary current.

In summary, rheostats are:

Two-terminal devices
Found in series with loads and voltage sources
Used to vary total current

Potentiometers are:

Three-terminal devices
Found to have end terminals connected across voltage sources
Used to tap off part of the voltage source

EQUIPMENT

DC power supply, 0–10 V
Voltmeter
Ammeter
Ohmmeter
Protoboard
Test leads

COMPONENTS

(1) 100-Ω, 1-W resistor
(1) 1-kΩ, 1-W potentiometer, linear taper

PROCEDURE

1. Connect the circuit shown in Fig. 31-5, where $V = 10$ V, $R_1 = 100\ \Omega$, and R_2 (pot) = 1 kΩ.

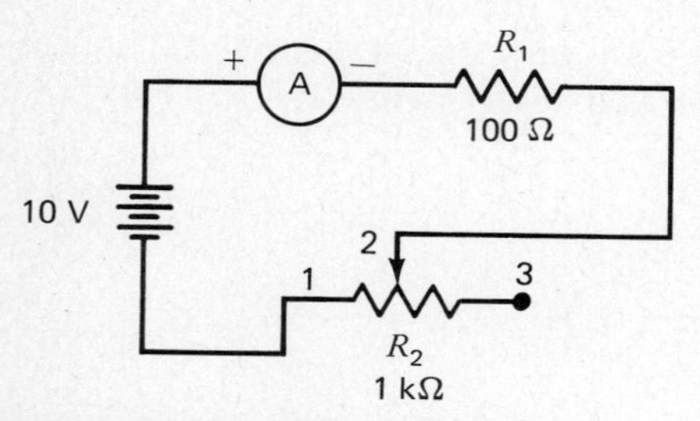

Fig. 31-5. Rheostat controlling current.

2. Turn on the power supply and adjust R_2 for a minimum resistance value (maximum I).

3. Remove R_2 from the circuit and connect it to an ohmmeter (points 1 and 2). Set R_2 to 100 Ω and reconnect R_2 to the circuit. Measure the current flow and record in Table 31-1.

4. Repeat step 3 in 100-Ω increments (100, 200, 300 Ω, etc.) up to 1000 Ω.

5. Make a graph of resistance (horizontal axis) versus current (vertical axis) from Table 31-1.

6. Connect the circuit shown in Fig. 31-6, where $V = 10$ V and R_2 (pot) = 1 kΩ.

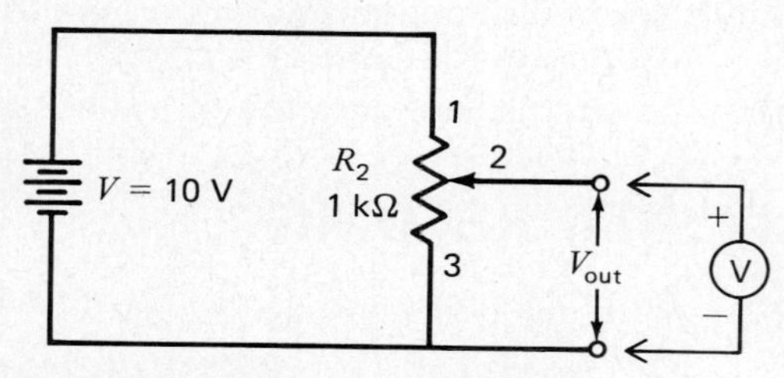

Fig. 31-6. Potentiometer voltage divider.

7. Turn on the power supply and adjust R_2 for a minimum resistance value (minimum V).

8. Remove R_2 from the circuit and connect it to an ohmmeter (points 2 and 3). Set R_2 to 100 Ω, and reconnect R_2 to the circuit. Measure the voltage drop across R_2 (pins 2 and 3). Record the results in Table 31-2.

9. Repeat step 8 in 100-Ω increments (100, 200, 300 Ω, etc.) up to 1000 Ω.

10. Make a graph of resistance (horizontal axis) versus voltage (vertical axis) from Table 31-2.

NAME _______________ DATE _______________

RESULTS FOR EXPERIMENT 31

QUESTIONS

1. How many circuit connections to a potentiometer are needed?

2. How many circuit connections to a rheostat are needed?

3. Determine maximum power consumption from the graphs you completed in steps 5 and 10. What are the actual necessary wattages of R_1 and R_2?

REPORT

Write a complete report. Discuss the measured and calculated results. Discuss the three most significant aspects of the experiment and write a conclusion.

TABLE 31–1

Resistance, Ω	Measured Current
100	________
200	________
300	________
400	________
500	________
600	________
700	________
800	________
900	________
1000	________

TABLE 31–2

Resistance, Ω	Measured Voltage
100	______
200	______
300	______
400	______
500	______
600	______
700	______
800	______
900	______
1000	______

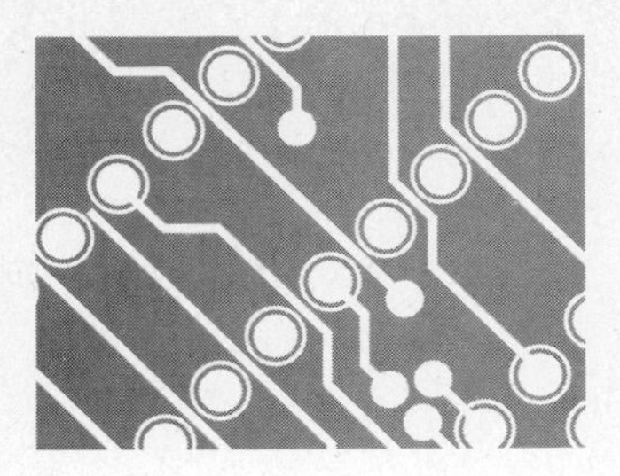

EXPERIMENT 32

INTERNAL RESISTANCE

OBJECTIVES

At the completion of this experiment, you will be able to:

- Validate the concept of internal resistance in a power source.
- Determine the internal resistance of a dry cell battery and a dc power supply (generator).
- Graph or plot decreasing terminal voltage versus load current.

SUGGESTED READING

Chapter 12, *Basic Electronics,* B. Grob, Eighth Edition

INTRODUCTION

Any source of electric power that produces a continuous output voltage can be called a *generator.* All generators have some internal resistance, labeled r_i. This internal resistance has its own *IR* voltage drop, because it is in series with any load connected to the generator. In other words, the internal resistance of a source subtracts from the generated voltage, resulting in a decreased voltage across the output terminals. In a battery, r_i is due to the chemical makeup inside; in a power supply, r_i is due to the internal circuitry of the supply.

For example, Fig. 32-1 is a schematic representation of a 9-V battery with 100 Ω of internal resistance.

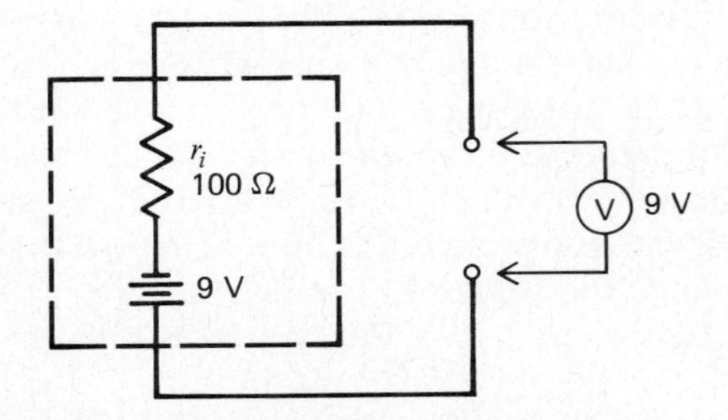

Fig. 32-1. A 9-V battery with $r_i = 100$ Ω.

Notice that the dotted line indicates that r_i is actually inside the battery. This battery has 9 V across its output terminals when it is measured with a voltmeter. If r_i were equal to 100 kΩ, the voltmeter would still measure 9 V across the output terminals. Thus, the value of r_i does not affect the output voltage. However, if a load is connected across the output terminals, then the value of r_i becomes significant. In any case, Fig. 32-2 shows that the battery's internal resistance now becomes a resistance in series with the load.

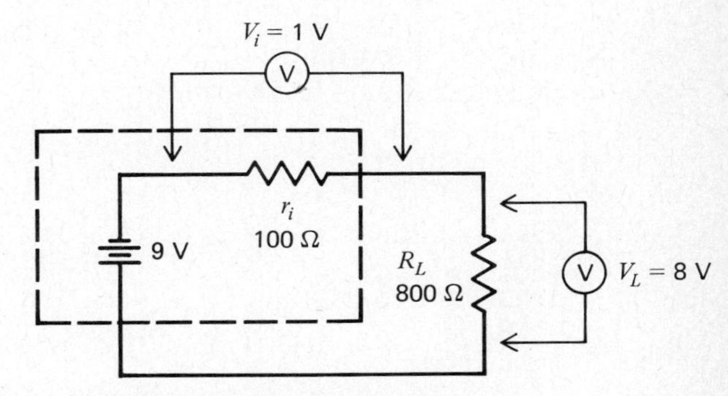

Fig. 32-2. A 9-V battery under load.

With a load resistance of 800 Ω connected across the output terminals, the voltmeter will now measure 8 V instead of 9 V. The other 1 V is now across the internal resistance of the battery. If r_i were equal to 100 kΩ, for example, the voltage across the output terminals would be almost 0 V due to the excessive value of r_i. In that case, the battery would be worn out or depleted.

Most bench power supplies have a fixed value of internal resistance that does not vary, regardless of the load value. Remember, without the load connected, the circuit is an open load. Therefore, the voltage drop across r_i equals zero. In this case, the total voltage is still available across the output, and it is called *open-circuit voltage,* or *no-load voltage.*

In the example of Fig. 32-2, the total circuit current I_T is equal to

$$I_T = \frac{V_L}{R_L} = \frac{8\text{ V}}{800\ \Omega} = 0.01\text{ A}$$

As the load resistance decreases, more circuit current will flow. If R_L decreases to 350 Ω, the current will increase and the load will require more current. Also, the voltage drop across the load will decrease and the voltage drop across V_i will increase.

Notice that as the load resistance decreased, the circuit current increased. Thus, the terminal voltage (the same thing as the load *IR* voltage) decreased. Therefore, the terminal voltage drops with more load current.

There is a method for determining the internal resistance of a source (generator) based on the examples given. Simply put, it is as follows.

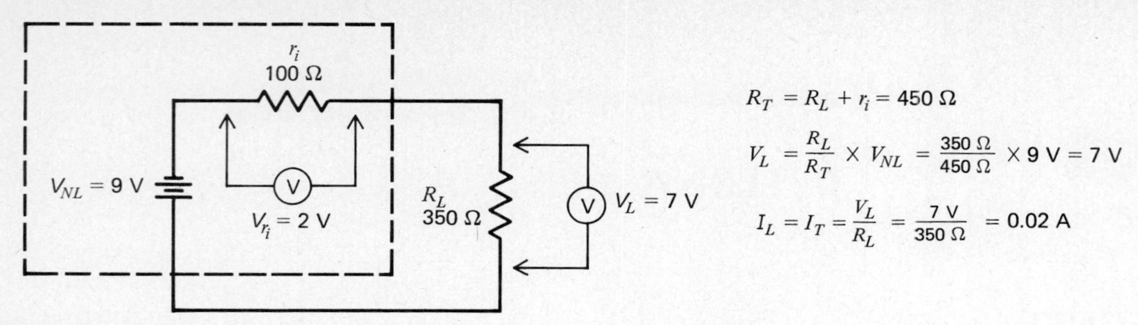

Fig. 32-3. Determining r_i.

1. Measure the no-load voltage.
2. Connect a load, and measure the voltage across the load and the circuit current.
3. Use the following formula to determine r_i:

$$r_i = \frac{V_{\text{no load}} - V_{\text{load}}}{I_{\text{load}}}$$

In Fig. 32-3, this would be

$$r_i = \frac{V_{NL} - V_L}{I_L} = \frac{9\ V - 7\ V}{0.02\ A} = \frac{2\ V}{0.02\ A} = 100\ \Omega$$

Finally, in general, if a generator has a very low internal resistance in relation to load resistance, it is considered a constant voltage source, because the voltage across r_i will subtract very little from the load voltage. If the value of r_i is very great in relation to load resistance, the generator is considered a constant current source, because the load resistance will have little effect upon the total resistance $(r_i + R_L)$ and the total circuit current.

EQUIPMENT

DC power supply
Voltmeter
Ammeter
VOM
1.5-V battery
Protoboard or springboard
Test leads

COMPONENTS

Resistors (all 0.25 W unless indicated otherwise):

(1) 220 Ω   (1) 2.2 kΩ
(2) 560 Ω   (1) 5.6 kΩ
(2) 1 kΩ   (1) 10 kΩ

PROCEDURE

1. Connect the circuit of Fig. 32-4. Do not connect the load yet. Measure and record in Table 32-1 the no-load voltage (V_{NL}) across the output terminals.

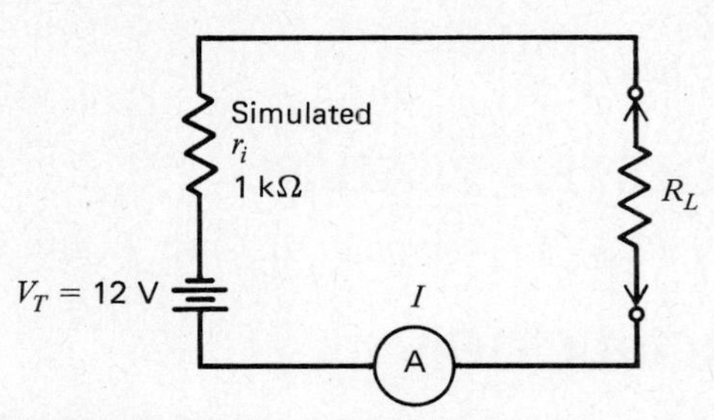

Fig. 32-4. Power supply with simulated r_i. Note that r_i is a 1-kΩ resistor in series.

2. Connect the following loads to the circuit of Fig. 32-4. Measure and record in Table 32-1 the load voltage and current for each load resistance.

R_L = 10 kΩ
= 5.6 kΩ
= 2.2 kΩ
= 1 kΩ
= 560 Ω
= 220 Ω

3. Calculate the value of r_i by using the measured values of load voltage and current for each load resistance. Show your calculations on a separate sheet of paper, and record the results in Table 32-1.
4. Change the value of r_i to 560 Ω and repeat steps 1 to 3 above. Record the results in Table 32-2.
5. Change the value of V_T to 6 V (using r_i = 560 Ω), and repeat steps 1 to 3. Record the results in Table 32-3.
6. Measure the voltage across a 1.5-V battery and record the value in Table 32-4.
7. Measure the short-circuit current of a 1.5-V battery by placing an ammeter across the output terminals of the battery for no longer than approximately 5 s, as shown in Fig. 32-5. Record the value in Table 32-4.

CAUTION: Use a VOM on its 10- or 12-A scale range. Some VOMs have special input jacks for this purpose.

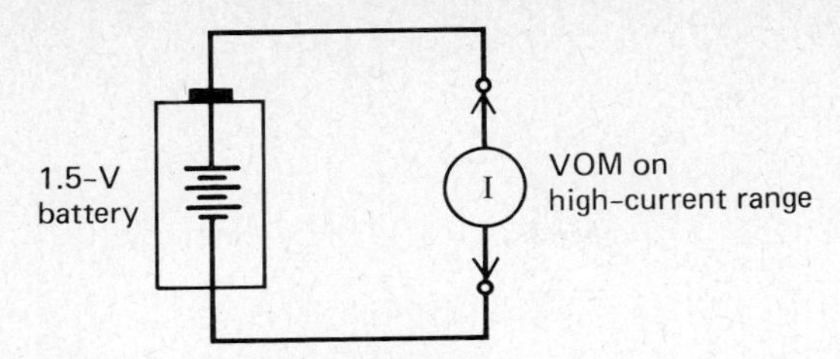

Fig. 32-5. Short-circuit method.

8. Calculate r_i by using Ohm's law. If available, repeat with a 22-V or any other size battery that will not damage the meter.

Note: You can do this for any value of battery, provided a meter of large enough current capacity is used.

9. Using the method for determining r_i (steps 1 to 3), use an unknown value of r_i (three times) and use a 1-kΩ load resistor. This can be done by disguising the value of a resistance with black electrical tape or by placing the resistance inside a chassis, as illustrated in Fig. 32-6. Use the circuit in Fig. 32-7 for this step. Record the results in Table 32-5.

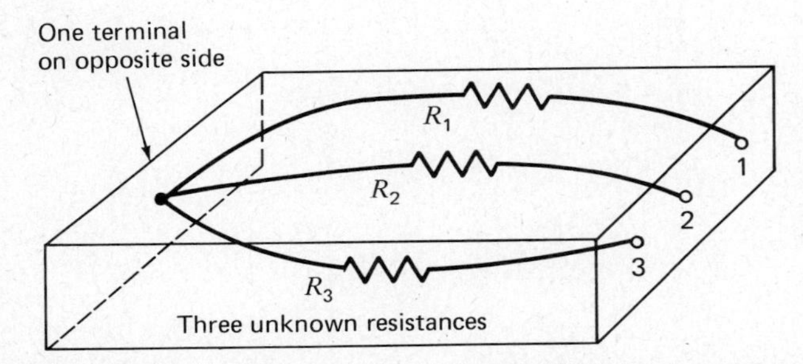

Fig. 32-6. Resistance box containing three unknown resistors.

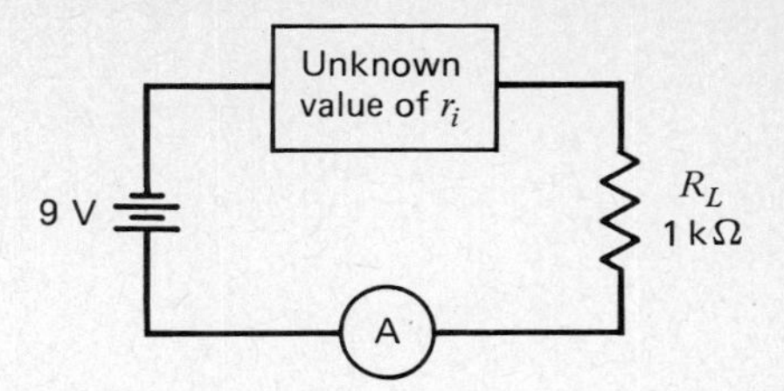

Fig. 32-7. Circuit for determining the internal resistance.

10. *OPTIONAL:* Plot the results of steps 1 to 3 (Table 32-1). For example, V_L versus I_L. Use regular graph paper, *not* semilog graph paper. See Fig. 32-8. See Appendix G for suggestions on how to make graphs.

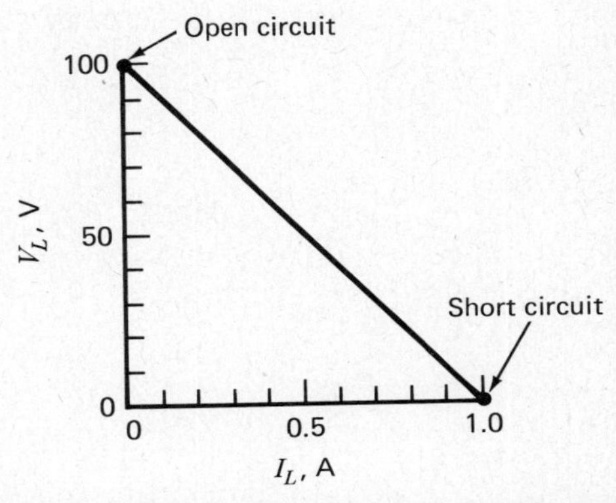

Fig. 32-8. How terminal voltage V_L drops with more load current I_L.

NAME ______________________ DATE __________

RESULTS FOR EXPERIMENT 32

QUESTIONS

Answer TRUE (T) or FALSE (F) to the following.

_____ **1.** Batteries have internal resistance, but dc power supplies do not.

_____ **2.** As load resistance increases, the terminal voltage decreases.

_____ **3.** As load current increases, terminal voltage increases.

_____ **4.** Connecting four batteries in parallel, each with $r_i = 100\ \Omega$, would increase the total r_i four times.

_____ **5.** Connecting four batteries in series, each with $r_i = 100\ \Omega$, would increase the total r_i four times.

_____ **6.** The internal resistance of a generator is always in parallel with a load.

_____ **7.** Subtracting the load voltage from the no-load voltage gives a remainder that is equal to the *IR* voltage drop in the internal resistance of the source.

_____ **8.** Internal resistance is in series with the load resistance.

_____ **9.** Short-circuiting a battery will not drain the battery.

_____ **10.** A 1.5-V dry cell battery with 1 Ω of internal resistance is probably a depleted battery.

REPORT

Write a complete report. Discuss the measured and calculated results. Discuss the most significant aspects of the experiment and write a conclusion.

TABLE 32–1. $r_i = 1\ k\Omega$ (Steps 1–3)

R_L	Measured V_L, V	Measured I_L, A	Calculated r_i, Ω
10 kΩ	______	______	______
5.6 kΩ	______	______	______
2.2 kΩ	______	______	______
1 kΩ	______	______	______
560 Ω	______	______	______
220 Ω	______	______	______

$V_{NL} =$ ______

TABLE 32–2. r_i = 560 Ω (Step 4)

R_L	Measured V_L, V	Measured I_L, A	Calculated r_i, Ω
10 kΩ	______	______	______
5.6 kΩ	______	______	______
2.2 kΩ	______	______	______
1 kΩ	______	______	______
560 Ω	______	______	______
220 Ω	______	______	______

TABLE 32–3. V_T = 6 V; r_i = 560 Ω (Step 5)

R_L	Measured V_L, V	Measured I_L, A	Calculated r_i, Ω
10 kΩ	______	______	______
5.6 kΩ	______	______	______
2.2 kΩ	______	______	______
1 kΩ	______	______	______
560 Ω	______	______	______
220 Ω	______	______	______

TABLE 32–4. Steps 6–8

	V_{NL}, V	Short-circuit I, A	Calculated r_i, Ω
1.5-V battery	______	______	______
Additional ______-V battery	______	______	______

Note: Only the instructor will know the value of the three unknown values of r_i. In this way, your lab techniques and your ability to follow procedures will be tested.

TABLE 32–5. r_i Unknown; r_L = 1 kΩ (Step 9)

	Measured V_L, V	Measured I_L, A	Calculated r_i, Ω
Measured V_{NL} = ______			
r_i No. 1	______	______	______
r_i No. 2	______	______	______
r_i No. 3	______	______	______

Chassis or box number (if applicable): ______

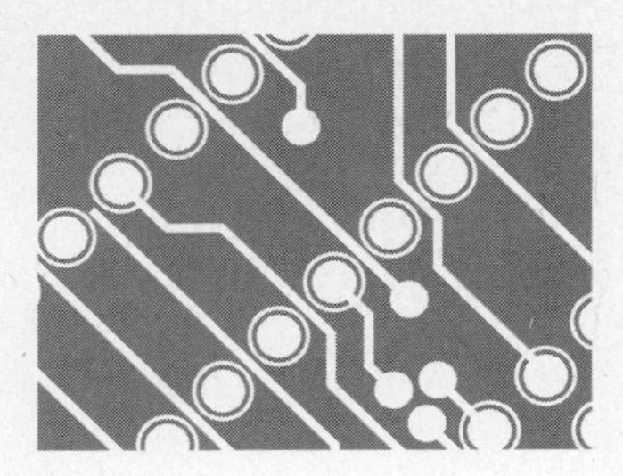

EXPERIMENT 33

LOAD MATCH AND MAXIMUM POWER

OBJECTIVES

At the completion of this experiment, you will be able to:

- Validate that maximum source power is transferred to a load when the value of source $r_i = R_L$.
- Plot a graph of load power for differing values of load resistance.
- Understand the concept of maximum efficiency versus maximum power.

SUGGESTED READING

Chapter 12, *Basic Electronics,* B. Grob, Eighth Edition

INTRODUCTION

When the internal resistance of a generator is equal to the load resistance, the load is considered matched to the source. The matching of load to source resistance is significant because the source can then transfer maximum power to the load.

Whenever $R_L = r_i$, maximum power is transferred to the load. When load resistance is more than r_i, the output voltage is more but the circuit current is less. When the load resistance is less than r_i, the output voltage is less but the circuit current is more. This experiment will provide data that you can analyze and thus prove that these concepts are valid.

The circuit of Fig. 33-1 and the accompanying graph of Fig. 33-2 illustrate the concept of matching a load to an internal source resistance to obtain maximum power transfer.

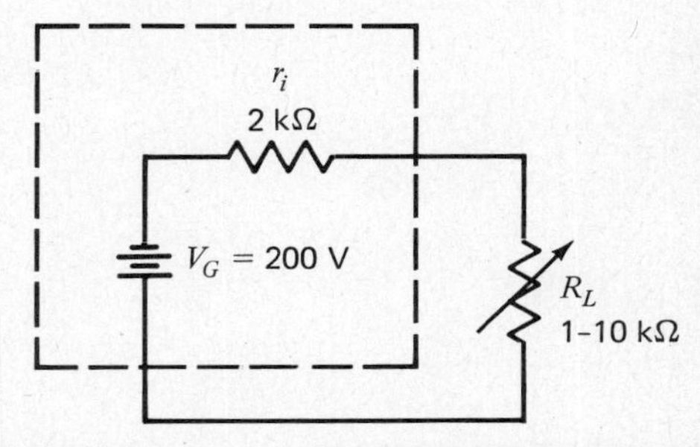

Fig. 33-1. Maximum power transfer circuit for analysis.

Because of the voltage divider formed by r_i and R_L, there is an equal voltage division: half of V_G is across r_i and half of V_G is across R_L. Under these circumstances, the load develops the maximum power that is possible using the particular source.

Referring to Fig. 33-1, as R_L increases, current decreases, resulting in less power dissipated in r_i. This results in more circuit efficiency because less power is lost across r_i. However, when $r_i = R_L$, the circuit efficiency is 50 percent.

$$\frac{P_L}{P_T} \times 100 = \text{circuit efficiency}$$

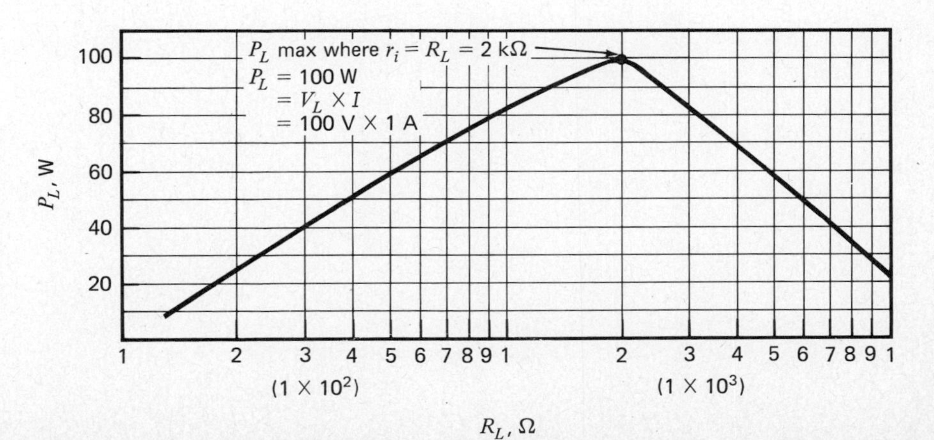

Fig. 33-2. Semilog graph of P_L versus R_L.

where P_T is the total power dissipated by the circuit, or

$$P_T = P_L + P_{r_i}$$

By this definition, 100 percent circuit efficiency means that absolutely no power is being dissipated.

EQUIPMENT

Ammeter
Voltmeter
DC power supply
Decade box
Protoboard or springboard
Leads

COMPONENTS

(1) 820-Ω, 0.25-W resistor

PROCEDURE

1. Connect the circuit of Fig. 33-3.

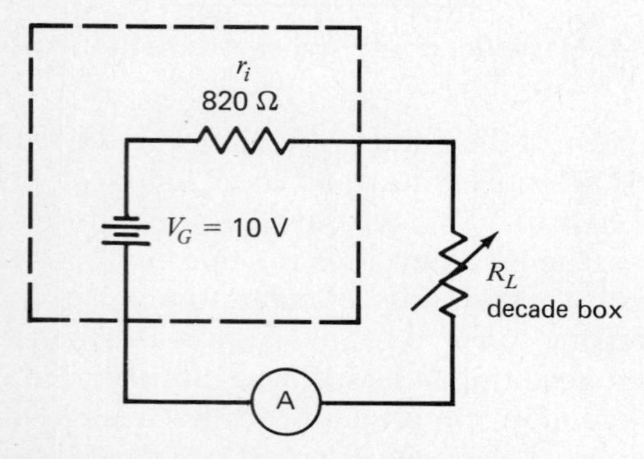

Fig. 33-3. Maximum power transfer circuit.

2. Increase the load resistance in 100-Ω steps from 100 Ω to 1 kΩ. Measure the voltage across R_L and the current at each step. Record the results in Table 33-1 for each step.

3. Increase the load resistance from 1 kΩ to 10 kΩ in 1-kΩ steps. Measure the voltage across R_L and the current at each step. Record the results in Table 33-1 for each step.

4. Calculate the *IR* voltage drop across r_i at each step, as $V_{r_i} = V_G - V_{R_1}$ and record the results in Table 33-1.

5. Calculate the load power dissipated at each step of R_L, as

$$P_L = V_L \times I$$

Record in Table 33-1.

6. Calculate the power dissipated across r_i at each step of R_L as

$$P_{r_i} = V_{r_i} \times I$$

Record in Table 33-1.

7. Calculate the total power dissipated in the circuit for each step of R_L as

$$P_T = V_G \times I$$

Note that

$$V_G = V_L + V_{r_i}$$

Record in Table 33-1.

8. Calculate circuit efficiency for each step of R_L as

$$\frac{P_L}{P_T} \times 100$$

expressed as a percentage.

9. Plot a graph of load resistance versus load power, using your data. Use two-cycle semilog paper. Prepare this graph as if it were to be used in a professional situation. It should be neat and well-organized, it should include a title and all possible values, and critical parameters should be labeled.

NAME DATE

RESULTS FOR EXPERIMENT 33

QUESTIONS

1. Explain the difference between circuit efficiencies of 1, 50, and 100 percent. In other words, explain what is meant by *circuit efficiency* as it relates to transfer of maximum power.

2. Explain what would happen if the circuit of Fig. 33-3 had an internal resistance of 100 kΩ.

3. Explain what would happen if the circuit of Fig. 33-3 had an internal resistance of 0.001 Ω.

4. Explain why semilog paper is used to graph the data.

5. Explain how you could get maximum power transferred to a 15-kΩ load if the internal resistance of your source were 10 kΩ.

REPORT

Write a complete report. Discuss the measured and calculated results. Discuss the three most significant aspects of the experiment and write a conclusion.

TABLE 33–1. Data for Circuit Fig. 33-3

R_L	Measured V_L, V	Measured I, A	Calculated V_{r_i}, V	Calculated P_L, W	Calculated P_{r_i}, W	Calculated P_T, W	% Efficiency
100 Ω							
200 Ω							
300 Ω							
400 Ω							
500 Ω							
600 Ω							
700 Ω							
800 Ω							
900 Ω							
1 kΩ							
2 kΩ							
3 kΩ							
4 kΩ							
5 kΩ							
6 kΩ							
7 kΩ							
8 kΩ							
9 kΩ							
10 kΩ							

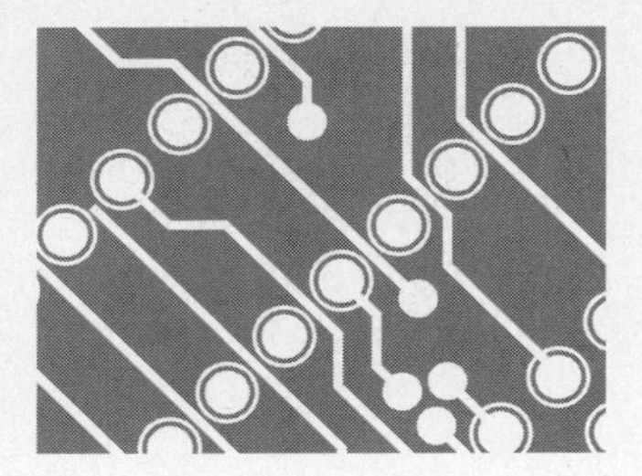

EXPERIMENT 34

MAGNETISM

OBJECTIVES

At the completion of this experiment, you will be able to:

- Validate that current in a conductor has an associated magnetic field.
- Understand the concept of shielding.
- Examine the left-hand rule to determine magnetic polarity.

SUGGESTED READING

Chapters 13, 14, and 15, *Basic Electronics*, B. Grob, Eighth Edition

INTRODUCTION

Any electric current has an associated magnetic field that can do the work of attraction or repulsion. Not only is the magnetic field useful for doing work, it is also the cause of unwanted attraction and repulsion. Thus, it is often necessary to shield particular circuits to prevent one component from affecting another.

The most common example of magnetic force is that produced by a magnet. The magnet, with its north and south poles, acts as a generator that produces an external magnetic field provided by the opposite magnetic poles of the magnet. The idea is like the two opposite terminals of a battery that have opposite charges. Also, the earth itself is a huge natural magnet, having both north and south poles. Thus, the needle of a compass (also a magnet) is attracted to the north pole, because the atoms that make up the needle have been aligned in such a way that their magnetic field is attracted to the magnetic field of the earth's north pole.

It is these magnetic fields that are the subject of electromagnetism. These fields are thought of as lines of force, called *magnetic flux*, as shown in Fig. 34-1.

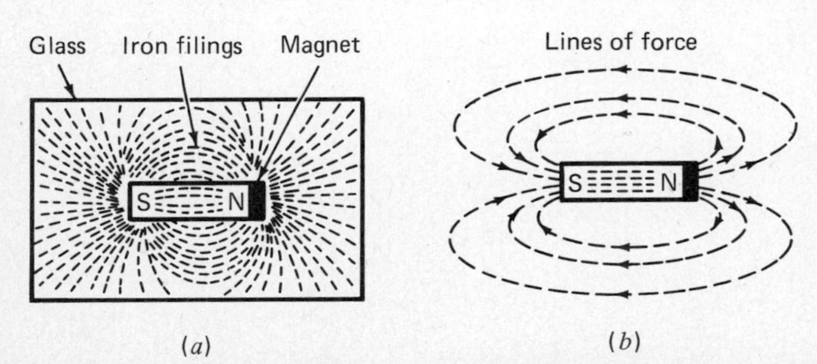

Fig. 34-1. Magnetic field of force around a bar magnet. (*a*) Field outlined by iron filings. (*b*) Field indicated by lines of force.

If current is flowing in a conductor, there is a similar magnetic field that can be used in conjunction with the fields of a magnet. For example, PM (permanent magnet) loudspeakers found in most radios, televisions, and public address systems all use the principles of magnetism to produce the audible sound we listen to.

Finally, the opposite effect of current moving through a conductor is a magnetic field in motion, forcing electrons to move. This action is called *induction*. Inductance is produced by the motion of magnetic lines of flux cutting across a conductor, thus forcing free electrons in the conductor to move, as shown in Fig. 34-2.

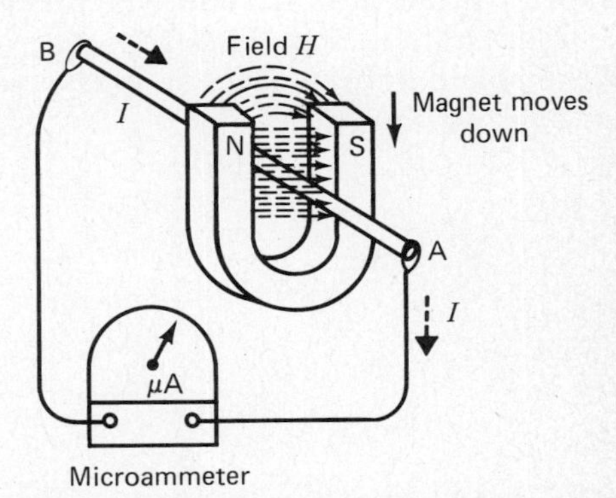

Fig. 34-2. Magnetically induced current in a conductor. Current I is electron flow.

EQUIPMENT

DC power supply
Galvanometer or microammeter
Heavy-duty horseshoe magnet (>20 lb pull)
Magnetic compass
Shield (6 × 6 in.) conductance sheet metal

COMPONENTS

2 to 3 ft of thin insulated wire
(1) No. 18 iron nail
Iron filings

PROCEDURE

1. Connect the circuit of Fig. 34-3. Have the compass

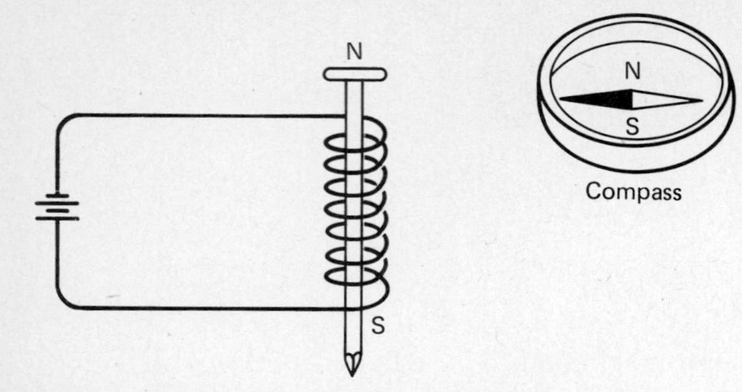

Fig. 34-3. Electromagnetic circuit for step 1.

and the iron filings nearby. Wrap the insulated wire evenly around the nail (about 10 to 15 turns).

2. The left-hand rule states that if a coil is grasped with the fingers of the left hand curled around the coil in the direction of electron flow, the thumb (extended) points to the north pole of the coil. Imagine your left hand grasped around the coil of wire wound around the nail. Determine which end is the north pole.

3. Turn the power on, and slowly move the compass close to both ends of the needle. Determine which end of the nail is north and which is south. Compare the results to step 2 above.

4. Place the shield between the compass and the nail in the circuit and repeat step 3. Note the results.

5. Turn the power off. Remove the nail and pass it through the iron filings. Note the results. Disconnect the circuit.

6. Connect the circuit of Fig. 34-4. Using the same wire as in steps 1 to 4 above, loop the wire around the magnet many times, making sure that the galvanometer is on the lowest range.

7. Move the horseshoe magnet up and down, as necessary, and note the amount of current produced. Try moving the magnet more rapidly, then slowly.

8. Disconnect the circuit.

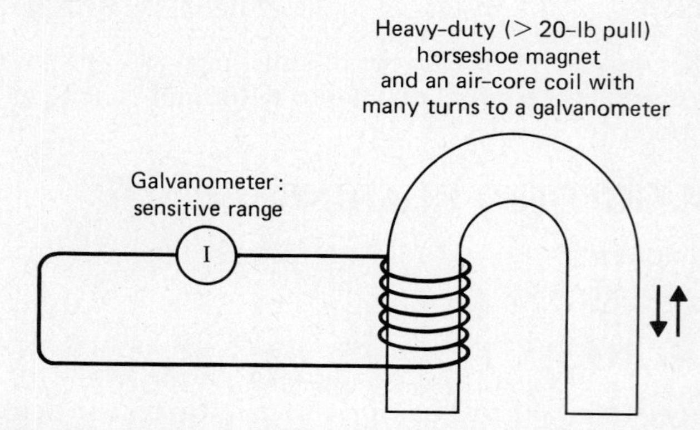

Fig. 34-4. Electromagnetic generator circuit for step 6.

NAME DATE

RESULTS FOR EXPERIMENT 34

QUESTIONS

1. Explain what is meant by shielding.

2. Discuss the results of moving the magnet (in step 7) faster or slower.

3. Explain which end of the nail attracted the iron filings, and why.

4. Discuss any differences between the results of steps 1 to 4 and steps 6 to 8.

5. Explain the left-hand rule as it was applied in this experiment.

REPORT

Write a complete report. Discuss the results. Discuss the three most significant aspects of the experiment and write a conclusion.

1N4001 thru 1N4007

Designers▲Data Sheet

"SURMETIC"▲ RECTIFIERS

. . . subminiature size, axial lead mounted rectifiers for general-purpose low-power applications.

Designers Data for "Worst Case" Conditions

The Designers▲ Data Sheets permit the design of most circuits entirely from the information presented. Limit curves — representing boundaries on device characteristics — are given to facilitate "worst case" design.

LEAD MOUNTED SILICON RECTIFIERS

50-1000 VOLTS DIFFUSED JUNCTION

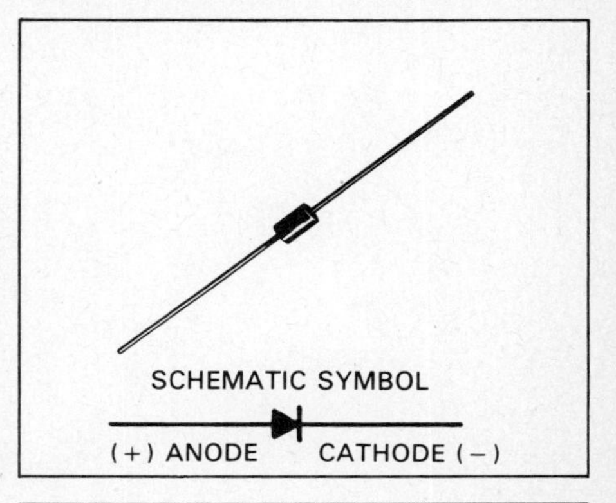

*MAXIMUM RATINGS

Rating	Symbol	1N4001	1N4002	1N4003	1N4004	1N4005	1N4006	1N4007	Unit
Peak Repetitive Reverse Voltage Working Peak Reverse Voltage DC Blocking Voltage	V_{RRM} V_{RWM} V_R	50	100	200	400	600	800	1000	Volts
Non-Repetitive Peak Reverse Voltage (halfwave, single phase, 60 Hz)	V_{RSM}	60	120	240	480	720	1000	1200	Volts
RMS Reverse Voltage	$V_{R(RMS)}$	35	70	140	280	420	560	700	Volts
Average Rectified Forward Current (single phase, resistive load, 60 Hz, see Figure 8, $T_A = 75^oC$)	I_O	1.0							Amp
Non-Repetitive Peak Surge Current (surge applied at rated load conditions, see Figure 2)	I_{FSM}	30 (for 1 cycle)							Amp
Operating and Storage Junction Temperature Range	T_J, T_{stg}	-65 to +175							^oC

*ELECTRICAL CHARACTERISTICS

Characteristic and Conditions	Symbol	Typ	Max	Unit
Maximum Instantaneous Forward Voltage Drop ($i_F = 1.0$ Amp, $T_J = 25^oC$) Figure 1	v_F	0.93	1.1	Volts
Maximum Full-Cycle Average Forward Voltage Drop ($I_O = 1.0$ Amp, $T_L = 75^oC$, 1 inch leads)	$V_{F(AV)}$	—	0.8	Volts
Maximum Reverse Current (rated dc voltage) $T_J = 25^oC$	I_R	0.05	10	μA
$T_J = 100^oC$		1.0	50	
Maximum Full-Cycle Average Reverse Current ($I_O = 1.0$ Amp, $T_L = 75^oC$, 1 inch leads	$I_{R(AV)}$	—	30	μA

*Indicates JEDEC Registered Data.

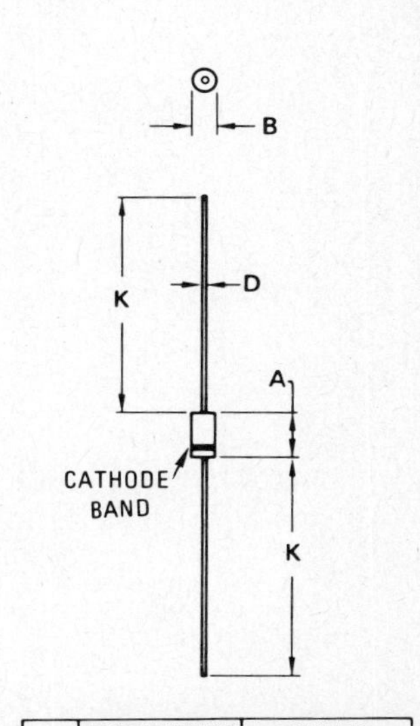

DIM	MILLIMETERS MIN	MILLIMETERS MAX	INCHES MIN	INCHES MAX
A	5.97	6.60	0.235	0.260
B	2.79	3.05	0.110	0.120
D	0.76	0.86	0.030	0.034
K	27.94	—	1.100	—

CASE 59-04
Does Not Conform to DO-41 Outline.

MECHANICAL CHARACTERISTICS

CASE: Void free, Transfer Molded
MAXIMUM LEAD TEMPERATURE FOR SOLDERING PURPOSES: 350^oC, 3/8" from case for 10 seconds at 5 lbs. tension
FINISH: All external surfaces are corrosion-resistant, leads are readily solderable
POLARITY: Cathode indicated by color band
WEIGHT: 0.40 Grams (approximately)

▲Trademark of Motorola Inc.

DS 6015 R3

Appendix B Transistor Data Sheet

2N3903 (SILICON)
2N3904

NPN SILICON ANNULAR TRANSISTORS

. . . designed for general purpose switching and amplifier applications and for complementary circuitry with types 2N3905 and 2N3906.

- Collector-Emitter Breakdown Voltage – BV_{CEO} = 40 Vdc (Min)
- Current Gain Specified from 100 μA to 100 mA
- Complete Switching and Amplifier Specifications
- Low Capacitance – C_{ob} = 4.0 pF (Max)

NPN SILICON SWITCHING & AMPLIFIER TRANSISTORS

***MAXIMUM RATINGS**

Rating	Symbol	Value	Unit
Collector-Base Voltage	V_{CB}	60	Vdc
Collector-Emitter Voltage	V_{CEO}	40	Vdc
Emitter-Base Voltage	V_{EB}	6.0	Vdc
Collector Current – Continuous	I_C	200	mAdc
Total Power Dissipation @ T_A = 25°C Derate above 25°C	P_D	350 2.8	mW mW/°C
Total Power Dissipation @ T_C = 25°C Derate above 25°C	P_D	1.0 8.0	Watts mW/°C
Junction Operating Temperature	T_J	150	°C
Storage Temperature Range	T_{stg}	-55 to +150	°C

THERMAL CHARACTERISTICS

Characteristic	Symbol	Max	Unit
Thermal Resistance, Junction to Ambient	$R_{\theta JA}$	357	°C/W
Thermal Resistance, Junction to Case	$R_{\theta JC}$	125.	°C/W

*Indicates JEDEC Registered Data

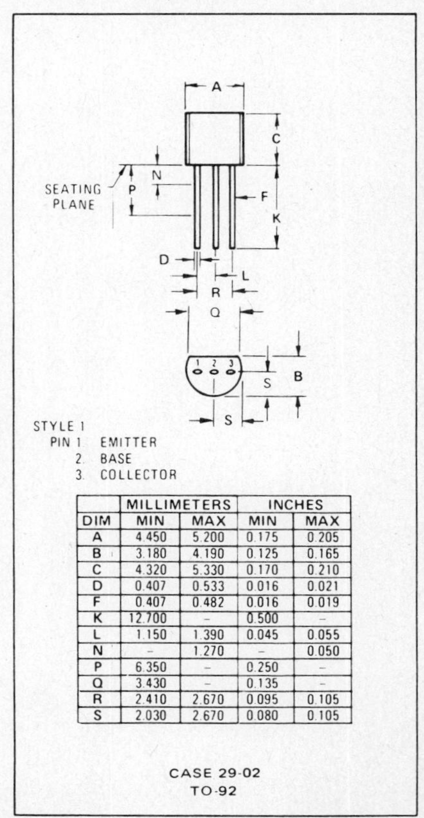

DIM	MILLIMETERS MIN	MILLIMETERS MAX	INCHES MIN	INCHES MAX
A	4.450	5.200	0.175	0.205
B	3.180	4.190	0.125	0.165
C	4.320	5.330	0.170	0.210
D	0.407	0.533	0.016	0.021
F	0.407	0.482	0.016	0.019
K	12.700	–	0.500	–
L	1.150	1.390	0.045	0.055
N	–	1.270	–	0.050
P	6.350	–	0.250	–
Q	3.430	–	0.135	–
R	2.410	2.670	0.095	0.105
S	2.030	2.670	0.080	0.105

CASE 29-02
TO-92

Appendix C Applicable Color Codes

TABLE C-1 Color Code for Carbon Composition Resistors

COLOR	DIGIT 1st	DIGIT 2nd	MULTIPLIER	TOLERANCE
Black	0	0	1	—
Brown	1	1	10	—
Red	2	2	100	—
Orange	3	3	1,000	—
Yellow	4	4	10,000	—
Green	5	5	100,000	—
Blue	6	6	1,000,000	—
Violet	7	7	10,000,000	—
Gray	8	8	100,000,000	—
White	9	9	1,000,000,000	—
Gold	—	—	0.1	± 5%
Silver	—	—	0.01	±10%
No band	—	—	—	±20%

TABLE C-2 Color Code for Carbon Film Resistors

COLOR	DIGITS 1st	DIGITS 2nd	DIGITS 3rd	MULTIPLIER	TOLERANCE
Black	0	0	0	1	
Brown	1	1	1	10	±1%
Red	2	2	2	100	±2%
Orange	3	3	3	1,000	
Yellow	4	4	4	10,000	
Green	5	5	5	100,000	±5%
Blue	6	6	6	1,000,000	±0.25%
Violet	7	7	7	10,000,000	±0.10%
Gray	8	8	8		±0.05%
White	9	9	9		±5%
Gold	—	—	—	0.1	±10%
Silver	—	—	—	0.01	

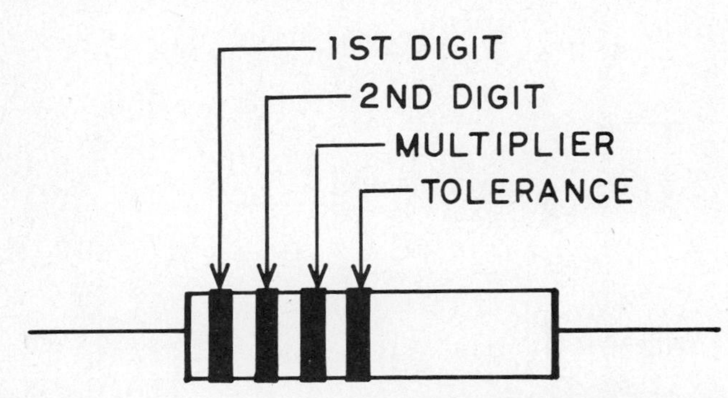

FIG. C-1 Color coding on a carbon composition resistor.

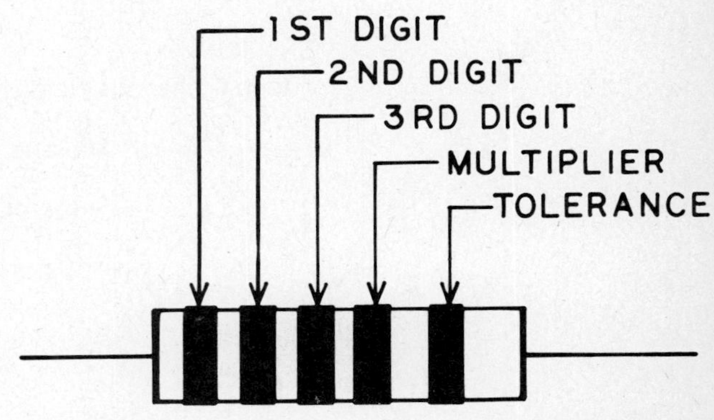

FIG. C-2 Color coding on a carbon film resistor.

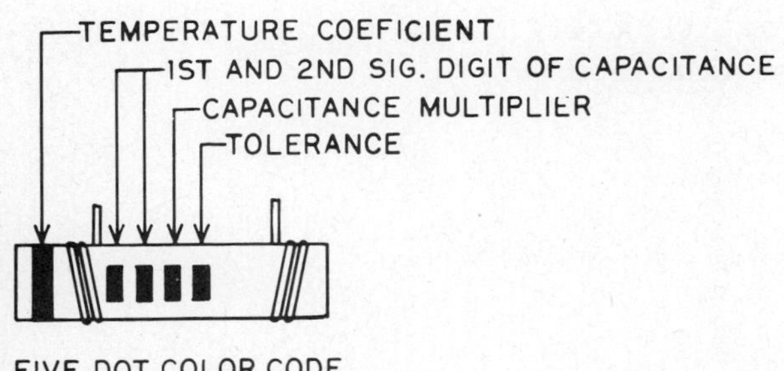

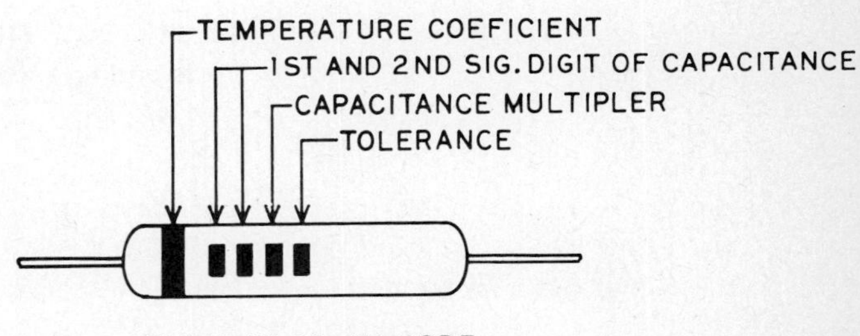

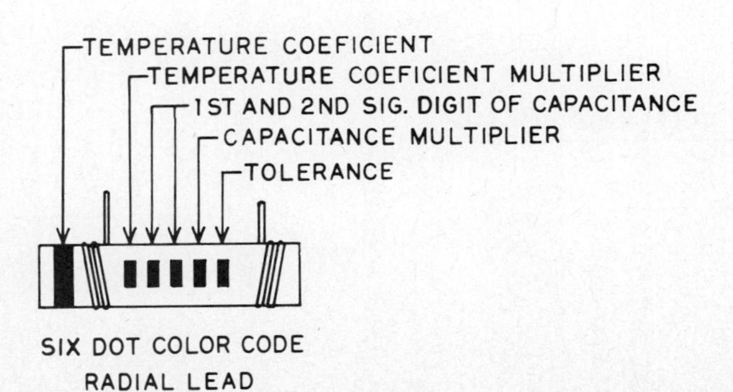

FIG. C-3 Color coding on tubular ceramic capacitors.

Reproduced from Baer/Ottaway, *Electrical and Electronic Drawing,* Fifth Edition, McGraw-Hill, 1986.

TABLE C-3 Color Codes for Tubular and Disc Ceramic Capacitors

BAND OR DOT COLOR	CAPACITANCE IN PICOFARADS SIGNIF-ICANT DIGITS 1st	2nd	CAPACITANCE MULTIPLIER	TOLERANCE ≤10 pF	>10 pF	TEMPERATURE COEFFICIENT pp °C (5-DOT SYSTEM)	TEMPERATURE COEFFICIENT 6-DOT SYSTEM SIG. FIG.	TEMPERATURE COEFFICIENT MULTIPLIER
Black	0	0	1	±2.0 pF	±20%	0	0.0	−1
Brown	1	1	10	±0.1 pF	±1%	−33		−10
Red	2	2	100		±2%	−75	1.0	−100
Orange	3	3	1000		±3%	−150	1.5	−1000
Yellow	4	4				−230	2.0	−10000
Green	5	5		±0.5 pF	±5%	−330	3.3	+1
Blue	6	6				−470	4.7	+10
Violet	7	7				−750	7.5	+100
Gray	8	8	0.01	±0.25 pF		+150 to −1500		+1000
White	9	9	0.1	±1.0 pF	±10%	+100 to −75		+10000
Silver	—	—						
Gold	—	—						

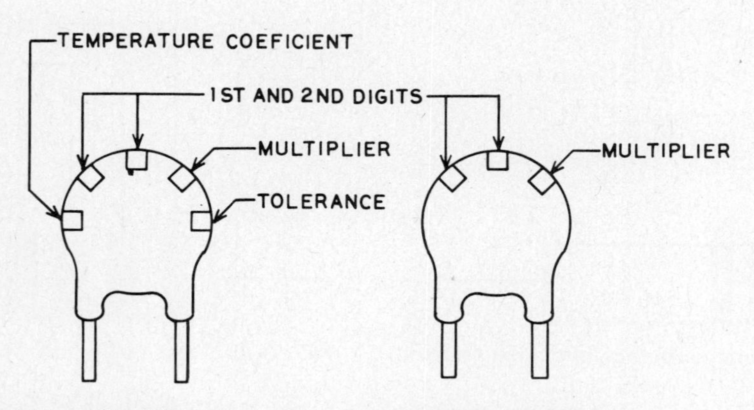

FIG. C-4 Color coding on a ceramic disk capacitor.

TABLE C-4 Color Code for Molded Paper Tubular Capacitors

COLOR	(CAPACITANCE IN PICOFARADS) SIGNIF-ICANT DIGITS 1st	2nd	MULTIPLIER	TOLERANCE	VOLTAGE
Black	0	0	1	±20%	—
Brown	1	1	10		100
Red	2	2	100		200
Orange	3	3	1000	±30%	300
Yellow	4	4	10000		400
Green	5	5			500
Blue	6	6			600
Violet	7	7			700
Gray	8	8			800
White	9	9			900
Gold	—	—			1000
Silver	—	—		±10%	—

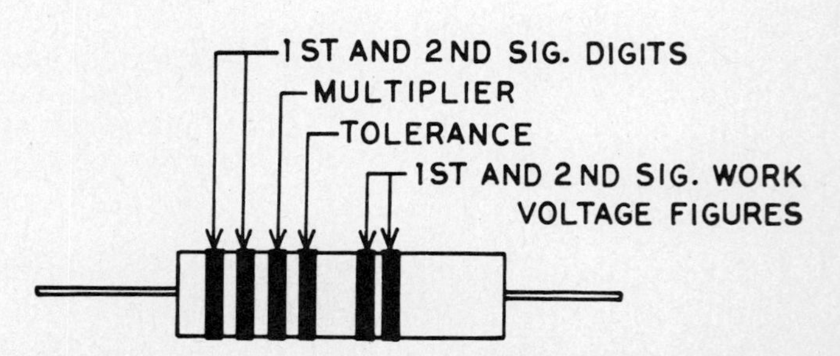

FIG. C-5 Color coding on a paper tubular capacitor.

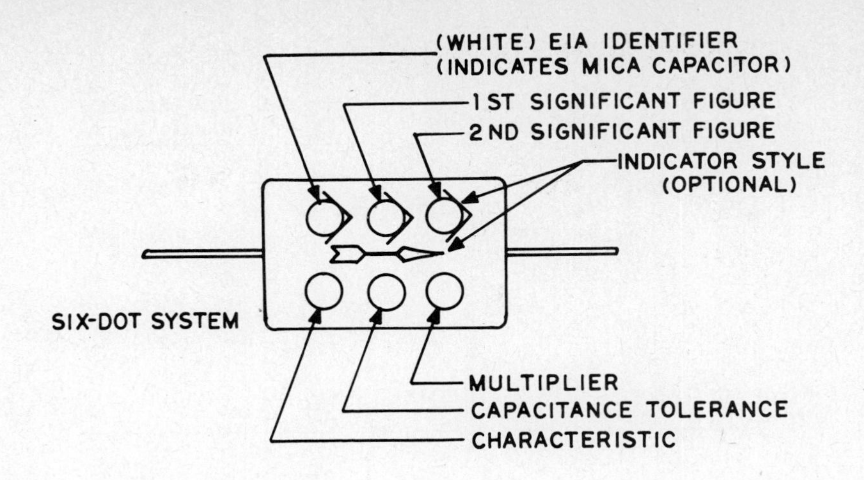

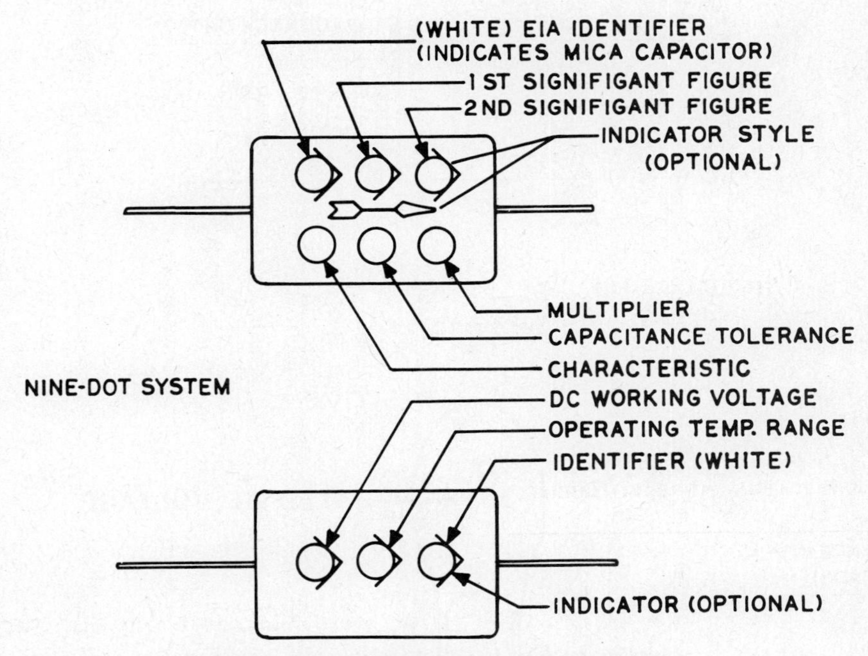

FIG. C-6 Color coding on mica capacitors.

TABLE C-5 Color Code for Mica Capacitors

COLOR	CHARAC-TERISTIC	DIGITS 1st	DIGITS 2nd	MULTI-PLIER	TOLER-ANCE	DC WORKING VOLTAGE	OPERATING TEMPERATURE RANGE
Black		0	0	1	±20%	100	
Brown	B	1	1	10	±1%		−55°C to +85°C
Red	C	2	2	100	±2%	300	
Orange	D	3	3	1,000			−55°C to +125°C
Yellow	E	4	4	10,000		500	
Green	F	5	5		±5%		
Blue		6	6				
Violet		7	7				
Gray		8	8				
White		9	9				
Gold		—	—	0.1	±½%	1000	
Silver		—	—	0.01	±10%		

TABLE C-6 Mica Capacitor Characteristics

CHARAC-TERISTIC	TEMPERATURE COEFFICIENT OF CAPACITANCE (ppm/°C)	MAXIMUM CAPACITANCE DRIFT
B	Not specified	Not specified
C	±200	±(0.5% + 0.5 pF)
D	±100	±(0.3% + 0.1 pF)
E	−20 to +100	±(0.1% + 0.1 pF)
F	0 to +70	±(0.05% + 0.1 pF)

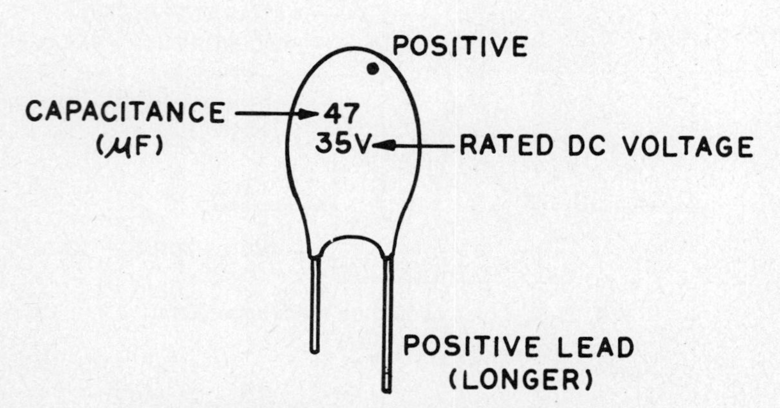

FIG. C-7 Marking of a tantalum capacitor.

Appendix D Lab Report Preparation

Appendix D-1: How to Write Lab Reports

1. Write short sentences whenever possible.
2. Use a dictionary and spell all words correctly.
3. Write neatly in blue or black ink.
4. Avoid personal pronouns: I, you, we, etc.
5. Never discuss results unless they are part of your data.
6. Do not copy or paraphrase textbook theory.
7. Label all data tables and graphs with titles, numbers, proper units, and column headings.
8. Never write in the margins of your paper.
9. Leave enough space between sentences for the instructor to make corrections.
10. Technical accuracy and completeness are the most important part of a lab report. Unless the report is well organized and easy to read, it is of little value.

Every instructor will have different standards and different ideas about report writing. However, most lab reports reflect the scientific method as follows:

- A hypothesis is formulated. This is like a statement of purpose.
- Data is collected and analyzed. This is like the procedure and results.
- The hypothesis is proven or disproven based upon the results. This is like the discussion and conclusion.

Refer to the two sample reports that follow in Appendixes D-3 and D-4. One is a poor report that does not follow these suggestions. The other is a good report that does use the suggestions.

Appendix D-2: Blank Style Sheet

Experiment No.

Name: ______________________

Date: ______________________

Class: ______________________

Instr: ______________________

Title:

Purpose:

Procedure:

Results:

Discussion of Results:

1.

2.

3.

Notes:

Conclusion:

Appendix D-3: Sample Poor Report

Experiment No. 3

Name: J. Doe

Date:

Title: Ohm's law

Class: Elec.

Instr: Jones

Purpose: To do Ohm's law experiment.

Procedure: 1–16 in manual.

Results:

Discussion of Results:

1. The more voltage I had the more current I had when I measured.

2. When we changed the resistors I saw more current but it was hard to read the meter because the needle was bent a little.

3. $I = \frac{V}{R}$ is ohm's law.

Notes: This experiment is good to learn about ohm's law but I had trouble hooking up the circuit.

Conclusion: Ohm's law works good.

Appendix D-4: Sample Good Report

Experiment No. 3

Name: John Doe

Date:

Title: Ohm's Law

Class: Elec. 1-A

Instr: Mr. R. Jones

Purpose: To validate Ohm's Law: $I = \frac{V}{R}$

Procedure: Experiments in Basic Electronics, pages 16-20, steps 1-16.

Results: Data tables 3-1 and 3-2, attached.

Discussion of Results:

1. With resistance held constant, the current varied in direct proportion to any changes in applied voltage.

2. With voltage held constant, the current was inversely proportional to any changes in circuit resistance.

3. Current can be held constant as long as voltage and resistance are kept in proportion. This is consistent with the formula $I = \frac{V}{R}$.

Notes: The pointer of meter number 16 was bent.

Conclusion: Ohm's Law is valid based upon the results of this experiment. Current is directly proportional to voltage and inversely proportional to resistance.

Appendix E Blank Graph Paper

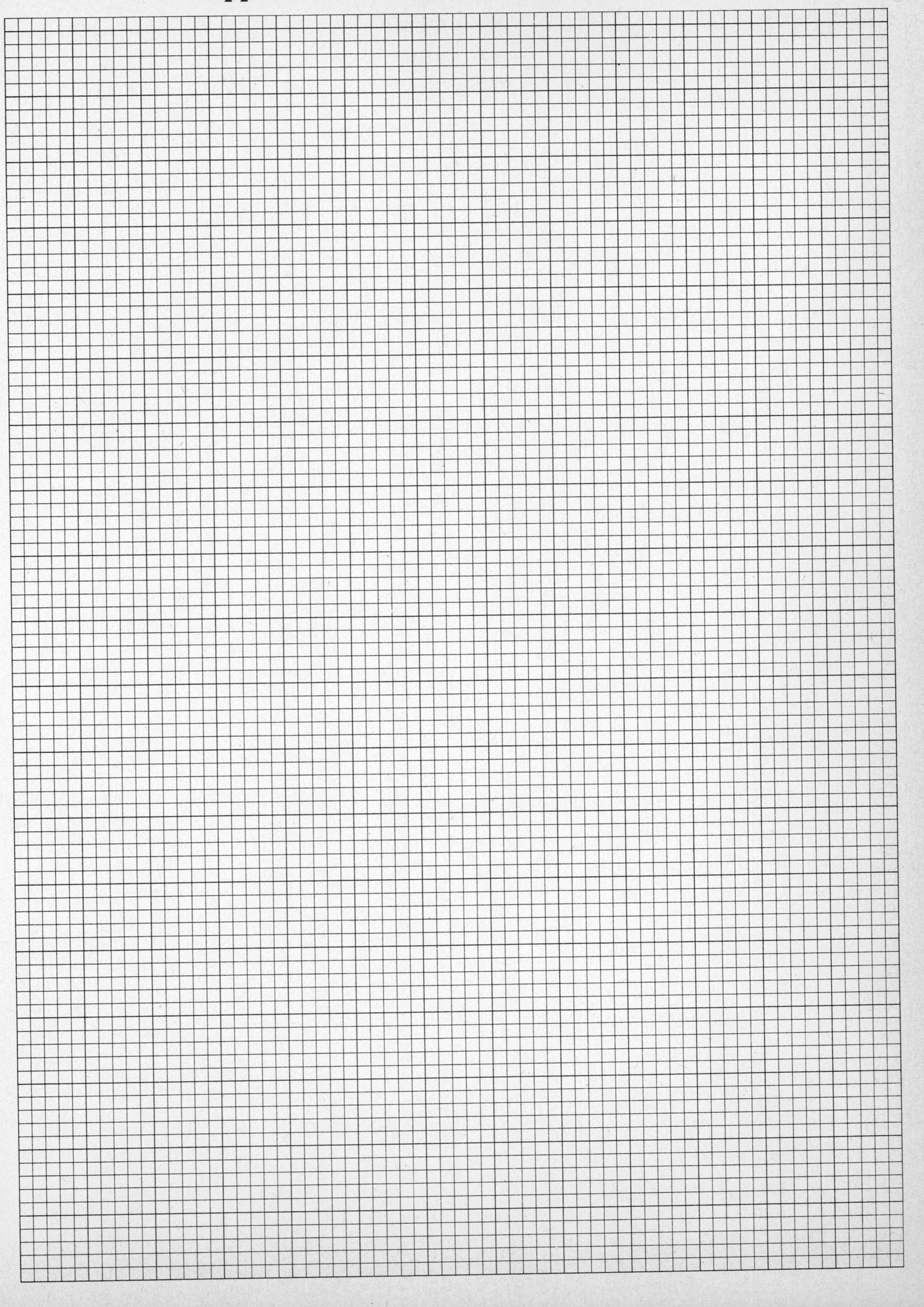

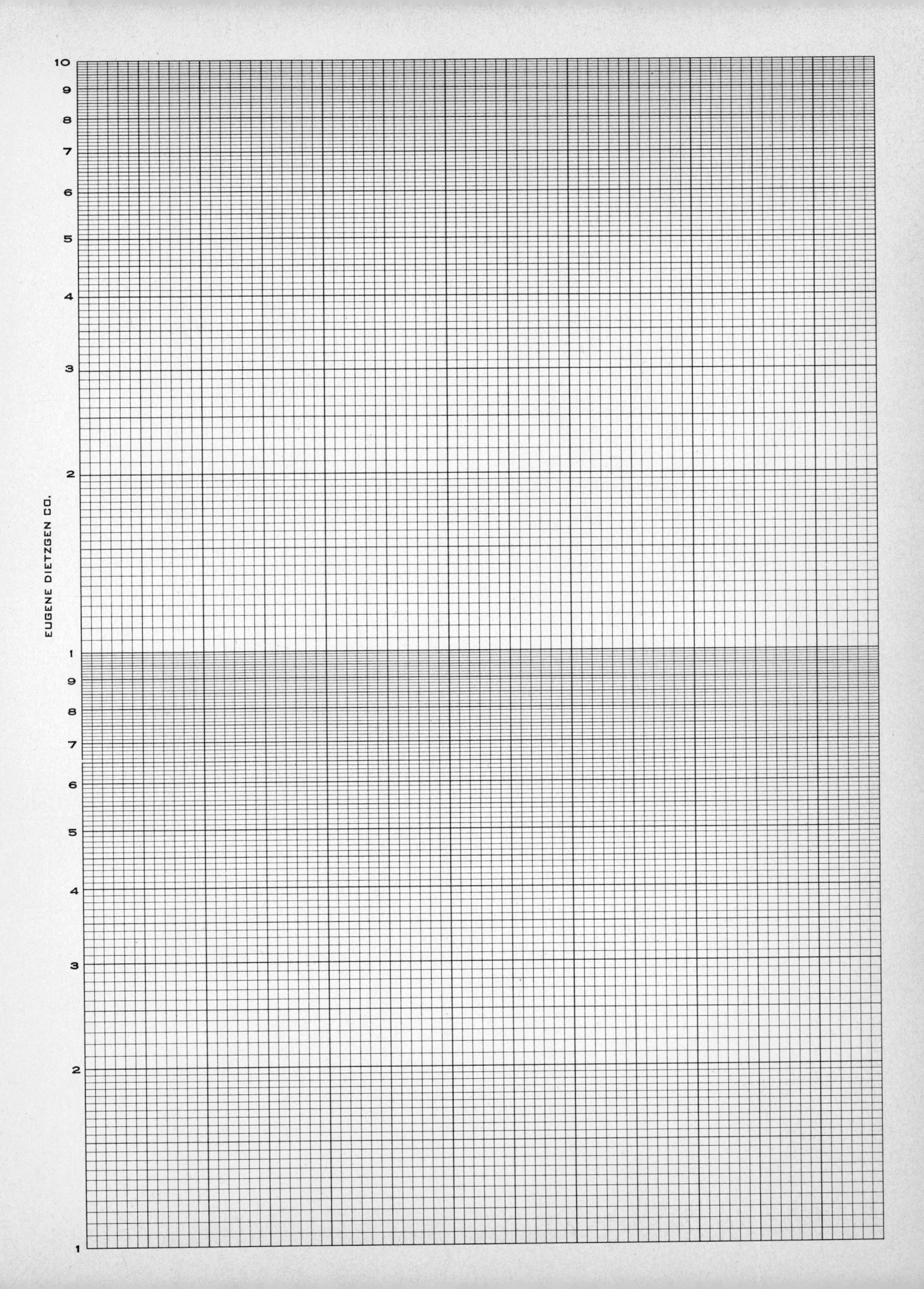
10
9
8
7
6
5
4
3
2
1
9
8
7
6
5
4
3
2
1
EUGENE DIETZGEN CO.

Appendix F Oscilloscope Graticules

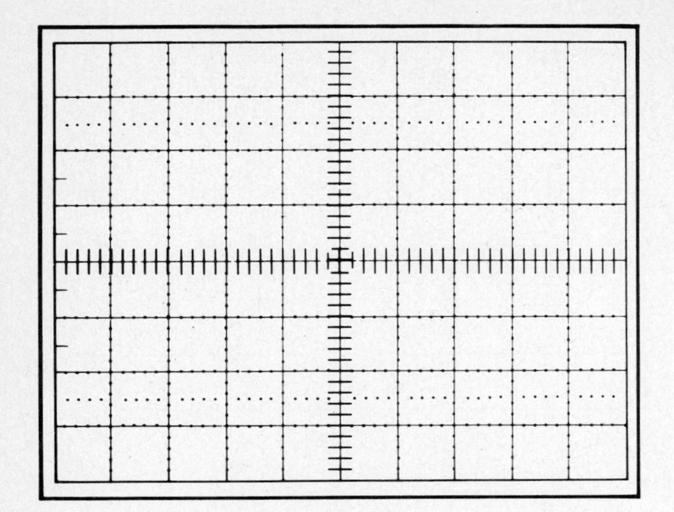

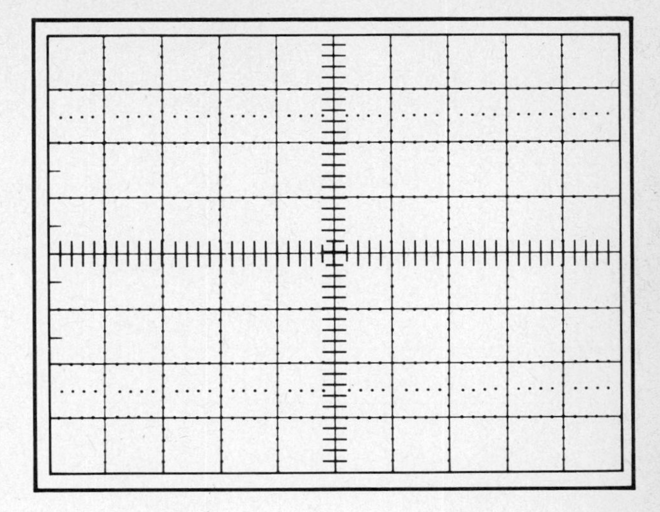

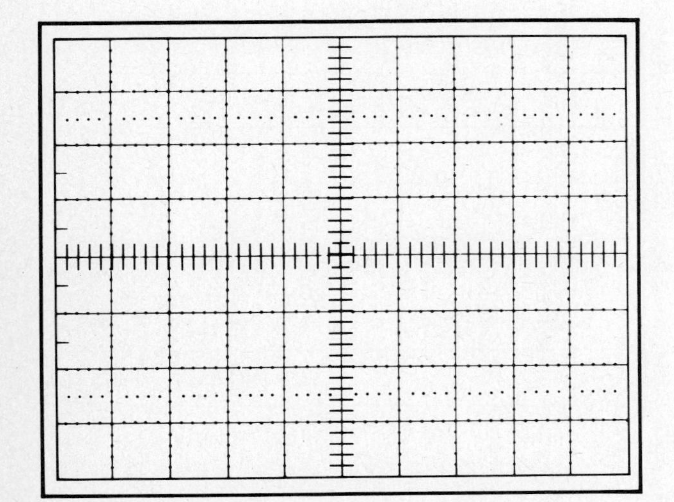

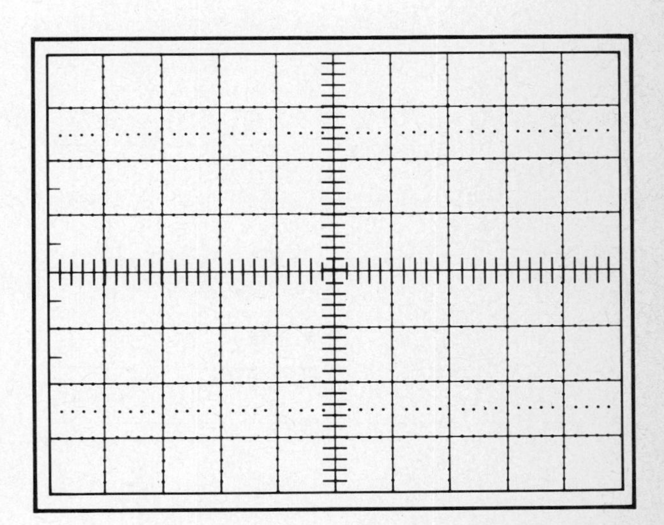

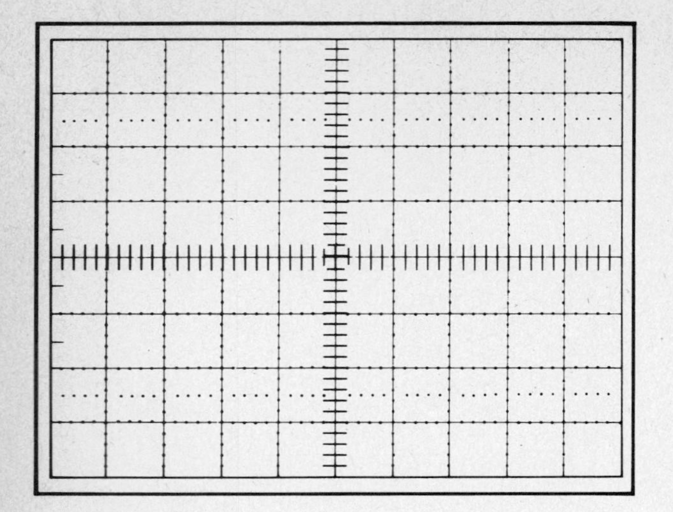

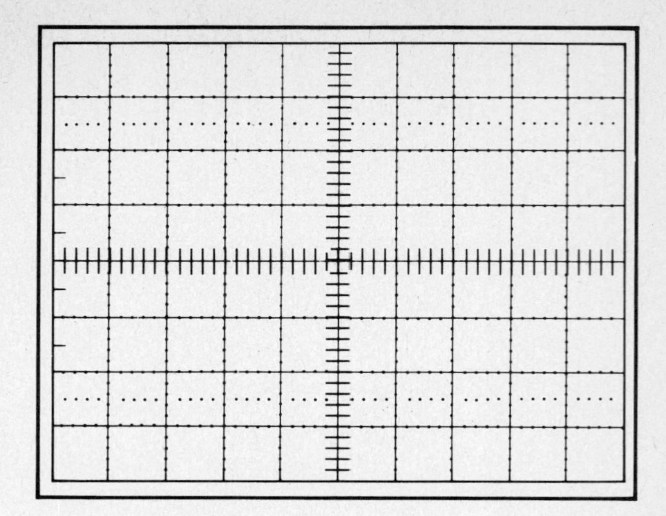

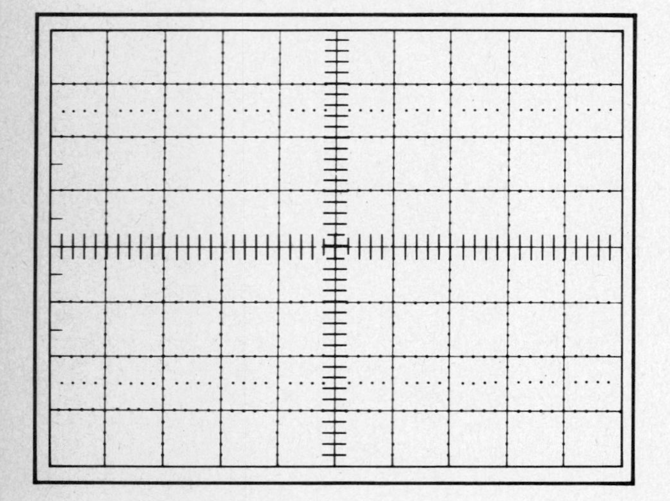

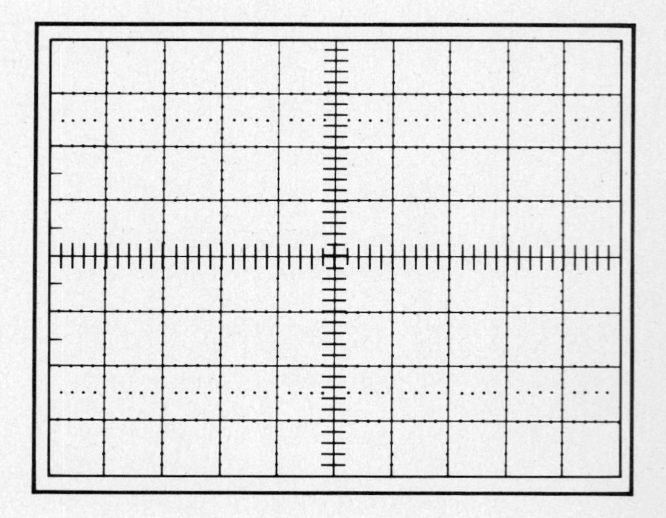

Appendix G How To Make Graphs

Graphs usually show the relationships of two or more variables. The relationship is actually the curve or line that results. Here are some things to remember when making graphs.

1. Be neat and complete.
2. Never connect points. Always show the characteristic of the curve.
3. There should be room in the margins to title the graph.
4. Use the fullest scales possible. Do not confine a graph to one corner of the paper.
5. Use semilog graph paper for exponential quantities. Label the X axis as 1×10^2 for 100s, 1×10^3 for 1000s, etc.

Examples

Incorrect

I

Ohm's Law *V*

Correct

(mA)

I

Ohm's Law Graph
R(100 Ω) held constant

Volts

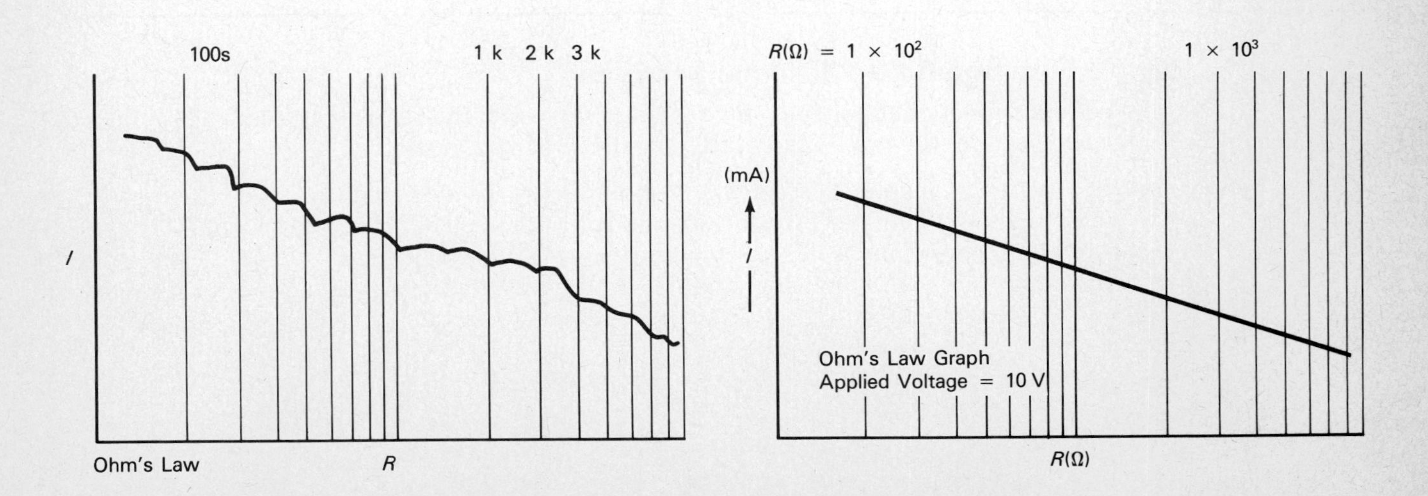

Appendix H The Oscilloscope

The purpose of this appendix on oscilloscopes is to help you learn to use this measurement tool accurately and efficiently. This introduction is divided into two sections: the first section describes the functional parts of the basic oscilloscope, and the second section describes probes.

The oscilloscope is the most important tool to an experienced electronics technician (see Fig. H-1). While working through this appendix, it is best to have your laboratory oscilloscope (or the one you will be using in your studies of electronics) in front of you so that you can learn, practice, and apply your newly acquired knowledge. This appendix will discuss fundamentals which apply to any oscilloscope; your instructor or laboratory aid will help you with the fine details and special provisions that apply to your particular oscilloscope.

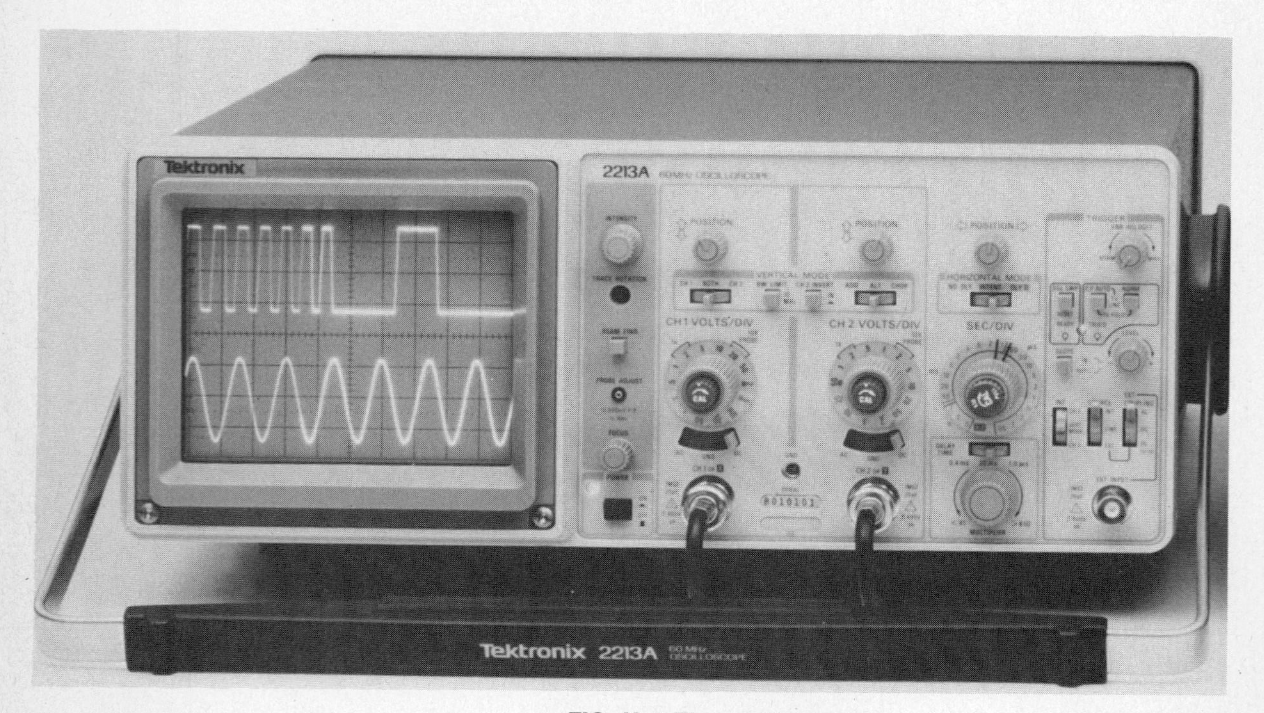

FIG. H-1 The oscilloscope.

Part 1: Functional Oscilloscope Sections

There are four functional parts to the basic oscilloscope: the display system, the vertical system, the horizontal system, and the trigger system.

Display System. Ths display system is a coordinated system of controls. It includes a cathode-ray tube (CRT), intensity control, and focus control. The CRT has a phosphor coating inside it. As an electron beam is moved across the phosphor coating, a glow is created which follows the beam and persists for a short time. A grid, also known as a graticule, is etched or painted on the screen of the CRT. This grid serves as a reference for taking measurements. Figure H-2 shows a typical oscilloscope graticule. Note the major and minor divisions.

The intensity control adjusts the amount of glow emitted by the electron beam and phosphor coating. The beam-trace should be adjusted so that it is easy to see and produces no halo. The focus control adjusts the beam for an optimum trace.

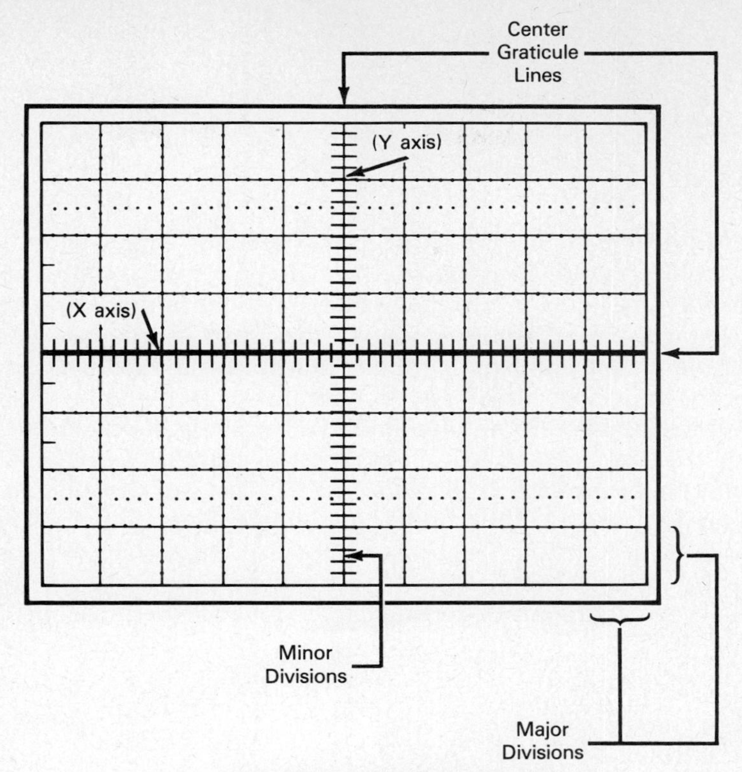

FIG. H-2 Oscilloscope CRT.

Vertical System. The vertical system controls and develops the deflection voltages which are displayed on the CRT. In this system, you typically find controls for vertical position, vertical sensitivity, and input coupling. The vertical position controls the placement of the trace. Adjusting this control will move the entire trace either up or down along the Y axis of the CRT. This control is adjusted as needed to help the operator make accurate measurements. The vertical-sensitivity control, also known as the volts-per-division switch, controls the Y axis sensitivity. The range is usually controlled from 1 mV to 50 V per division. For example, if you were to observe a trace occupying 4 divisions on the CRT, and the volts-per-division switch was turned to 1 mV/div., then the measured voltage would equal 1 mV × 4 divisions, or 4 mV. If the switch were turned to the 50 V/div. position and a 4 division trace was observed, then the oscilloscope would be measuring 200 V. The input-coupling switch lets the operator determine how the circuit under examination is connected to the oscilloscope. The three positions of this switch are ground, dc coupling, and ac coupling. When the switch is in the ground position, the operator can adjust the position of the trace with no input signal applied to the oscilloscope. This function is used primarily to align the oscilloscope to a reference point prior to taking a measurement. When in the dc-coupling position, the oscilloscope allows the operator to see the entire signal. However, when the input-coupling switch is in the ac-coupling position, only the ac signal components are displayed on the CRT. All dc components are blocked when the switch is in the ac position.

Horizontal System. As the oscilloscope trace is moved across the CRT (from left to right), it moves at a rate of speed which is related to frequency. The horizontal system is dominated by two main controls: the horizontal-position control and the time-base control. The horizontal-position control performs the same task as the vertical-position, but utilizes the X axis. The time-base, or seconds-per-division control, is used to select the appropriate sweep necessary to see the input signal. Ranges typically found on the time-base control extend from 0.1 μs to 0.5 μs per division on the CRT.

Trigger System. The trigger system allows the operator to select a part of the input signal and synchronize it with the trace displayed on the CRT. Normally, a trigger-level control is available. The position of the trigger-level control determines where on the selected trace the oscilloscope triggering will occur.

Each oscilloscope has different features. Your instructor is the best source for varying operational procedures.

Part 2: Oscilloscope Probes

Probes should accurately reproduce the signal for your oscilloscope. Probes can be divided by function into two main areas: current sensing and voltage sensing. Voltage-sensing probes can be further divided into passive and active types. For most applications, the probes that were supplied with your oscilloscope are the ones you should use. An operator picks the type of probe based on the voltage intended to be measured. For example, if you are measuring a 50-V signal, and the largest vertical sensitivity available is 5 V, then that particular signal will occupy 10 divisions on the CRT. This is a situation where attenuation is needed, and a $\times 10$ probe would reduce the amplitude of your signal to a reasonable proportion. The best way to ensure that your oscilloscope and probe measurement system have the least effect on the accuracy of your measurements is to use the probe recommended for your oscilloscope.

Appendix I Component List

Resistors

All resistors 0.25 W, 5% unless indicated otherwise.

(1) 10 Ω
(1) 15 Ω
(1) 56 Ω
(1) 68 Ω
(1) 100 Ω
(12) 100 Ω, 1 W
(1) 120 Ω
(8) 150 Ω, 1 W
(2) 150 Ω, 1 W
(7) 220 Ω
(1) 270 Ω
(2) 330 Ω
(5) 330 Ω, 1 W
(7) 390 Ω
(5) 470 Ω, 1 W
(8) 560 Ω
(3) 680 Ω
(3) 820 Ω
(1) 1000 Ω
(1) 1500 Ω
(1) 2200 Ω
(1) 3900 Ω
(1) 5600 Ω
(8) 1 kΩ
(1) 1 kΩ, 1 W
(3) 1.2 kΩ
(2) 1.5 kΩ
(3) 2.2 kΩ
(1) 2.7 kΩ
(1) 3.3 kΩ
(1) 3.9 kΩ
(3) 4.7 kΩ
(1) 5.6 kΩ
(1) 8.2 kΩ
(4) 10 kΩ
(1) 12 kΩ
(4) 22 kΩ
(1) 22 kΩ, 2 W
(1) 27 kΩ
(1) 33 kΩ
(1) 39 kΩ
(2) 47 kΩ
(1) 68 kΩ
(2) 82 kΩ
(1) 86 kΩ
(2) 100 kΩ
(1) 100 kΩ, 1 W
(1) 150 kΩ
(1) 220 kΩ
(1) 470 kΩ
(1) 1 MΩ
(1) 1.2 MΩ
(1) 3 MΩ
(1) 3.3 MΩ

Capacitors

All capacitors 25 V or greater.

(1) 0.0068 μF
(1) 0.068 μF
(4) 0.01 μF
(2) 0.1 μF
(4) 10 μF
(2) 25 μF
(2) 47 μF electrolytic
(2) 47 μF
(2) 4 μF or 1 μF
(1) 100 μF

Inductors

(2) 33 mH
(1) 100 mH
(1) 1 H (or optional value)
(4) Varying values from 10 mH to 0.5 H
(1) 0.5 H
(1) 0.01 H

Potentiometers

(1) 1 W
(1) 5 kΩ
(1) 100 kΩ
(1) 1 MΩ

Batteries

(4) D cells
(4) D-cell holders

Diodes

(4) 1N4004 or equivalent
(4) LEDs
(1) Zener, 5 V (1 W)
(2) IR#S1M solar cells or equivalent photo diode

Transistors

(1) 2N3638
(2) 2N3904

FET

(1) 2N3823 or equivalent

Op Amps and ICs

(1) 741
(1) 7408
(1) 7432

Vacuum Tube (Optional)

6J5 or equivalent

Transformers

(1) 60–Hz with two or three taps

Bench Equipment

Ammeter with 30-mA capacity;VOM/DMM
Voltmeter: DVM, VTVM, VOM, DMM
DC power supply, 0–30 V (± 15 V for op amps experiment)
High-voltage power supply with 120 : 12.6 V center-tap @ 6.3 V filament transformer
Galvanometer or microammeter movement
Signal generator (sine wave, to 1 MHz preferred)
Oscilloscope (solid-state, auto-trigger, dual-trace, with operator's manual preferred)
Frequency counter
Breadboard
AC signal generator

Miscellaneous Parts

(1) Circuit board; proto springboard or breadboard
(2) SPST switch
(1) SPDT switch
(1) 0–1 mA meter movement
(1) 50 μA meter movement
6 test leads
(1) Decade box
(1) Magnetic compass
(1) Heavy-duty horseshoe magnet, 20 lb plus pull
(1) Sheet-metal shield, 6 × 6 in
(1) Grease pencil
2–3 ft, thin insulated wire
Iron filings
No. 18 steel nail
(4) light bulbs: 25, 60, 100, 150 W
(1) Clear glass functioning fuse (any current rating)
(1) Clear glass nonfunctioning fuse (any current rating)
(1) Neon bulb, approximately 60 V